S346 Drug design and synthesis
Science: Level 3

Drug Design

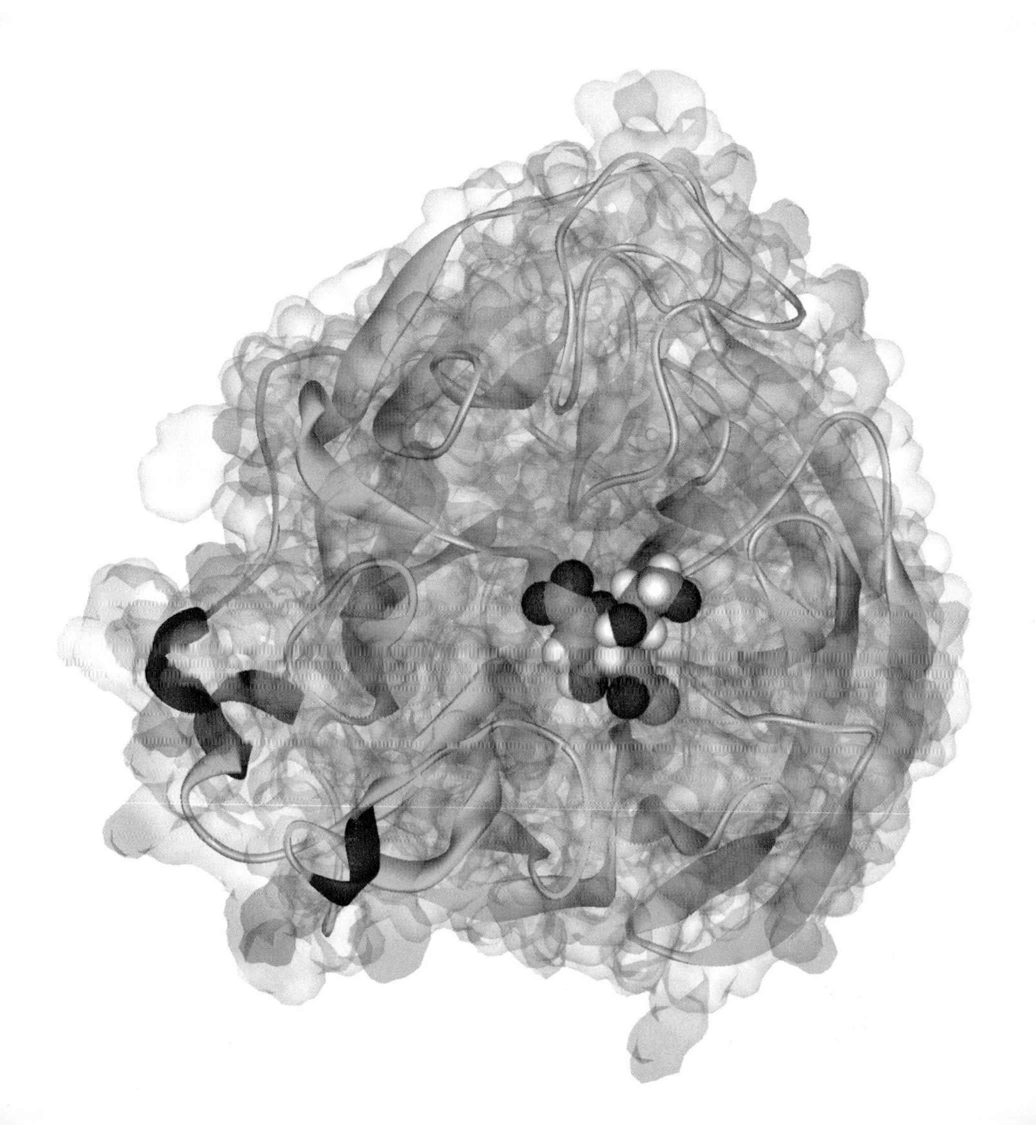

This publication forms part of an Open University module S346 *Drug design and synthesis*. Details of this and other Open University modules can be obtained from the Student Registration and Enquiry Service, The Open University, PO Box 197, Milton Keynes MK7 6BJ, United Kingdom: tel. +44 (0)845 300 60 90, email general-enquiries@open.ac.uk

Alternatively, you may visit the Open University website at http://www.open.ac.uk where you can learn more about the wide range of modules and packs offered at all levels by The Open University.

To purchase a selection of Open University materials visit http://www.ouw.co.uk, or contact Open University Worldwide, Walton Hall, Milton Keynes MK7 6AA, United Kingdom for a brochure. tel. +44 (0)1908 858793; fax +44 (0)1908 858787; email ouw-customer-services@open.ac.uk

The Open University
Walton Hall, Milton Keynes
MK7 6AA

First published 2009. Second edition 2010. Third edition 2012.

Edited and designed by The Open University.

Typeset by The Open University.

Printed in the United Kingdom by Latimer Trend and Company Ltd, Plymouth.

ISBN 978 1 7800 7339 2

3.1

Contents

1 Proteins and protein structure

1.1 Proteins and amino acids

Proteins are a chemically defined class of macromolecular compound, and are fundamental constituents of every living organism. Humans have about 100 000 different proteins in our bodies. At first acquaintance, it seems remarkable that substances as diverse in their function as lysozyme (an enzyme, i.e. a catalyst), collagen (a structural fabric), insulin (a chemical regulator) and haemoglobin (a chemical carrier) can all have the same type of molecular structure. Proteins also form part of our defence mechanisms (immunoglobulins), they help adhesion between cells and enable movement within the cell. The reason for this diverse range of functionality becomes more understandable when one looks in detail at the basis of their chemical classification. Consider the synthetic substance polyglycine (**1.2**). This is formed when the **amino acid** glycine (**1.1**), or a suitable derivative, is polymerised through the formation of amide bonds. Hence polyglycine clearly has the same unit (the glycine residue) repeated throughout the sequence.

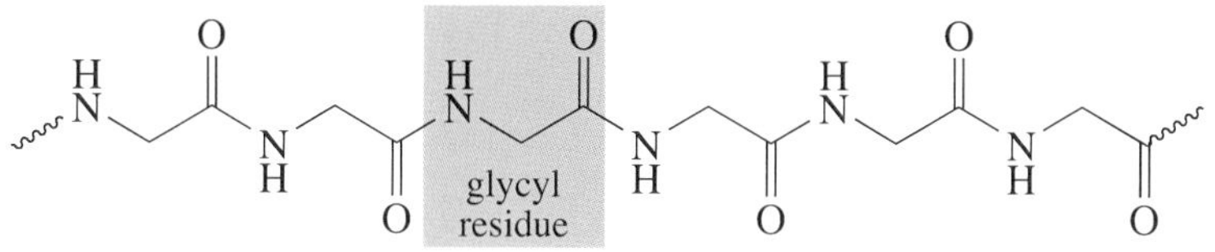

$H_2N-\overset{\alpha}{C}H_2-CO_2H$

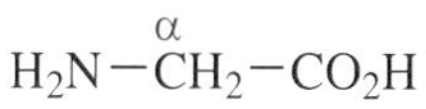

1.1

glycyl residue

1.2

All proteins have the same basic structure as polyglycine, with the polyamide 'backbone', but they are not strictly **polymers**. In a protein, an individual unit, or amino acid residue, is derived not from a single amino acid, but from any one of a list of 20 amino acids. Of the 20, glycine has the simplest structure, and all the others are related to glycine by replacing one of the hydrogen atoms on the α-carbon, that is the carbon next to the carboxylic acid group, by a side chain (**1.3**). (This is why they are known as α-amino acids.)

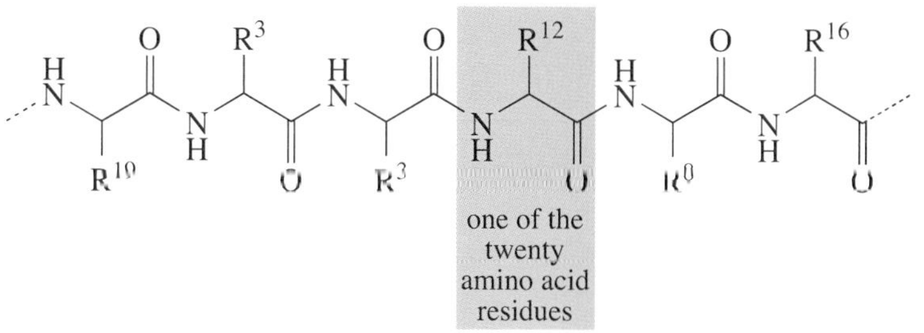

$H_2N-CH(R)-CO_2H$

1.3

one of the twenty amino acid residues

1.4

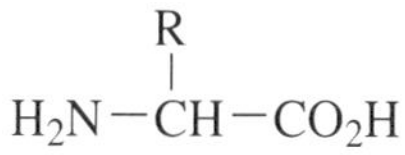

As there appears to be no limitation on the sequence of the different amino acid residues in a protein (**1.4**), it is easy to appreciate that the number of different proteins containing, say, 100 residues is inconceivably large. Each residue can be chosen in 20 ways, so 20^{100} such 100-residue proteins are possible – a number exceeding by far the supposed number of atoms in the whole universe. Moreover, most proteins contain many more than 100 amino acid residues.

But do you think that this information alone is sufficient as a satisfying explanation for the functional diversity of proteins in living organisms? You might say that it is, if the side chains $R^1 – R^{20}$ are sufficiently different. Well, have a look at them in Figure 1.1. What do you conclude?

There is no denying that there are fundamental differences between the side chains, although the differences could have been much greater. For instance, the largest side chain is in the tryptophyl residue in tryptophan, and further scope for variety seems to have been 'overlooked' by including the very similar valyl, leucyl and isoleucyl residues. The amino acids can be divided into four classes, depending upon their functionality: basic, acidic, nonpolar and polar uncharged. Also, note that residues that incorporate amino or carboxyl groups in their side chains (lysyl and aspartyl, for example) are never found to use those groups to form part of the polyamide backbone of a protein. The backbone is always derived from the α-substituted type of structure.

Whilst we may represent amino acids as in **1.3**, to highlight their amino and acid functional groups, in aqueous solution the acid –COOH group is acidic enough to protonate the basic amino group to give what is known as a **zwitterion (1.5)**, from the German, *zwitter*, meaning hybrid. So this is a more realistic representation of their structure.

$$H_3\overset{+}{N}-\underset{}{\overset{R}{\overset{|}{C}}}H-COO^-$$

1.5

Humans can only synthesise 11 of the 20 amino acids found in proteins, and these are called the *nonessential* amino acids. The other nine *essential* amino acids are only synthesised by plants and microorganisms; thus, we need to obtain them through our diet.

Returning to the issue of the functional diversity of proteins, even if the differences in amino acid structure are significant, do proteins with different biological functions differ markedly in their amino acid composition? To take an extreme case, we might well expect to find polyglycine, polyhistidine and polyaspartic acid to be very different substances and to fulfil differing functions if they occurred in a biosystem.

■ Examine Figure 1.2, what do you conclude?

□ The data in Figure 1.2 indicate very strongly that amino acid composition is only significant as an explanation of biofunctional diversity in some cases, and silk fibroin is obviously one of these. The other four proteins analysed have amino acid compositions that do not differ to anything like the extent that their differing biological roles might suggest they should.

So we have to look further than the mere availability of different side chains for an explanation of functional diversity. In short, we have to ask what are the consequences of a particular sequence of amino acid residues that leads ultimately to a highly specialised function. The answer can be seen if you look first at the amino acid sequence representations of, say, collagen, myoglobin and lysozyme (Figure 1.3) and then their three-dimensional (3D) structures using Discovery Studio®.

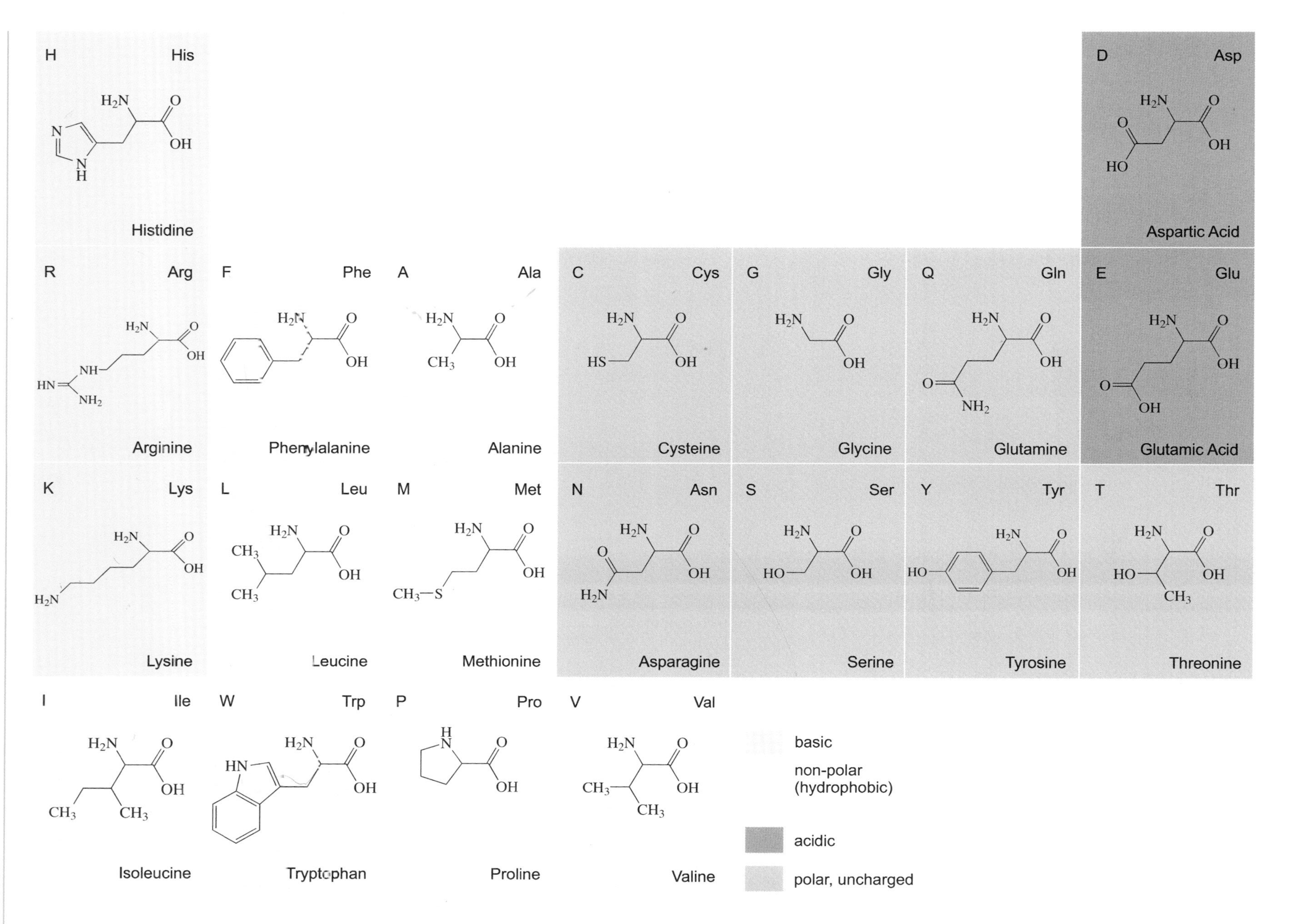

Figure 1.1 The 20 amino acid residues found in nearly all proteins. (A copy of this figure is available as a separate PDF file on the module website.)

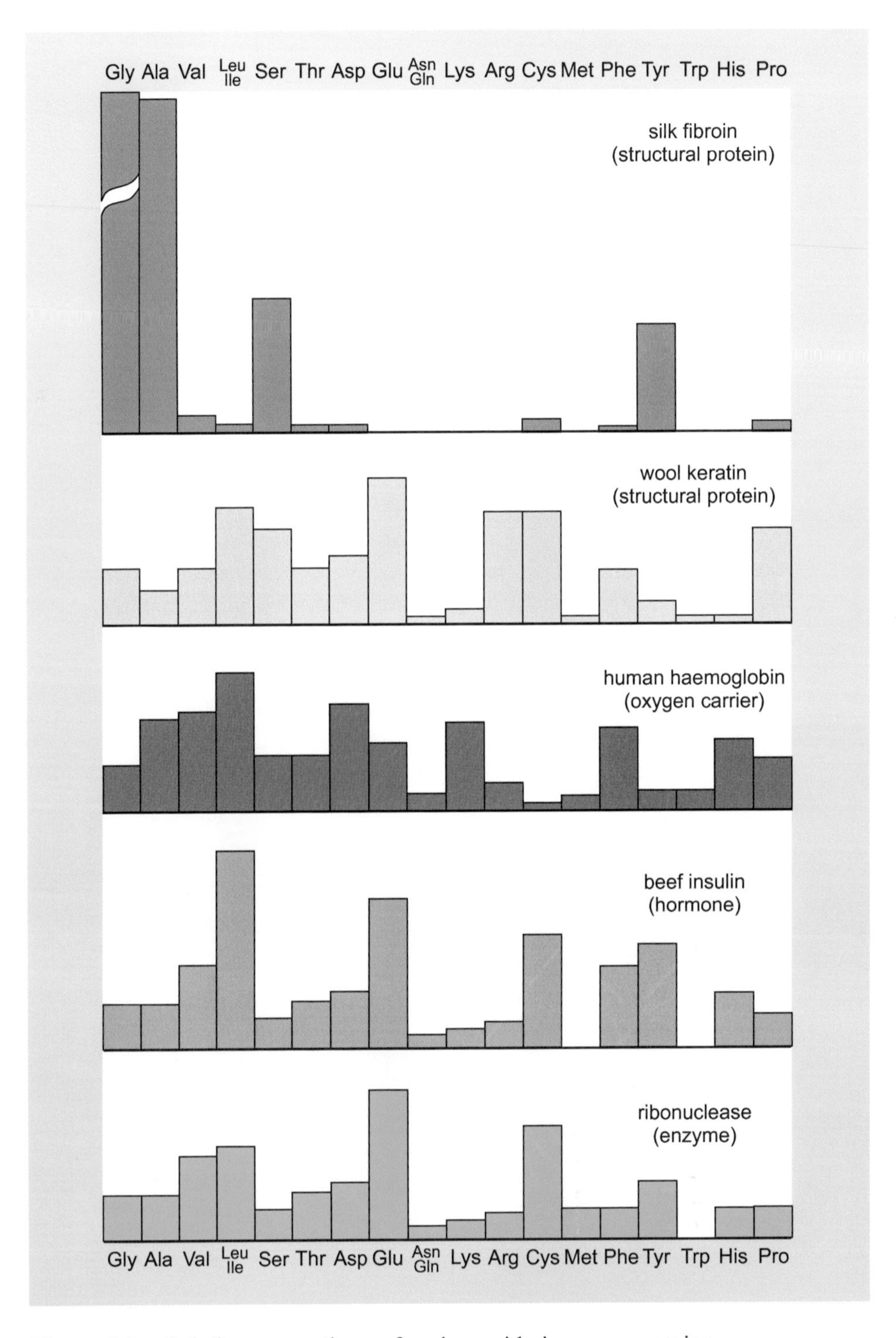

Figure 1.2 Relative proportions of amino acids in some proteins.

H-GlyTyrAspGluLysSerAlaG yValSerValProGlyProMetGlyProSerGlyProArgGlyLeu HO-Pro
Gly
HO-Pro GluGlyHO-ProGluGlyHO-ProProGlyGlnPheGlyGlnProGlyHO-ProAlaGlyHO-Pro Pro
Gly
Ala SerGlyProMetGlyProArgGlyProHO-ProGlyProHO-ProGlyLysAsnGlyAspAspGlyGlu Ala
Gly
Thr GlyHO-ProLeuGlyArgAlaGlyGlnProGlyHO-ProProGlyArgGlnGlyHO-ProArgGlyPro Lys
Ala
Gly LeuHO-ProGlyMetHO-LysGlyHisArgGlyPheSerGlyLeuAspGlyAlaLys GlyAsnThrGly Pro
Ala
Glu ArgProGlyMetGlnGlyHO-ProAlaGlyAsxGlxGlyHO-ProSerGlyHO-ProGluGlyLysPro Gly
Leu
HO-Pro GlyGluArgGlyArgHO-ProGlyProHO-ProGlySerAlaGlyAlaArgGlyAspAspGlyAla Val
Gly
Ala Gly AlaAlaGlyHO-ProPheGlyHO-ProProGlyThrProGlyThrProGlyHO-ProProGlyAla Ala
Lys
Gly GluAlaGlyProGlnGlyAlaArgGlySerGluGlyProGlnGlyValArgGlyGlu…→563 residues

(a)

H-ValLeuSerGluGlyGluTrpGlr LeuValLeuHisValTrpAla LysValGlu AlaAspValAlaGlyHis Gly
Gln
Thr LysLeuHisLysPheArgAspPheLysGluLeuThrGluProHisSerLysPheLeuArgIleLeuIle Asp
Glu
Ala GluMetLysAlaSerGluAspLeu LysLysHisGlyValThrValLeuThrAlaLeuGlyAlaIleLeu Lys Lys
Lys
Glu LeuTyrLysIleProIleLysHisLysThrAlaHisSerGlnAlaLeuProLysLeuGluAlaGluHisHis Gly
Phe
Ile SerGluAla Ile IleHisVal Leu His Ser Arg His Pro Gly Asn PheGlyAlaAspAlaGlnGlyAla Met
Asn
Gly-OHGlnTyrGlyHO-LeuGluLysTyrLysAlaAlaIleAspLysArgPheLeuGluLeuAla Lys

(b)

H-Lys Val Phe Gly Arg Cys Glu Leu Ala Ala Ala Met Lys
Arg
HO-Leu Arg Cys Gly Arg Ile Try His
Ala Gly
Gln Leu
Asn Arg Cys Lys Thr Asp Val Asp
Arg Asn
Try Tyr
Ala CysValTryAsnGlyLeuSerTyrGlyArg
Val Ala
Try AlaLysPheGluSerAsnPheAsnThrGln
Ala Ala
AsnMetGlyAspGlyAspSerVal Thr
Ile Asn
Lys Arg
SerAspIleThrAlaSerValAsnCysAlaLys Asn
Ser Thr
LeuLeuAlaSerCysProIleAsnCysLeuAsnArg Asp
Ser Gly
CysAspAsnGlyArgThrProGly Ser
Try Thr
TryArgSerAsnIleGlnLeuIleGlyTyrAsp

(c)

Figure 1.3 Amino acid sequence of (a) part of one chain of rat collagen; (b) sperm whale myoglobin; (c) hen egg-white lysozyme. 'OH-Pro' in the collagen sequence refers to γ-hydroxyproline, which occurs rarely in proteins other than collagen.

Activity 1.1

Open the following molecule files in Discovery Studio® collagen (pdb file 1cgd), myoglobin (1vxa) and lysozyme (2yvb), and view the proteins in separate 3D windows as ball-and-stick models. Advice on using Discovery Studio is given in Unit 1. (The molecule files are available from Unit 2 resources on the module website.)

It is clear that a change in amino acid sequence results in a change in structural form, and it is this, surely, that leads to widely different physical, chemical and hence biological properties. Like every other molecular chain, the backbone of a protein has conformational preferences. In fact, any protein invariably prefers just one conformation for its biological function – its so-called **native conformation**. It is reached in the first instance by successive bond rotations along the main chain, and in the side chains. These give rise to localised regular and irregular structures within the chain, including, in many proteins, sharp bends that allow the chain as a whole to fold back on itself. Thus, amino acid residues widely separated in sequence along the chain are brought close to one another in space, allowing interactions that further stabilise the conformation to take place between them. The sulfur-sulfur bonding between the cysteine residues in lysozyme (Figure 1.3) is an example. These localised conformations of a protein along the chain are part of the so-called secondary structure, and the folding of the whole chain is known as the tertiary structure of the protein. (You will have an opportunity to revise these and other aspects of protein structure in a moment.)

It is not difficult to see how the regular form of the native conformation of a fibrous protein like collagen or α-keratin (Figure 1.4) fits the molecule perfectly for its role in nature.

The long thread-like shape is ideal for packing laterally with others to form the fibrous structure that gives the material the strength necessary for its function. In contrast, most physiologically active proteins, such as myoglobin or lysozyme, resemble balls of tangled baling wire, and the 'fitness' of these conformations for their biological roles is not so obvious. But, as you probably know, one only needs to look briefly at the detail of how any one of these proteins functions to be convinced that the conformation is crucially specific. For instance, an enzyme's catalytic activity depends on it having just the right size of cavity in its tertiary structure to accommodate the substrate, just the right geometric disposition of groups to hold the substrate in a particular conformation, and just the right groups strategically located to stabilise the transition state of the reaction. Even a minor adjustment to the 'tangle' could make the structure useless.

One cannot but be impressed by the economy of chemistry in the structural and functional diversity of proteins. The same fundamental units can lead to molecular structures of widely differing form and properties because of interactions within the chain that contains them.

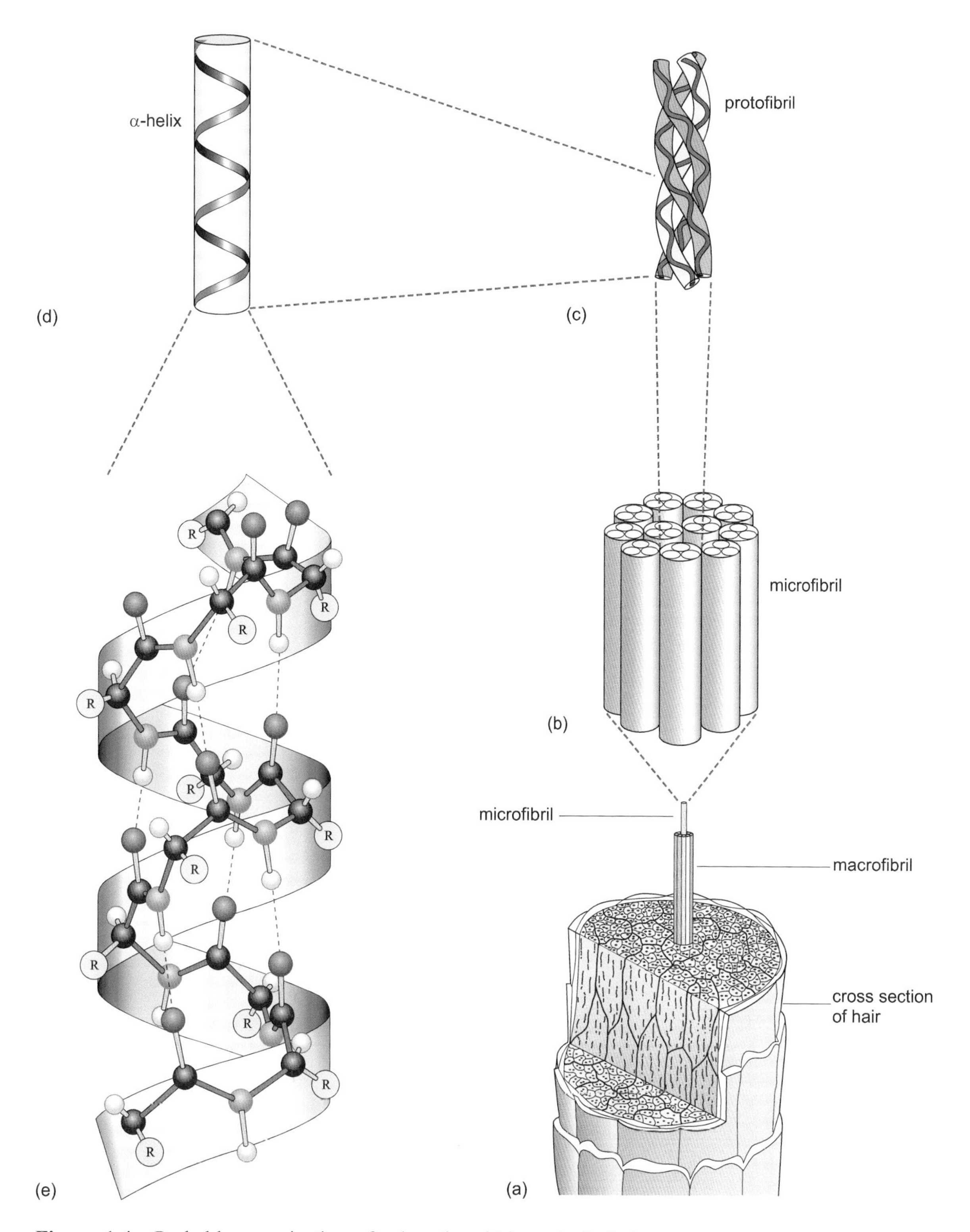

Figure 1.4 Probable organisation of α-keratin within a single hair.

We recommend that, before proceeding any further, you revise or become familiar with a few aspects of the language of protein structure.

1 You will find that an ability to recall the names and structures of all 20 amino acid residues will ease your study of what follows considerably, although you may prefer to print out Figure 1.1 to use as a reference.

2 In the context of amino acid and protein chemistry, the amide bond that links the residues is known as a **peptide bond**. We shall also use the following related definitions in this module:

- A **peptide** – a compound composed of 2 to 50 amino acid units, linked through peptide bonds. There appears to be no generally accepted demarcation between a large peptide and a small protein, although few proteins have less than 80 amino acid residues. We shall refer to the linear sequence of residues in a protein as its peptide chain or **backbone**.
- A dipeptide, tripeptide, etc. – compounds containing two residues, three residues, etc. respectively.
- A poly-α-amino acid – a polymer of an α-amino acid.
- A **polypeptide** – although logic demands that this term should be restricted to a polymer of a peptide, we shall adopt its common usage as any long sequence of amino acid residues.

We shall follow the established convention of naming peptides by regarding them as acylated derivatives of the last amino acid residue. Thus, following the abbreviations given in Figure 1.1, the peptide **1.6** is named valylalanylglycine and abbreviated H–Val-Ala-Gly–OH. So the amino end of a peptide always appears on the left and the carboxyl end on the right. We shall also use the notation L and D to distinguish enantiomers, because this is the one used principally by protein chemists (they are called L amino acids because of their stereochemical similarity to the L sugars). All protein amino acids (other than glycine, which is achiral) occur naturally as the L-enantiomer **1.7**.

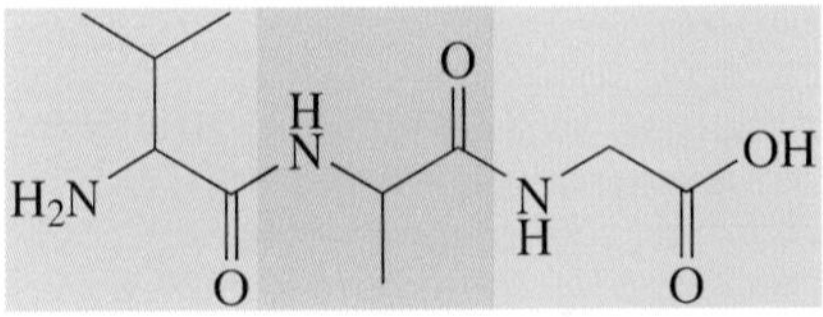

1.6

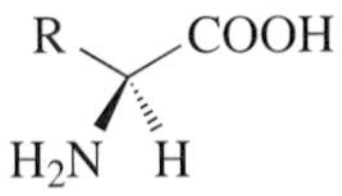

1.7

As we shall see in Unit 4, we can also assign an *R* or *S* designation to the chiral centre.

3 Although we have already mentioned secondary and tertiary structures, it is as well to review the classification of structural elements in proteins.

- The **primary structure** is simply the sequence of amino acids in the peptide chain, or in any one of the chains if there are more than one.
- The **secondary structure** refers to the sequence of local conformations within the chain. Each regular local conformation is an element of secondary structure and commonly incorporates 4 to 20 residues.
- The **tertiary structure** of a protein refers to the folding of the chain as a whole, together with its secondary structural elements.

- Finally, the term **quaternary structure** is reserved for the way the peptide chains fit together in a protein that contains more than one polypeptide chain.

4 As regards the classification of proteins, we shall be concerned only with whether the protein is fibrous (that is, its overall shape is long and thin) or globular (that is, its overall shape is spherical or ovular). In general, globular proteins are enzymes, receptors and transport proteins, whereas fibrous proteins are structural. However, this distinction is not unambiguous; some globular proteins have structural roles (the protein 'coat' of a virus, for example), although few protein chemical agents are fibrous.

5 The last term we want to elaborate at this point is the word 'conformation'. You may have come across the term conformation used to refer to any one of the infinite number of arrangements in space of the atoms of a molecule that can be interconverted by single-bond rotations at room temperature.

The term 'conformation' has a slightly different meaning in the context of protein chemistry. Although both the components of the secondary structure and the tertiary structure as a whole are derived formally by bond rotations along the chain, it is misleading to think that the conformations found in a protein or that of the entire molecule can interconvert freely with many others at room temperature. Indeed, you will see that it is only under special circumstances that the overall 3D structure of a protein changes at all. Nevertheless, the shape of a protein is almost universally described as its native 'conformation', and we shall follow the convention.

6 When, in response to an environmental effect, a protein undergoes a conformational change that destroys the tertiary and secondary structures of its native conformation, it is said to be **denatured**. Some denatured proteins can undergo 'renaturation' to their native conformations.

1.2 Protein conformation

One of the most widely occurring types of fibrous proteins are the keratins (Figure 1.4), which are conveniently classified in two groups. The α-keratins have a high sulfur content (they are rich in cysteine residues) and include the hard, brittle proteins of horns and nails as well as the softer more flexible keratins of skin, hair and wool (Figure 1.2). The β-keratins contain no cysteine, but are rich in residues with small side chains, particularly glycine, alanine and serine. They are found in thc fibres spun by spiders and silkworms, as well as in the scales, claws and beaks of reptiles and birds. Another important difference between the two classes is that the α-keratins stretch when heated, whereas the β-keratins do not. In the early 1930s, W. T. Astbury, a British crystallographer, noted that proteins in the α-keratin class gave similar X-ray diffraction patterns, which indicated that they possessed a major repeat unit of about 0.5 nm along their axes. On the other hand, the β-keratin of silk fibres has a distinctly different X-ray diffraction pattern, which indicated a repeat unit of about 0.7 nm. Significantly, when hair or wool is stretched after steaming, it produces an X-ray pattern similar to that of the β-keratins.

In the late 1930s, L. Pauling and R. B. Corey in the United States used X-ray diffraction data to show that the peptide bond in simple peptides is a relatively rigid structure. The peptide C–N bond and the four atoms attached to it lie in a single plane and the N–H bond is *trans* to the C=O bond. This means that the backbone of the polypeptide chain may be pictured as a series of relatively rigid planes separated by substituted methylene groups (–CHR) (Figure 1.5).

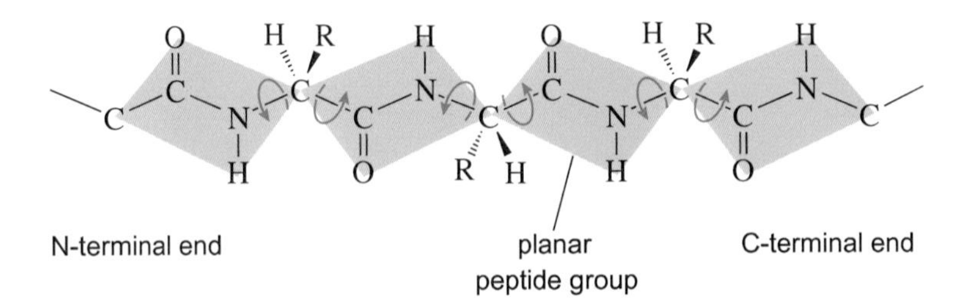

Figure 1.5 Restricted rotation around the single bonds of a polypeptide chain. Only the single bonds to the α-carbon atoms are free to rotate; the C–N single bonds of the planar peptide groups are rigid.

- ■ Why do you think the C–N bond and the four atoms attached to it lie in a single plane?

- □ Two resonance forms of the amide group can be drawn:

  The nitrogen is sp^2 hybridised and the non-bonded pair on the nitrogen occupies a p orbital which needs to overlap with the π bond of the C=O as shown below. Thus the atoms are forced to lie in the same plane.

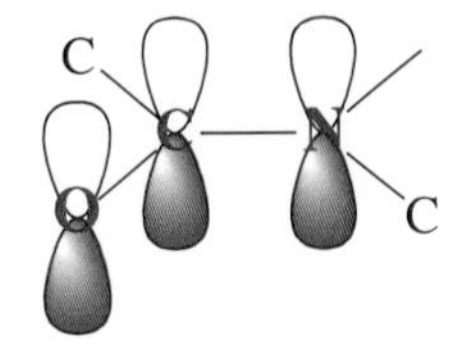

- ■ Why do you think the N–H bond is generally *trans* to the C=O bond?

N−H and C=O *trans*

N−H and C=O *cis*

- □ The *trans* conformation would be energetically more favorable than the *cis* conformation since it contains less steric hindrance. (Note this is not necessarily true of proline residues, which have no N–H bond in a protein.)

Using models, Pauling and Corey found that they could account for the 0.5 nm repeat units in α-keratin if the molecule adopted a helical structure, where the repeat unit is one complete turn of the helix containing the equivalent of 3.6 amino acid residues.

Activity 1.2

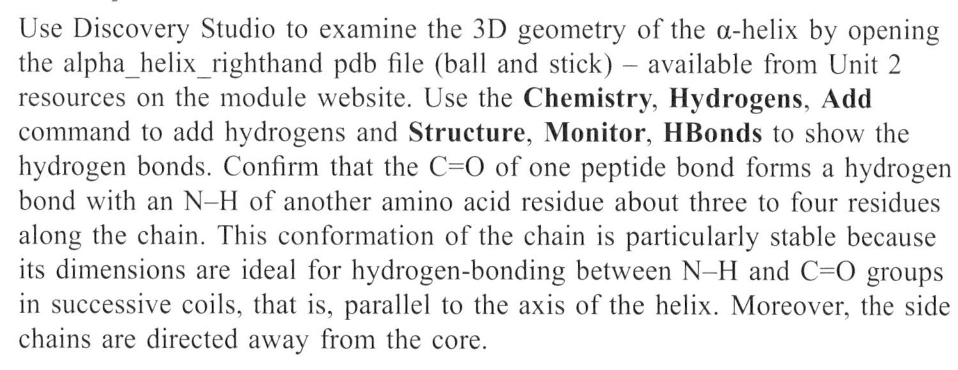

Use Discovery Studio to examine the 3D geometry of the α-helix by opening the alpha_helix_righthand pdb file (ball and stick) – available from Unit 2 resources on the module website. Use the **Chemistry**, **Hydrogens**, **Add** command to add hydrogens and **Structure**, **Monitor**, **HBonds** to show the hydrogen bonds. Confirm that the C=O of one peptide bond forms a hydrogen bond with an N–H of another amino acid residue about three to four residues along the chain. This conformation of the chain is particularly stable because its dimensions are ideal for hydrogen-bonding between N–H and C=O groups in successive coils, that is, parallel to the axis of the helix. Moreover, the side chains are directed away from the core.

- ■ A helix can be either right-handed or left-handed. What would be the stereochemical relationships between right- and left-handed helices of polyglycine, and the polypeptide chain of a protein?

- □ The two polyglycine helices would be enantiomeric, since the helix is the only source of chirality. The two polypeptide helices would be diastereomeric because both would contain L-amino acid residues, giving rise to the combinations L with right-handed helix and L with left-handed helix.

Models show that the right-handed version of the helix is likely to be more stable than the left, because in the latter the side chains are in closer contact with the carbonyl groups.

Activity 1.3

You should be able to see this using Discovery Studio. Open the pdb file alpha_helix_left_handed in a separate 3D window. (The molecule file is in Unit 2 resources on the module website.)

The right-handed helix has since been shown to be widely distributed in stable conformations of proteins and of synthetic polypeptides, and, because of its historical connection with α-keratin, it has always been known as the **α_R-**

helix. Moreover, as the left-handed helix is comparatively rare, the subscript R is often omitted. In globular proteins, a helical sequence will, on average, include 12 amino acid residues, although some proteins have up to 50 amino acid residues in an α-helix.

Whilst the α-helix is the most common form of helix, a number of different helical structures have been identified in proteins. These helices vary depending upon the number of amino acid residues per turn (rarely an integer) and the pitch, the distance the helix rises along its axis per turn (Figure 1.6).

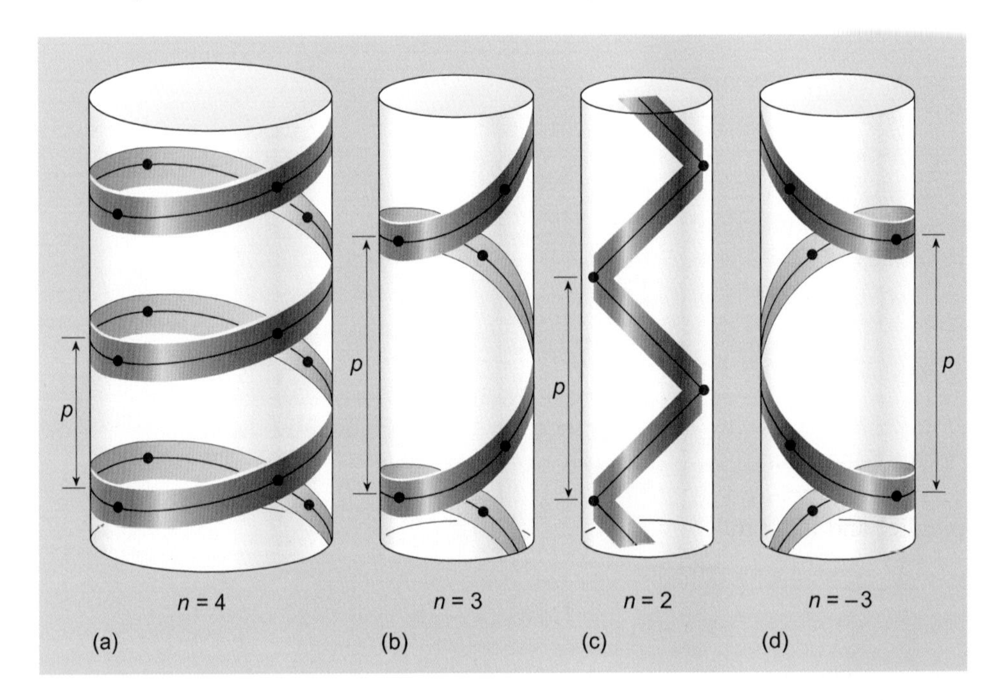

Figure 1.6 Examples of helices occurring in proteins indicating the parameters of pitch p, number of units per turn n and handedness (+ or –). The black circles denote amino acid residues.

1.2.1 Pleated sheets

Pauling and Corey concluded that the adoption by an α-keratin of a β-keratin-type structure on heating corresponded to the breaking of the hydrogen bonds in the α-helix and the consequent stretching to a more extended zigzag conformation of the chain, this being the preferred conformation of the β-keratins themselves. Individual stretched chains can then form intermolecular hydrogen bonds with other chains in a side-by-side arrangement, producing an overall pleated sheet-like structure.

Activity 1.4

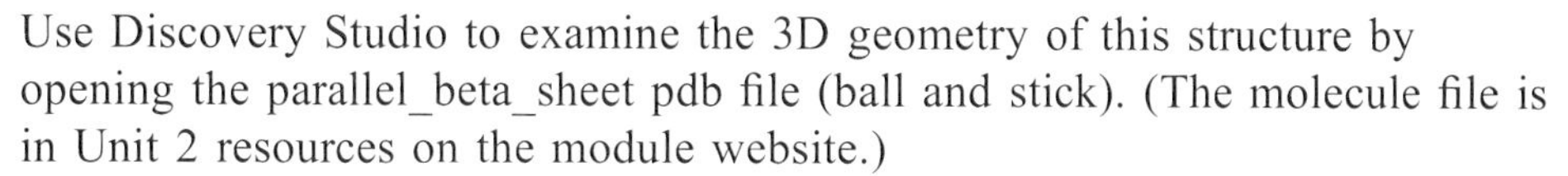
Use Discovery Studio to examine the 3D geometry of this structure by opening the parallel_beta_sheet pdb file (ball and stick). (The molecule file is in Unit 2 resources on the module website.)

There is a significant difference between the 'natural' pleated sheets of a β-keratin and those of a stretched α-keratin. It turns out that the helices in a bundle of α-keratin chains run in the same direction from N-terminal end to C-terminal end (see the protofibril in Figure 1.4). So when they are stretched in the β-form, the chains are parallel (Figure 1.7b). The chains in a β-keratin sheet, on the other hand, are antiparallel; that is adjacent chains run in the opposite direction (Figure 1.7a).

Activity 1.5

Use Discovery Studio to examine the 3D geometry of this structure by opening the betasheet_antiparallel pdb file (ball and stick). You may need to rotate the structure to identify the β-sheet network. It is easier to compare the parallel and antiparallel structures on the screen, if you place the 3D windows next to each other.

These extended sheet-like structures are also found as conformational features in single polypeptide chains, folding back on themselves, and again, because of the historical development, they have become known as β-structures, **β-pleated sheets (antiparallel** or **parallel**)or *extended structures*. Notice that the strands are not fully extended but have a zigzag shape, which gives the sheet formation, in both parallel and antiparallel structures, a pleated appearance when viewed edge-on (Figure 1.8). The α-carbon atoms of successive residues are at, alternately, the top and bottom of each pleat, with the side chains pointing away from the sheet. In globular proteins antiparallel β-pleated sheets can contain from two to 15 polypeptide strands, with the average being six strands. Each individual strand can contain up to 15 amino acid residues with the average being six. Parallel β-pleated sheets appear to be less stable than antiparallel β-pleated sheets and rarely contain fewer than five polypeptide chains.

- Clearly, a single polypeptide chain must undergo considerable folding to generate β-conformations. Imagine that a protein with 150 residues contains two such conformations, one parallel and one antiparallel. In one it is found that residue 78 is hydrogen bonded to residue 89 and in the other that residue 32 is hydrogen bonded to residue 115. Which two residues are part of the parallel β-structure?

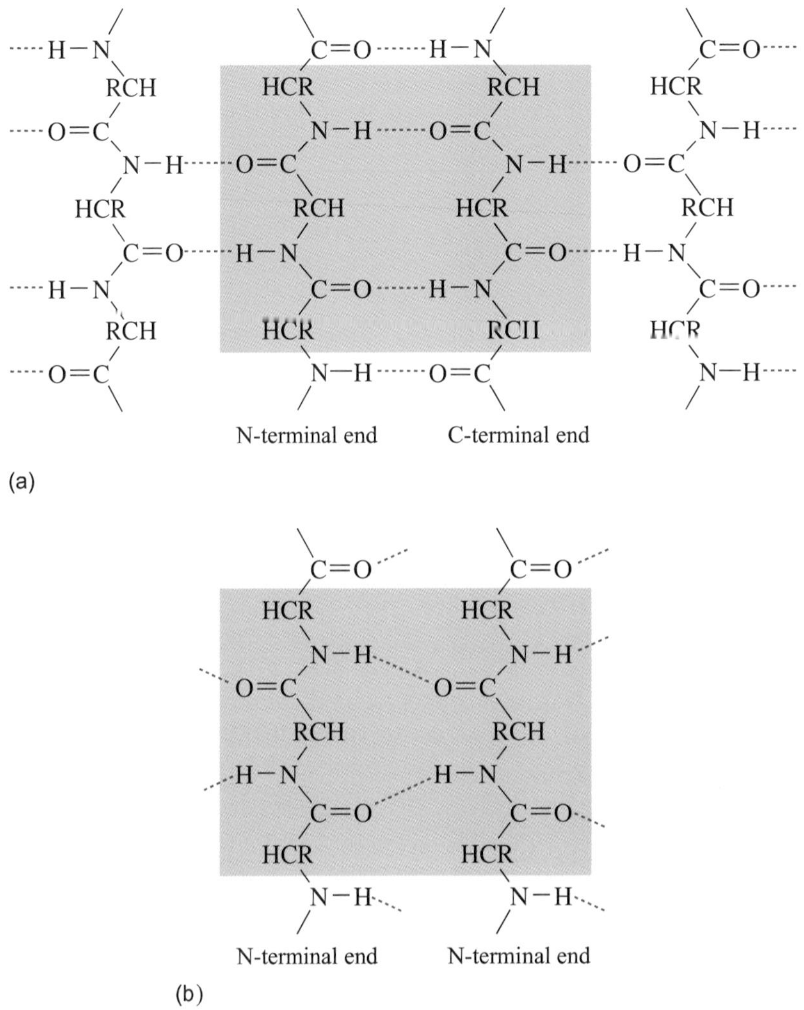

N-terminal end C-terminal end

(a)

N-terminal end N-terminal end

(b)

Figure 1.7 Schematic diagram illustrating the hydrogen-bonding arrangements in (a) the antiparallel-chain sheet and (b) the parallel-chain sheet model for β-structures. The shaded frames enclose the same number of residues in each type of sheet. Notice that in (a) the hydrogen bonds are horizontal, but in (b) they are not.

□ When hydrogen-bonded residues in a β-sheet are close in sequence, that part of the sheet must be formed by a single 180° turn, thus creating an antiparallel arrangement (Figure 1.9a). Hydrogen-bonded residues in a parallel β-conformation must be widely separated in the sequence in order for the two strands to be going in the same direction when associated (Figure 1.9b). Hence, residues 32 and 115 are part of the parallel β-structure.

The function of fibrous proteins demands a regular conformation for most of the polypeptide chains. One finds that globular proteins contain only segments of regular structures, usually of the α- or β-type, and segments of non-regular conformation. Remember that the linear arrangement of these segments constitutes the secondary structure of the protein. The tertiary structure is derived from the secondary structure by introducing loops and sharp bends that cause the linear arrangement to fold back on itself. (Indeed, sharp bends

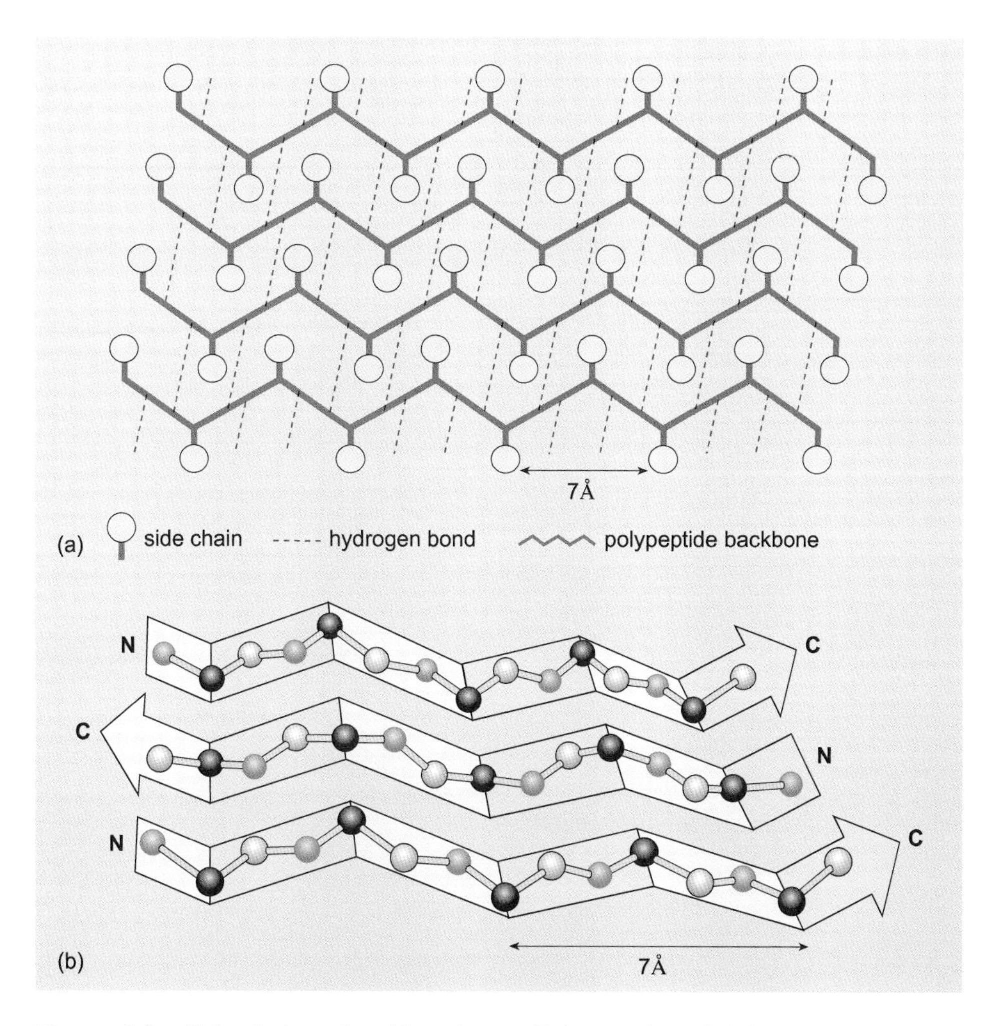

Figure 1.8 Side chains of residues in parallel or antiparallel β-sheet point away from the sheet, with successive side chains alternatively above and below.

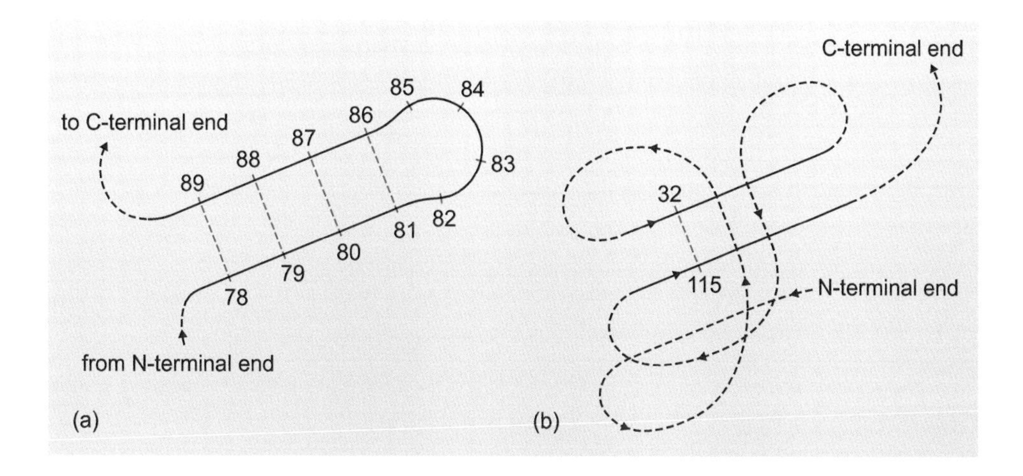

Figure 1.9 Typical folding in (a) antiparallel β-sheets and (b) parallel β-sheets.

are needed to create most antiparallel β-structures in the first place – see Figure 1.10, which illustrates the different kinds of connection that can occur between adjacent strands in pleated sheets.)

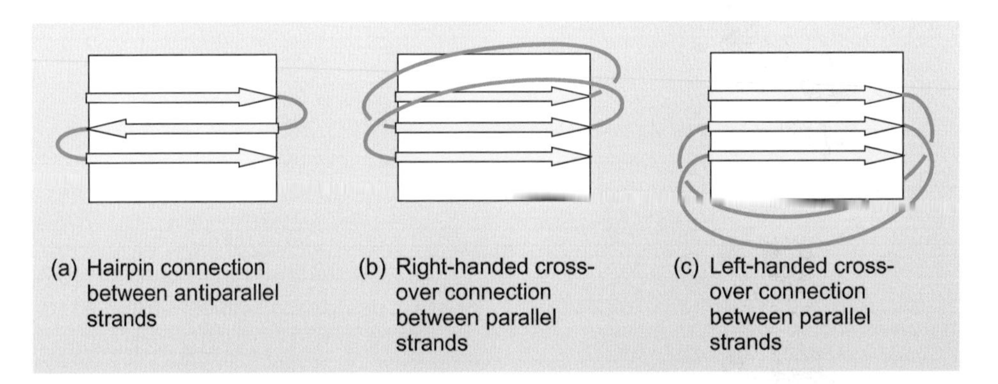

Figure 1.10 Types of linkage between adjacent β-sheet strands. (a) Simple hairpins in antiparallel structures. (b) and (c) Crossover connections in parallel β-pleated sheets – these connections can be very long and contain other elements of secondary structure such as α-helices.

The tertiary structure is then stabilised by interactions between sequentially remote parts of the chain; we shall discuss these in Section 1.5. But clearly an important aspect of protein conformation is the form of these sharp bends or **β-turns** as they have become known, which lead to antiparallel β-pleated sheets. β-turns are usually formed from a four-unit segment folded in the middle. Two types are recognised, as shown in Figure 1.11.

Activity 1.6

Use Discovery Studio to examine the 3D geometry of these structures by opening the pdb files betabend_typeI and betabend_typeII (ball and stick). (The molecule files are in Unit 2 resources on the module website.)

Type I has the C=O bond (arrowed) of the second residue pointing away from the plane of the bend on the opposite side to the second and third side chains, R^2 and R^3, whereas the C=O bond in Type II is located on the same side of the plane as the second and third side chains, R^2 and R^3.

Notice that β-bends are tighter than the turn in the α-helix. The amino acid on the $C_{\alpha 2}$ residue is frequently proline, which readily adopts the required conformation for such a turn. β-bends are usually located at the surface of a protein.

1.3 Representations of secondary structure

The secondary structure of proteins, such as α-helices and β-sheets can be highlighted in a protein's structure using the **ribbon notation**.

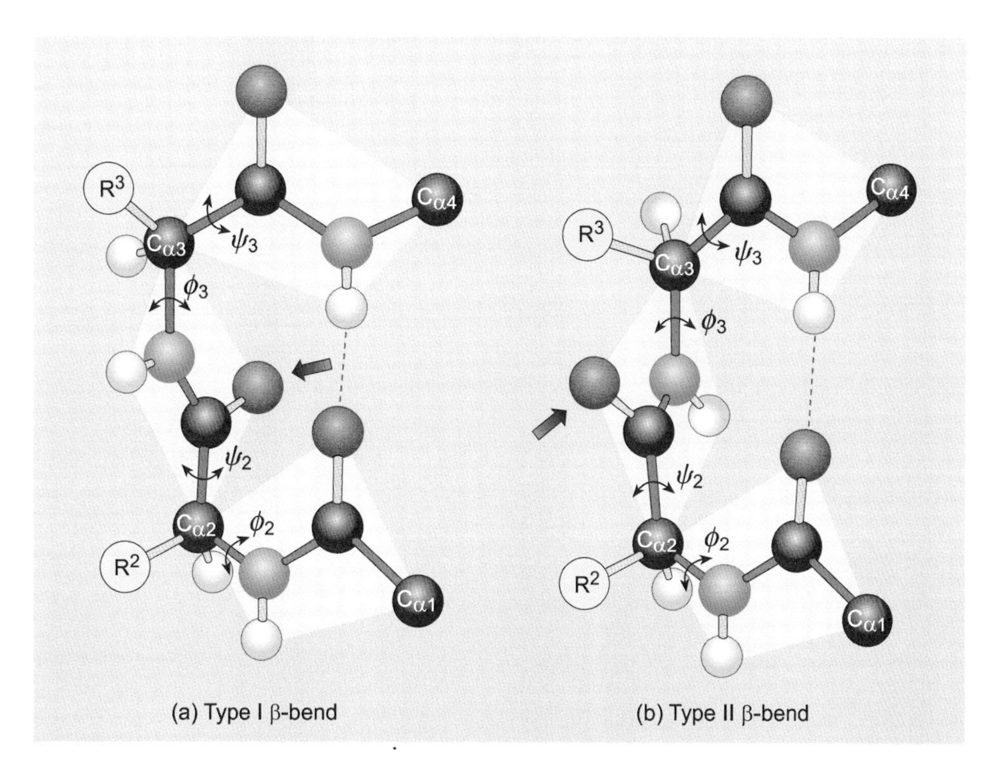

Figure 1.11 (a) Type I β-bend with any L-residue at any of the four positions $C_{\alpha 1}$–$C_{\alpha 4}$. (b) Type II β-bend with only glycyl being possible at position $C_{\alpha 3}$.

Activity 1.7

In this slightly longer activity, you will use Discovery Studio to examine the structure of a number of proteins and look at the different ways in which proteins can be represented. In particular, you will look at elements of protein secondary structure, α-helices and β-pleated sheet.

You should start by watching the following three video clips 'Modelling the structure of proteins' and then work through Activity 1.7 as described in *Unit 2 Activities* which is available from Unit 2 resources.

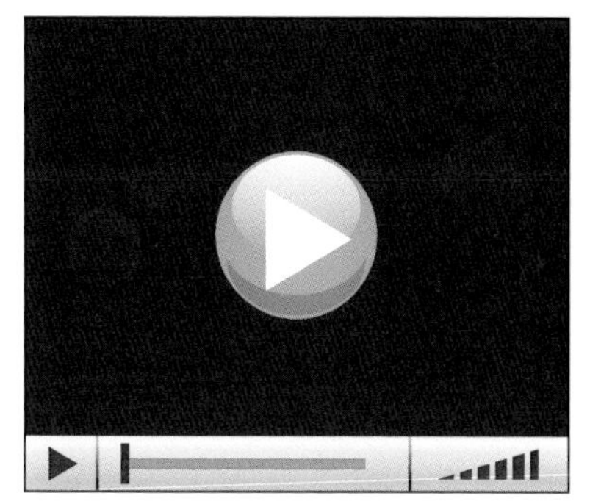

The three video clips can be viewed from the online version of this text or from Unit 2 resources on the module website – they are identical.

Modelling the structure of proteins

The files for the various molecular structures mentioned in the video are available from Unit 2 resources on the module website.

1.3.1 Analysing protein structures

Later in Unit 2 you will learn how to download protein structures for yourself from the RCSB protein database. But in general, once you have opened a protein structure in the 3D window of Discovery Studio you should:

- Look in the hierarchy window to identify if the protein is made up of more than one protein chain. By highlighting the different chains in the hierarchy window you can discover if there are subunits and if they are identical.
- Look at each non-identical subunit in turn by switching off the others and examine the secondary structure of the protein chain – identify the α-helices and the β-sheets and whether the sheets are parallel or antiparallel. Are there clear twists or turns of the overall secondary structure?
- Examine any substrate or non-proteinaceous functionality, such as the haem, in the structure. These can often be seen by highlighting a second 'chain A' if present in the hierarchy window and also opening the folder associated with the second 'chain A'.
- Open the protein groups in the hierarchy window to examine any special features such as active sites.
- View the active sites with the rest of the protein structure turned off and then add the substrate or heteroatoms into the window to see how the molecules are disposed relative to each other. Use the hydrogen bond monitor to examine the interactions.

1.4 Determining the structures of proteins

As we have seen, proteins are complex large molecules and thus require special techniques to discover their 3D structure. Common spectroscopic analyses are mainly aimed at small molecules and need a great deal more sophistication before they can be used to reveal the structure of a protein containing thousands of atoms. The main techniques used are X-ray crystallography and nuclear magnetic resonance (NMR), although NMR has only been used for about 7% of the total structures discovered to date.

The first detailed and complete structure of a protein (sperm whale myoglobin) as afforded by high-resolution X-ray diffraction, was published in 1958. By 1971 over 40 such analyses had been carried out. But, in contrast with the usual rate of growth of scientific developments, only a further ten or so analyses were added in the succeeding 4 years. Clearly, the structures of the most easily available and relatively small proteins were the prime candidates for X-ray diffraction. With developments in protein purification and X-ray methodology this had increased to about 150 proteins in 1984, but by 2000 this had increased to about 12 000 structures. This increase has continued unabated, such that by early 2009 about 50 000 structures were stored on the **RCSB protein database** – The Research Collaboratory for Structural Bioinformatics based at Rutgers University, the University of California in San Diego and the University of Wisconsin-Madison. Data specifying the coordinates of every atom in the molecule or complex are stored in the form of pdb files. Many proteins have more than one pdb file in this data bank, corresponding to different sets of data collected; for example, using different techniques or conditions, with or without a bound ligand, or for various species or various mutant versions of a protein. We will look in more detail at the RCSB protein database in Section 1.6.

One of the first steps in the experimental determination of the structure of a protein is to identify the primary structure, i.e. the sequence of amino acids.

In the next few sections we describe some very complex techniques. You are not expected to understand each in detail but rather to be aware of the processes by which protein structures are determined.

1.4.1 Primary structures – sequencing

The primary structure of an unknown protein can be determined by first identifying what amino acids are present, then how much of each amino acid is present and then their order. What amino acids are present and in what quantities is answered using an amino acid analyser. This is an automated instrument that first chemically breaks the polypeptide chain into its constituent amino acids. The disulfide bonds are reduced and the remaining –SH groups of the cysteine amino acids capped by an S_N2 reaction with iodoacetic acid.

$$R{-}CH_2{-}SH + ICH_2COOH \rightarrow R{-}CH_2{-}S{-}CH_2COOH \qquad (1.1)$$

- ■ Write out the mechanism of Reaction 1.1.
- □ The mechanism is given in Scheme 1.1:

$$R-CH_2-\ddot{S}H \quad H_2C(I)(COOH) \longrightarrow R-CH_2-\overset{+}{S}(H)-CH_2-COOH + I^-$$

$$\downarrow -H^+$$

$$R-CH_2-S-CH_2-COOH$$

Scheme 1.1

The amide bonds are then hydrolysed using 6 mol dm^{-3} HCl at 100–110 °C for 24 hours, giving a mixture of amino acids that can be analysed using high performance liquid chromatography (HPLC) or ion-exchange chromatography (Figure 1.12).

The retention time on the column provides information on the identity of the amino acid and the peak area allows the calculation of the relative amount of amino acids.

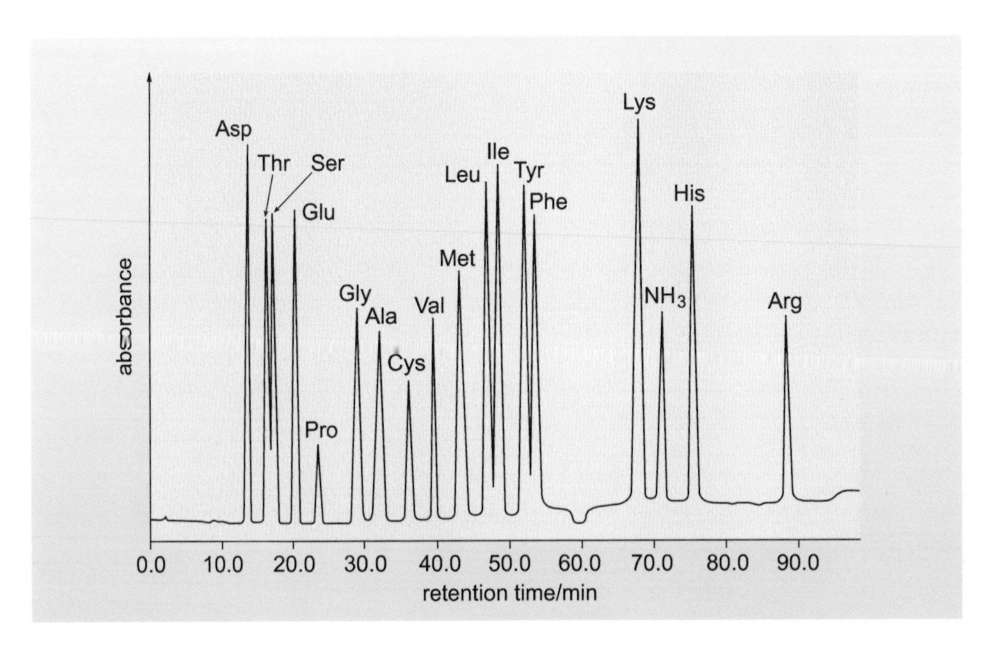

Figure 1.12 Amino acid analysis of an equimolar amino acid mixture.

Having determined what amino acids are present and their amounts, we can now determine their sequence. The two common methods of determining the primary structure of a protein are mass spectroscopy and the **Edman degradation**.

The Edman degradation (shown in Scheme 1.2) involves treating the peptide with phenyl isothiocyanate (Ph–N=C=S) followed by trifluoroacetic acid. This effectively cuts off the first amino acid residue from the N-terminal end of the peptide chain to yield a anilinothiazolinone, **1.8**, which rearranges to a phenylthiohydantoin, **1.9**, in acid. The nature of the original amino acid can be identified using HPLC based on the retention time of **1.9**.

The sequence of amino acids can be determined by cleaving one amino acid at a time from the N-terminal end. This can be automated so that an **amino acid sequencer** can identify up to the first 50 amino acid residues in the chain. Whilst each degradation reaction has a very high yield, after about 50 cycles there is too much byproduct present where one amino acid has not been removed because of incomplete reaction and this can complicate the analysis. However, proteins with more than 400 amino acids can be sequenced if a large polypeptide chain is first cleaved by partial hydrolysis to give a number of smaller fragments. These are then sequenced and the individual fragments fitted together by examining overlapping patterns. The strength of this technique is that the amino acid analyser can analyse less than 0.1 μg of protein. The cleavage into smaller fragments can be achieved by enzymatic hydrolysis, using trypsin or pepsin which only cleaves the amide bond between specific amino acid residues, giving reproducible smaller fragments. Using different enzymes means that different fragments can be obtained to ease the mapping. The knowledge of the relative amounts of amino acids can be used to confirm the structure or resolve ambiguities in the mapping.

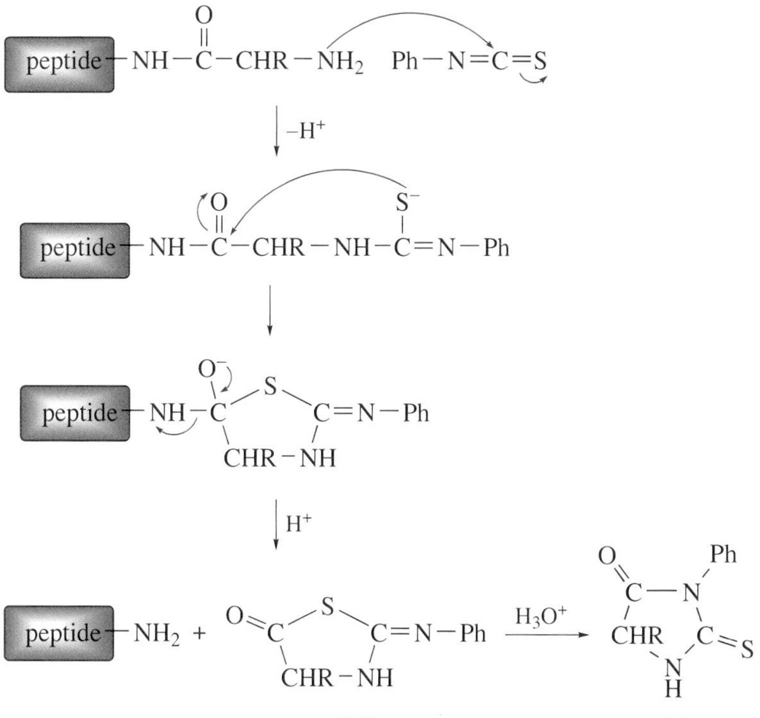

Scheme 1.2

Mass spectrometry is a technique which determines the mass of a molecule by creating a charged species and examining its path in a magnetic and/or electric field. Depending on the mass to charge ratio m/z, the ion will be deflected by different amounts by the magnetic and/or electric field and this deflection can be measured accurately.

Proteins tend to be involatile polar compounds, and so special techniques are required to get them into the gas phase for mass spectrometric analysis. The two most common techniques are matrix-assisted laser desorption/ionisation (**MALDI**) and **electrospray ionisation**.

- In MALDI, a laser is used to vaporise and ionise the protein. The matrix is employed to reduce the amount of decomposition by the laser beam.
- In electrospray ionisation, a solution of the protein is sprayed from a narrow capillary to form an aerosol. As the solvent evaporates, the charged proteins repel each other and break up the droplet eventually to leave the protein in the gas phase.

In both cases only very small amounts of material are required to produce a mass spectrum. This makes it ideal for proteins, since often only minute amounts of purified protein are isolable. In 2002 John B. Fenn and Koichi Tanaka were awarded the Nobel Prize in Chemistry 'for their development of soft desorption ionisation methods for mass spectrometric analyses of biological macromolecules'.

Mass spectrometry provides two key pieces of information: the accurate mass of a molecule (which provides the elemental constitution of the molecule) and a fragmentation pattern that provides evidence of structural fragments that can be recombined to deduce the overall structure and, thus, the sequence of amino acid residues. Fragmentation of a protein molecule occurs in a fairly predictable fashion; so, even though there are a large number of fragmentations from a protein, computer programs can be used to analyse the data and generate the most likely sequence. As with the Edman reagent, it is often useful to break large proteins up into smaller pieces by enzymic digestion first to simplify the mass spectral analysis.

Having identified the primary structure, the next step is to determine the conformation – how the chain is folded in space.

1.4.2 Protein structures using X-ray crystallography

Start this section by watching the following video. This video introduces you to the technique of single crystal X-ray crystallography, as applied to proteins. This was recorded a number of years ago and the technique and equipment have developed since then, but the principles are still the same.

This sequence can be viewed from the online version of this text, or from Unit 2 resources – they are identical.

The X-ray structure of barnase

X-ray crystallography is used to determine the structure of crystals. The key property of a crystal is that it consists of regular arrays of atoms, ions or molecules in three dimensions. Because the structure is regular, or 'periodic', a crystal can act as a 3D diffraction grating to radiation of a suitable wavelength, in this case X-rays. This is illustrated in two dimensions in Figure 1.13.

The X-ray diffraction patterns obtained from crystals are extremely complicated. However, in most cases the position and intensity of the diffracted peaks can be interpreted to give a complete analysis of the internal structure of the crystal providing accurate values of the bond lengths and bond angles. The process is difficult enough for simple molecules but proteins provide specific challenges. First, proteins are very large containing thousands of atoms and so the diffraction patterns they generate are complex. Second, in order for X-ray crystallography to be of any use, the individual protein molecules need to crystallise into a regular array. It was overcoming these problems that meant that X-ray crystallography of proteins has only become routine in recent years.

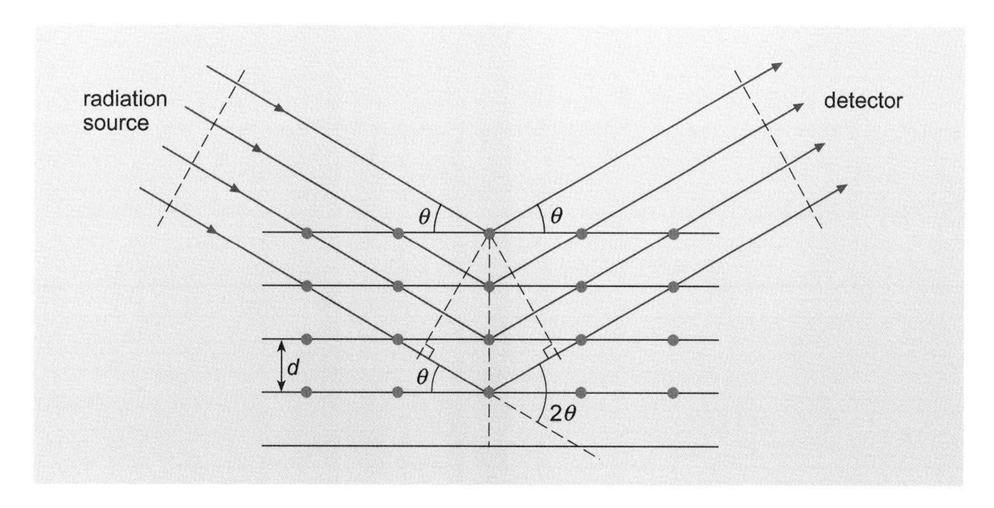

Figure 1.13 Diffraction of electromagnetic radiation incident at angle θ to crystal planes distance d apart.

Tens or even hundreds of milligrams of pure protein, may be required to obtain crystals of sufficient quality and size to carry out X-ray analysis, and obtaining protein in these quantities can be a challenge in itself. The art of crystallisation is to identify the conditions that allow protein molecules to come out of solution and associate in an ordered 3D array. Therefore hundreds of trials may be necessary to optimise the conditions for crystallisation. Recombinant DNA technology is widely used to produce many proteins in sufficiently large quantities and in a highly purified form. The time-consuming process of optimizing crystallisation conditions has been accelerated by the use of automated techniques.

Having obtained a satisfactory crystal of the protein it is aligned in an X-ray beam and the diffraction pattern determined. The fixed locations of the atoms cause this scattering to be amplified and concentrated in defined directions to produce a series of spots on a diffraction photograph (Figure 1.14). The spacing of the spots in a diffraction image is inversely related to the size of the unit cell. The intensity of the spots gives information about the type of atoms and their relative positions.

In order to reconstruct an image of the protein from the diffracted X-rays, one needs to be able to recombine the scattered waves. How this is done is beyond the scope of this module, suffice it to say that with complex protein structures this is a relatively time-consuming, but achievable, task. Since the X-rays are scattered by the electron density around the atoms, we end up with an electron density map of the unit cell.

Protein crystals typically contain 30–70% solvent. The large amount of solvent within the crystal structure means that there are large spaces between molecules, which renders the intermolecular forces between them relatively weak. This, in turn, means that the positions of the molecules vary slightly within the crystal. So, the diffraction patterns of proteins may not be as clear as those of small molecules. But there are also advantages: in a crystal containing a high proportion of solvent, a protein molecule is in an environment that does not differ substantially from that in its natural state.

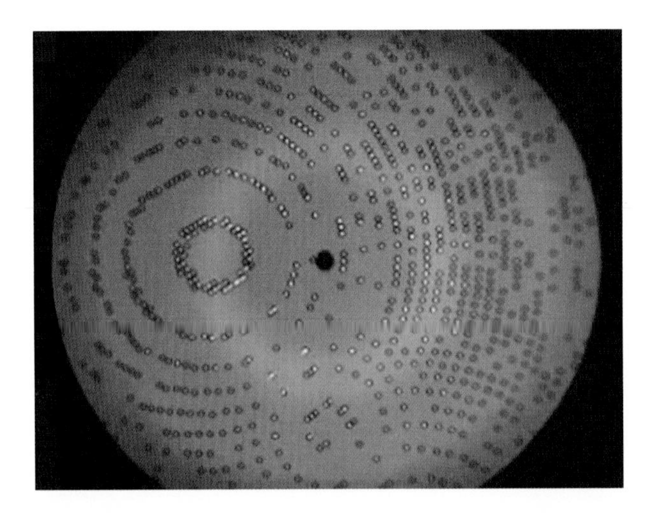

Figure 1.14 An X-ray diffraction pattern obtained with a crystal of barnase.

The electron density within a unit cell can be contoured and displayed using computer graphics. The aim is to take the known amino acid sequence of the protein and build it into the 'chicken wire' of electron density. The resulting model of the protein is only an interpretation of the observed distribution of electron density, although a highly refined one. The amount and quality of the original diffraction data will influence the sharpness of the electron density map, and hence, the level of detail (known as the resolution) that can be gleaned about a molecule's structure. Crystallographers usually quote values for resolution in angstroms (Å).

- Data to 7 Å (or 0.7 nm) resolution, for instance, include only a small portion of the diffraction pattern and the electron density map gives information limited to the path traced by the backbone chain of the protein. Stretches of regular backbone structure, such as α-helices, can be detected at this level.
- Data to 3 Å (0.3 nm) include more of the diffraction pattern, and the electron density map will reveal the structure of amino acid side chains as well as the backbone chain.
- Data to 2 Å (0.2 nm) include more information still, and the atomic positions are sufficiently well defined for experienced researchers to identify those parts of the protein where interactions such as hydrogen bonding can take place.

1.4.3 Protein structures using nuclear magnetic resonance (NMR) spectroscopy

You should now watch the following video sequence. It introduces you to the technique of NMR spectroscopy and how it is used to determine the structure of proteins. This was recorded a number of years ago and the technique and equipment have developed since then, but the principles are still the same.

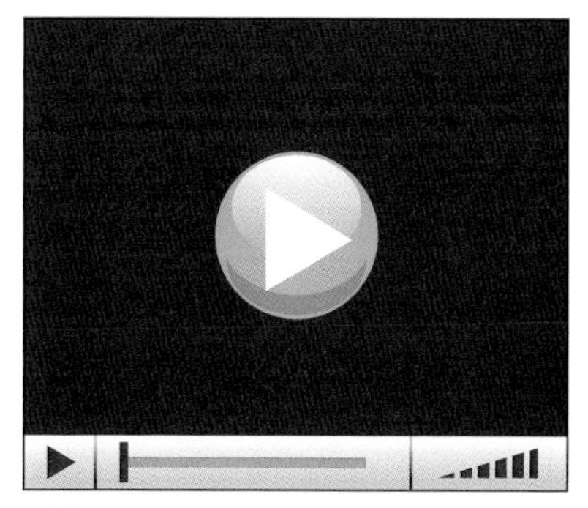

This sequence can be viewed from the online version of this text, or from Unit 2 resources – they are identical.

The NMR structure of barnase

NMR has a number of advantages over X-ray crystallography, including:

- insights on dynamics as well as structure
- information on proteins in an environment closely similar to that in vivo
- structural information on proteins that do not readily form crystals.

Like X-ray crystallography the number of structures determined has increased greatly in recent years due to improvements in instrumentation and computing. In 2002 Kurt Wüthrich was awarded the Nobel Prize in Chemistry 'for his development of nuclear magnetic resonance spectroscopy for determining the 3D structure of biological macromolecules in solution'.

1.4.4 Theoretical background of NMR

The **NMR technique** relies on a particular property of some atomic nuclei. For proteins, most importantly this is ^{1}H, ^{15}N and ^{13}C. The nuclei of these isotopes have what is known as angular momentum or magnetic spin, which allows them to behave like small bar magnets. In the presence of a magnetic field, the magnetic nuclei align with the applied field. Input of energy in the radio-frequency region of the electromagnetic spectrum can excite the nucleus such that its spin changes and becomes opposed to the applied field (Figure 1.15). When the excited nucleus returns to its aligned state, it emits radio-frequency radiation. The difference in the energy levels of the aligned and opposed nuclei, and hence the matching radiation, is dependent both on the strength of the magnetic field and on the nature of the nucleus.

^{1}H is the most commonly used nucleus for studying proteins, because 99.9% of hydrogen atoms occur naturally as this isotope and it gives strong signals compared to most other NMR-active nuclei. In contrast, the natural abundances of both ^{15}N and ^{13}C, the most suitable NMR-active isotopes of nitrogen and carbon, are low and samples must be enriched in these isotopes. Fortunately, for cloned proteins this can readily be achieved by growing bacteria in media with ^{15}N-labelled and ^{13}C-labelled compounds as the only nitrogen and carbon sources.

As with X-ray crystallography, NMR analysis requires a pure sample of protein. The protein sample dissolved in a suitable solvent is placed inside a magnet and is irradiated with a pulse of radio-frequency radiation. The

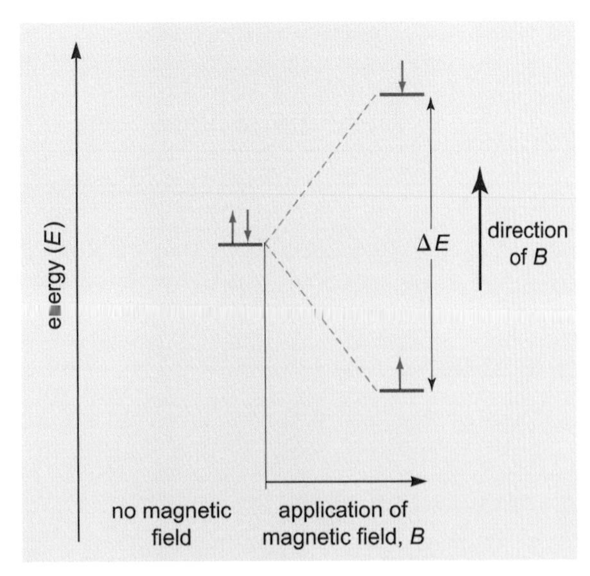

Figure 1.15 The effect of a magnetic field on the energies associated with the spin of certain types of atomic nuclei. Short arrows represent alternative spin states.

resulting radio-frequency emission is then followed as a function of time and is converted into a spectrum as a function of frequency using a mathematical process known as a Fourier transformation. As you may remember if you have done the Level 2 chemistry module, each carbon nucleus in a molecule usually resonates at a slightly different frequency, leading to different chemical shifts, δ, which are measured in parts per million (ppm) – although coincidences do occur. This is the origin of correlation tables that allowed us to assign particular structural features. So it is in a protein; the ^{1}H, ^{15}N and ^{13}C spectra reveal different nuclear environments. The ^{1}H spectrum of a protein is shown in Figure 1.16.

The chemical shift of a nucleus (^{1}H, ^{13}C or ^{15}N) in a protein is dependent on two factors:

- The atoms to which the nucleus is bonded. For example, the carbon of a methyl group will have a different chemical shift to the carbon of an amide group.
- The surroundings of the nucleus in the folded protein. Interactions of a nucleus with other parts of the protein molecule, particularly the proximity of aromatic rings and the formation of hydrogen bonds, leads to substantial changes in the chemical shift of a particular atom. As a result of the folded structure these groups may be much further down the protein chain, but still in close proximity.

One of the most useful aspects of NMR is the ability of the technique to identify nuclei geometrically near to one another. The identification of adjacent nuclei relies on two types of interaction. Nuclei can interact *through bonds* via a process known as *J* coupling. This is the result of the field produced by the magnetic polarity of neighbouring nuclei between one and four bonds away.

■ This is the source of the multiplicity obtained in the ^{13}C spectra that you may have seen before (if you have done the Level 2 chemistry module). What groups do a quartet, triplet, doublet and singlet in a ^{13}C spectrum correspond to?

□ A quartet corresponded to a CH_3 group, triplet to a CH_2 group, a doublet to a CH group and a singlet to a carbon with no hydrogens attached.

J coupling is very useful as it enables the covalent connections between nuclei in a molecule to be traced.

Nuclei can also interact *through space* via the so-called nuclear Overhauser effect (NOE). In proteins, NOEs can be seen between protons physically less than 0.5 nm apart, but a long way away in terms of the number of bonds along the backbone.

The NMR spectrum shown in Figure 1.16 is a plot of intensity against frequency, expressed as chemical shift. Since this kind of spectrum contains a single frequency dimension, it is referred to as a **one-dimensional (1D) NMR**

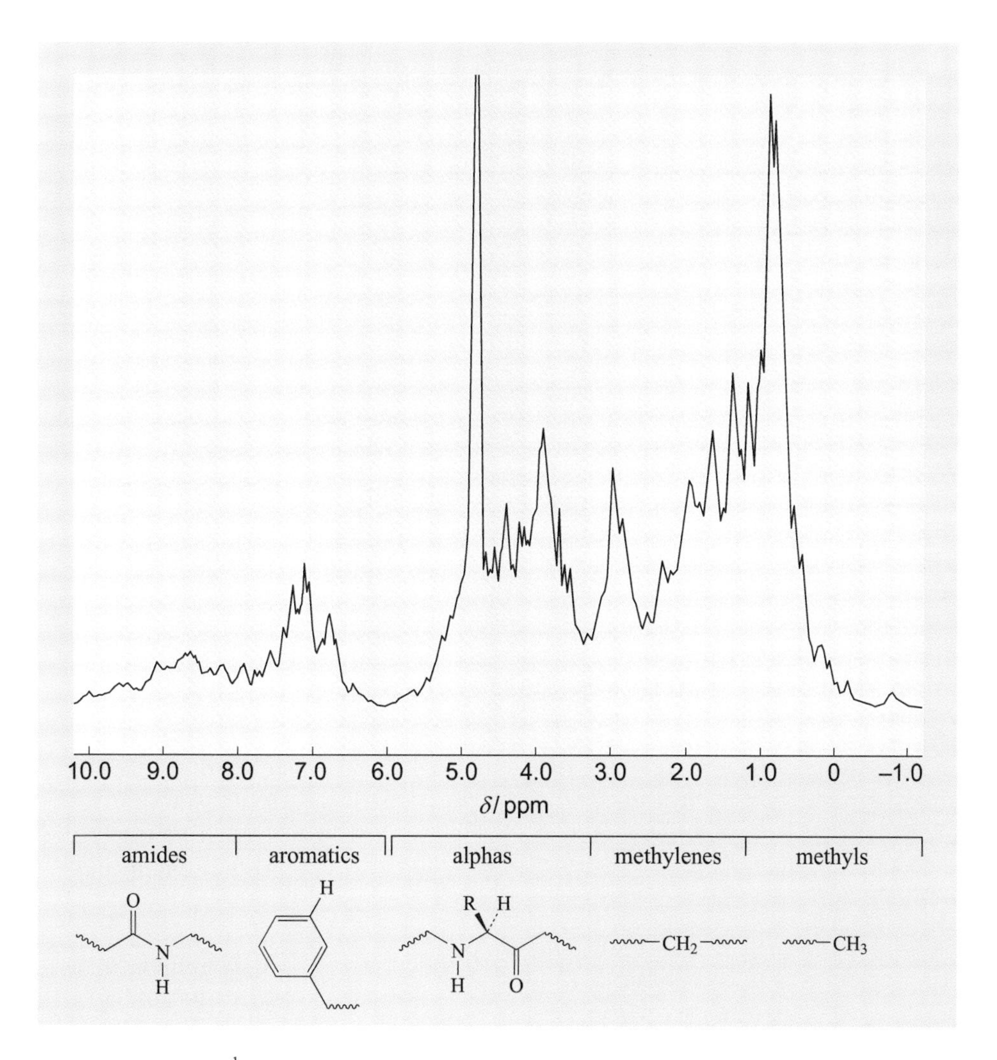

Figure 1.16 A ^{1}H, one-dimensional (1D) spectrum of a protein together with the regions corresponding to different types of hydrogen environments.

spectrum. For molecules as complex as proteins, it is not possible to obtain all the available structural information from 1D NMR spectra; however, NMR experiments can be designed that have more than one frequency dimension. Figure 1.17 shows a typical **two-dimensional (2D) NMR spectrum**. Both the horizontal and vertical axes correspond to the ^{1}H NMR spectrum in parts per million. Intensities are not discernible, as they would appear as peaks rising vertically from the plane of the diagram. The diagonal represents a plan view of the normal 1D spectrum. The off-diagonal peaks, seen in section as circles or black dots, are the result of interactions between different protons. Depending on the nature of the experiment, the off-diagonal peaks represent interactions between protons *through bonds* via *J* coupling (correlated spectroscopy, **COSY**) or *through space* via the NOE (nuclear Overhauser effect spectroscopy, **NOESY**), as in Figure 1.17.

The second frequency dimension can also be used for a different NMR-active nucleus; these so-called heteronuclear 2D NMR experiments normally correlate through bond interactions between different nuclei such as ^{1}H and ^{15}N, or ^{1}H and ^{13}C. Such a heteronuclear 2D NMR spectrum is shown in

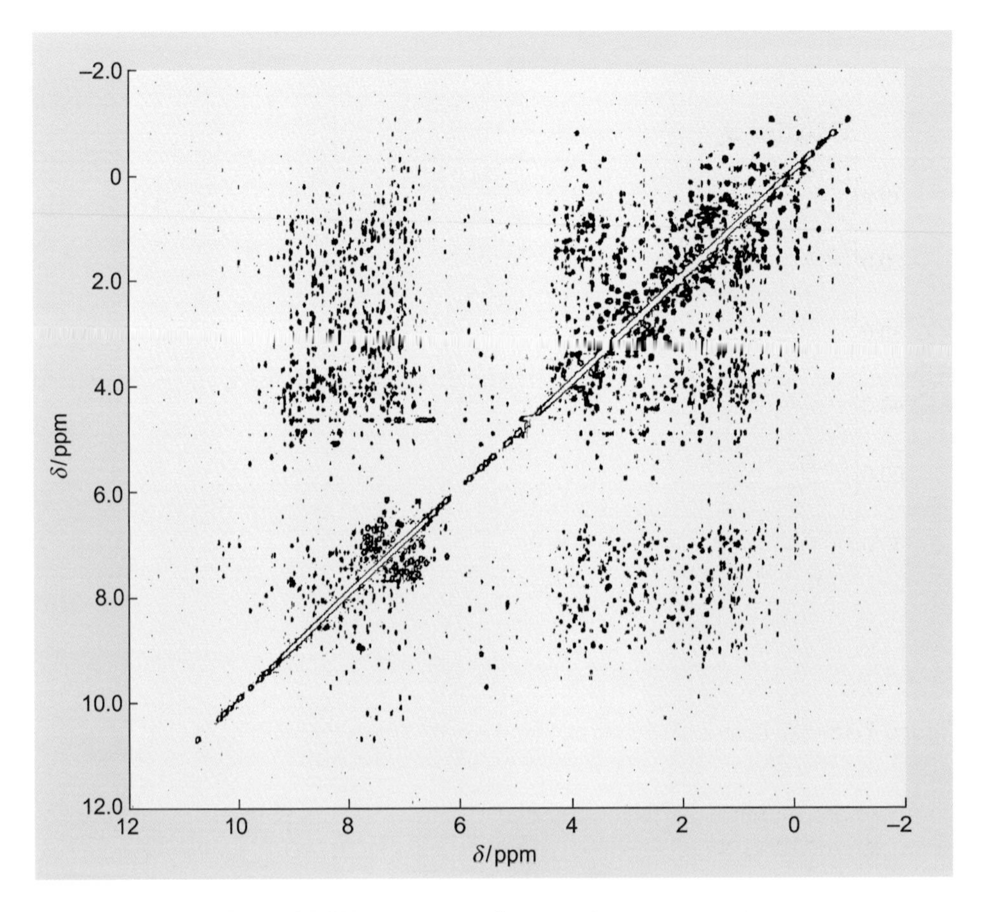

Figure 1.17 A 2D NOESY spectrum of a protein.

Figure 1.18, which shows the interaction between ^{13}C nuclei on one axis with adjacent ^{1}H nuclei on the other axis. Again the circles or black dots correspond to peaks rising from the paper and reflect adjacent protons and carbons. It is possible to combine these two types of experiment to produce 3D and 4D spectra where one or two of the dimensions are ^{1}H and the other dimensions are either ^{15}N or ^{13}C.

1.4.5 Assignment of protein NMR spectra

As with X-ray crystallography, we don't need to go into the detail of how a structure is determined. With a knowledge of the amino acid sequence of a protein and based on the multidimensional spectra described earlier, we can work out which atoms are coupling through bonds and which through space to give structural models that are consistent with the spectra. The experimental information does not define a unique structure, as many conformations will equally well satisfy the data. A series of structures (typically 20 to 30), therefore, are calculated and compared. The spread of the structures reflects how well the conformation of the protein has been defined. Certain regions in the structures will be well defined (e.g. hydrophobic cores), while other regions (e.g. surface loops) will be poorly defined.

In contrast to X-ray diffraction, NMR has the major advantage that the measurements are made on proteins in solution at physiological pH values and

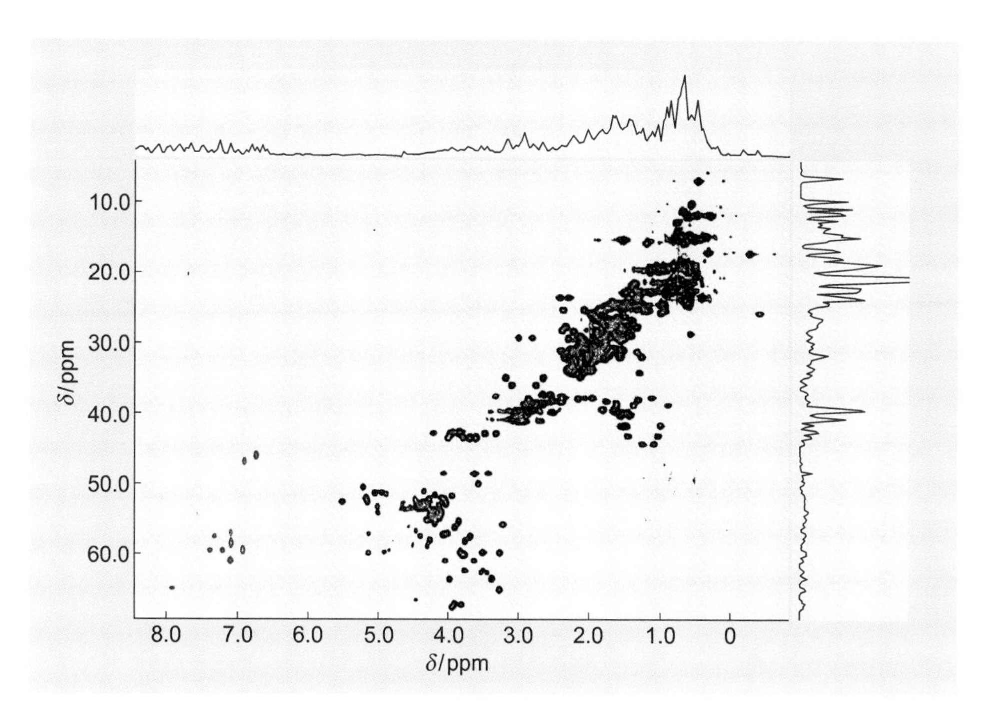

Figure 1.18 A heteronuclear ^{13}C, ^{1}H 2D NMR of a protein.

temperatures, rather than in the crystalline state. The most important limitation of protein NMR is the size of the molecules that can be studied. As the size of a protein increases, the spectral overlap becomes too great to accurately assign signals to particular nuclei. In addition, for large proteins, the width of the lines in the spectrum increases and they eventually become too broad to observe. This drawback is not, however, as serious as it seems: first, because many proteins are made up of a series of domains, each of which can be studied separately; second, because NMR spectrometers are being developed with increasingly larger fields that are able to show better separation of peaks.

1.5 Constraints on protein conformation

Until now, we have considered the polypeptide chain as a series of units, each unit corresponding to an amino acid residue (Figure 1.19a and b). Now we would like you to think of the chain in a different way – as a series of *peptide* units (Figure 1.19c and d). As discussed earlier, numerous physical studies with simple amides and polypeptides have shown that the six atoms within each peptide unit are virtually always found to lie in a single plane. Moreover, of the two planar geometries possible, the one in which the NH and CO bonds are on opposite sides (*trans*) of the backbone is usually found in proteins (Figure 1.19c).

So a polypeptide chain can be considered as a series of planes each joined at a corner to the next by a shared α-carbon atom (Figure 1.19d). The α-carbon atoms are tetrahedral and so apply another constraint to molecular geometry – the tetrahedral bond angle. In addition, we must take into account the fact that each of these atoms in a polypeptide chain are also bonded to a hydrogen atom and to a side chain. The importance of the α-carbon atom to

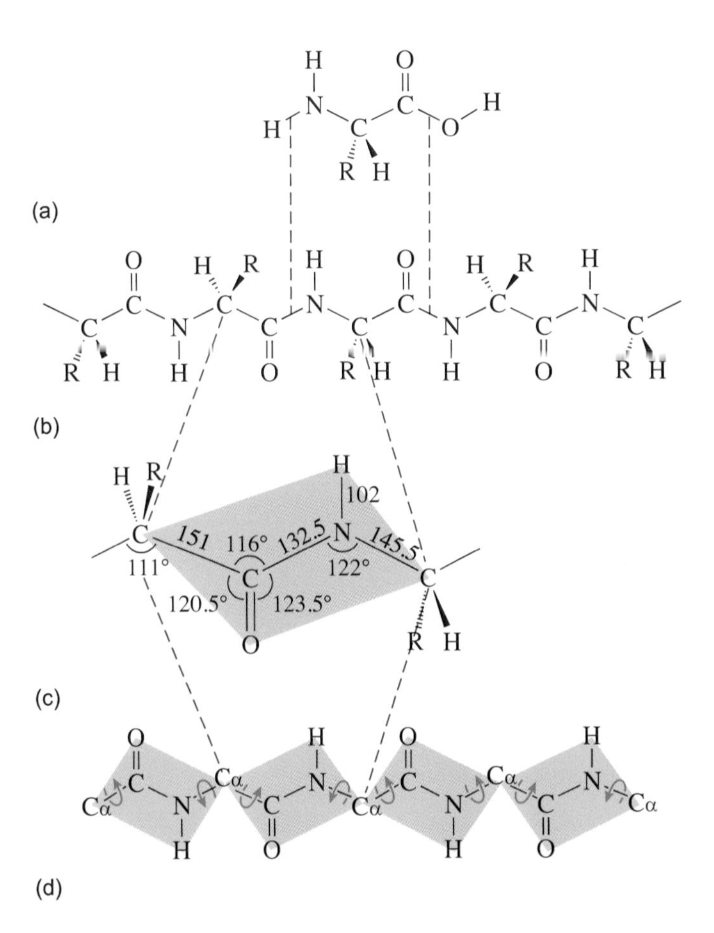

Figure 1.19 Peptide units in a polypeptide chain: (a) amino acid unit; (b) polypeptide as a series of amino acid units; (c) peptide unit; (d) polypeptide as a series of peptide units.

conformation lies in the uniqueness of its configuration in protein structures. All the chiral α-carbon atoms are of the L configuration.

Figure 1.19d shows how conformation of a protein will depend on, and, indeed, be completely defined by, the sequence of rotation angles about the two backbone bonds to each α-carbon atom. A segment of chain in which all the rotation angles about C_α–N are the same, and all those about C_α–C are the same will be a regular structure such as an α-helix. If, on the other hand, each of the two kinds of rotation angle has different values along the chain, then the segment will be in a non-regular conformation. Rotation angles, in turn, are dictated by non-covalent interactions, and we consider these in detail in a moment.

Before leaving covalent interactions, note that there is one of these that is outside the backbone/side chain structure that is important to stabilizing the conformation: the **disulfide S–S bond** that often bridges cysteine residues across a folded protein chain (Scheme 1.3 and Figure 1.20). It is weak as covalent bonds go (~200 kJ mol^{-1}; compare C–C ~350 kJ mol^{-1}), but much stronger than any *individual* non-covalent interaction. Within an individual protein, however, S–S bonds are few in number, and their cumulative effect on tertiary structure is probably much weaker than the cumulative effect of all the non-covalent interactions. Thus these covalent linkages do not affect the conformation of the protein, and are only formed when the folding is complete. They act, therefore, to secure the conformation and increase the stability of the protein. The amino acid dimer formed when two cysteine residues are linked by a disulfide bond is known as **cystine**.

$$\begin{array}{c}\text{C=O} \\ | \\ \text{CH}-\text{CH}_2-\text{SH} \\ | \\ \text{NH}\end{array} + \begin{array}{c}\text{O=C} \\ | \\ \text{HS}-\text{CH}_2-\text{CH} \\ | \\ \text{HN}\end{array} \underset{\text{reduction}}{\overset{\text{oxidation}}{\rightleftharpoons}} \begin{array}{c}\text{C=O} \qquad\qquad\qquad \text{O=C} \\ | \qquad\qquad\qquad\qquad | \\ \text{CH}-\text{CH}_2-\text{S}-\text{S}-\text{CH}_2-\text{CH} \\ | \qquad\qquad\qquad\qquad | \\ \text{NH} \qquad\qquad\qquad\qquad \text{HN}\end{array}$$

Scheme 1.3

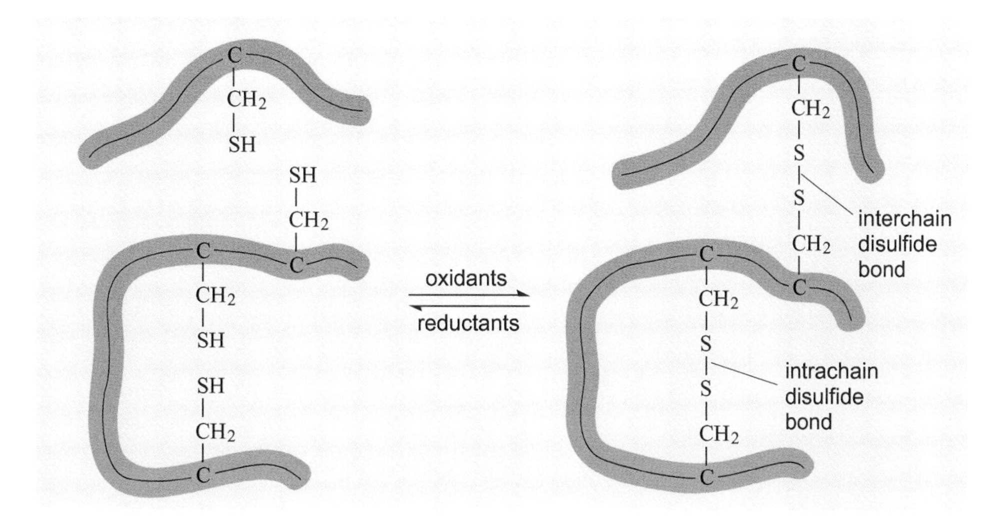

Figure 1.20 An example of how the formation of a disulfide bond between cysteine side chains stabilises existing structures in a polypeptide. These bonds can form between two polypeptide strands or between residues in the same polypeptide.

The conformation of a polypeptide chain is determined completely by the succession of rotational angles around the N–C_α and C_α–C bonds (Figure 1.19d). We have just said that when these angles vary along a segment of chain, the chain is in a non-regular conformation. The conformation lacks regularity, but it is by no means a random one. Randomness implies completely free rotation about the bonds. As you will see, the polypeptide non-regular conformation exists only within a limited range of angles of rotation for each of the two kinds of bond. Strong restrictions on those angles are imposed principally by electrostatic interactions, van der Waals interactions, hydrogen bonding and hydrophobic interactions, with other types of interaction playing a significant but lesser part. We find it convenient to think about these interactions in terms of the range, with respect to amino acid sequence, over which they can operate. We define **short-range interactions** as those that operate within a single dipeptide unit (Figure 1.21).

Medium-range interactions are those that occur between the atoms of one dipeptide unit and those of the dipeptide units that overlap with it on either

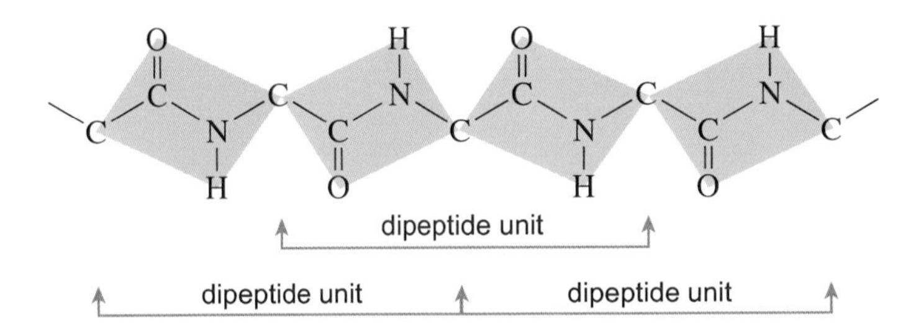

Figure 1.21 Dipeptide units in a polypeptide chain.

side, and of one more overlapping dipeptide in either direction. Interactions between atoms more remote (sequentially) along the chain we define as **long-range interactions**. In some chemical and biochemical contexts, the term 'long range' refers to physical separation. In our context, 'long range' interactions between groups occur when the groups are physically close to one another, but are separated in the chain by more than three dipeptide units; that is, more than five amino acid residues.

■ Assign to each of the interactions a–g in Figure 1.22 one of the labels 'short range', 'medium range' or 'long range' according to the above definitions.

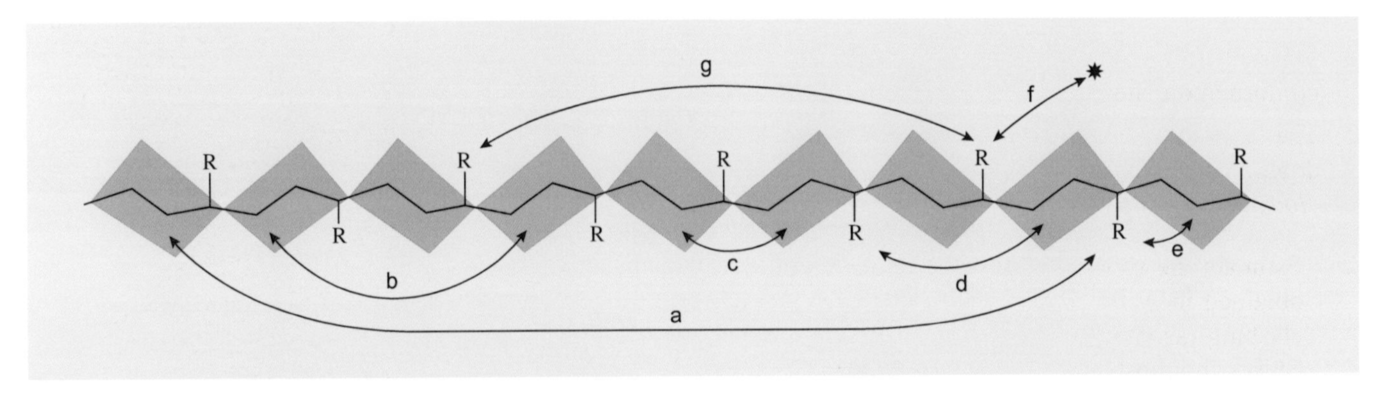

Figure 1.22 The interaction marked with the star is to another side chain, 50 residues away, but close across space.

□ Long range: a, f

medium range: b, d, g

short range: c, e

1.5.1 Short-range interactions

Activity 1.8

You should start this section by carrying out an activity in which you use Discovery Studio to examine the 3D geometry of a dipeptide. The instructions for this activity are in *Unit 2 Activities*.

Before proceeding further, we must define more precisely the two rotation angles within the dipeptide unit about the C_α–C bond and about the C_α–N bond. The angle of rotation in the C_α–C bond is designated the symbol ψ (pronounced psi) and measures the angle between the two C–N bonds at each end of the C_α–C bond, Figure 1.23.

The angle of rotation in the C_α–N bond is designated the symbol ϕ (pronounced phi) and measures the angle between the C_α–C bond and the N–C bond at respective ends of the C_α–N bond.

Note carefully two points:

1 We shall follow the convention where the fully extended conformation shown in Figure 1.23 corresponds to $\phi = \psi = \pm180°$.

2 The sense of rotation for each bond is such that when you look down either (in either direction), you rotate the *rear* group *clockwise* for a *positive* rotation.

■ Estimate the values of ψ and ϕ for the conformation you obtained in Activity 1.8 in which the two oxygen atoms are clashing (as shown in the *Unit 2 Activities* booklet). (b) What causes the most severe repulsion when $\phi = \psi = 0°$.

□ (a) $\psi(C_\alpha\text{–}C) = \pm180°$, $\phi(C_\alpha\text{–}N) = 0°$. ψ, associated with the C_α–C bond, was unchanged from the fully extended conformation; ϕ, associated with the C_α–N bond, was rotated through 180° from the fully extended conformation, making it 360° or 0°.

(b) Repulsion between an NH hydrogen and an oxygen atom. Note that you would have to widen bond angles to produce a hydrogen bond between these atoms (in a seven-membered ring). If you are not sure of this open the dipeptide_00rot file (ball and stick) in Discovery Studio which shows this conformation.

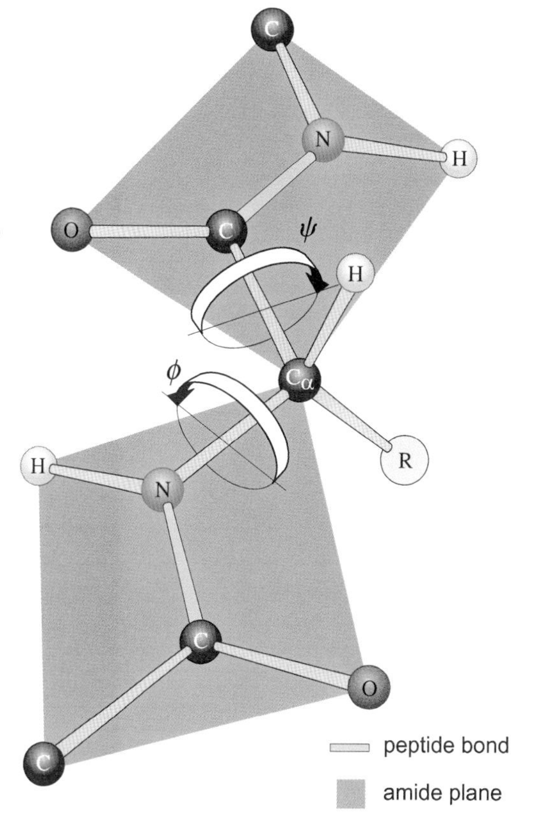

Figure 1.23 ϕ and ψ parameters in a dipeptide unit. The sense of the rotations depicted are relative to a fixed α-carbon atom.

Values for the closest approach between particular pairs of atoms (minimum contact distances) have been calculated from van der Waals radii. If each atom in a dipeptide unit is considered to occupy a volume of space similar to that of a hard sphere with the corresponding van der Waals radius (Figure 1.24), conformations that are 'disallowed' because of steric overlaps can be determined.

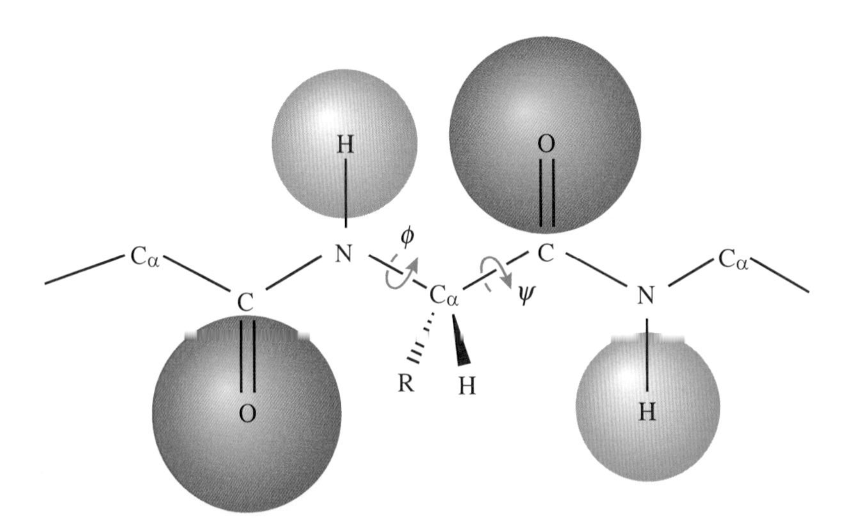

Figure 1.24 van der Waals radii of oxygen and NH hydrogen atoms in a dipeptide unit. When ϕ approaches 0° and ψ is 180°, the carbonyl oxygen atoms (the red tone) overlap and prevent further rotation. Similarly, when ϕ is 180° and ψ approaches 0°, the hydrogen atoms (the grey tone) overlap. The rotational senses of ϕ and ψ are relative to a fixed α-carbon atom.

1.5.2 Ramachandran plots

This approach was first taken by the Indian protein chemist, G. N. Ramachandran. Using a computer, he varied both ψ and ϕ of a given unit in small increments and rejected all conformations that involved the overlap of any two spheres. He expressed the result as a *steric map,* and such maps have since become known as **Ramachandran plots** or **hard-sphere plots**. Figure 1.25 shows the steric map for the L-alanyl residue, that is, the dipeptide unit that corresponds to the model you viewed with Discovery Studio in Activity 1.4. Where there is no conflict between the van der Waals radii of non-bonding atoms, a conformation is 'allowed'. These conformations lie in the blue areas in Figure 1.25. Conformations requiring interatomic distances at the limit of that which is permissible are defined as 'outer limit' conformations. They lie in the green areas in Figure 1.25. Theoretical conformations that require any two non-bonding atoms to be closer to each other than their van der Waals radii allow are sterically 'forbidden'. These lie in the white areas in Figure 1.25.

Notice that the values of ψ and ϕ in Figure 1.25 range from −180° to +180°. Turning the peptide group through 360° will, of course, bring it back to its starting position, and −180° and +180° correspond to the same position. Thus, the green strip at the bottom left corner of the plot in Figure 1.25 is contiguous with the field at the top left corner. The most obvious feature of this plot is that the majority of (ϕ , ψ) combinations are not allowed. There are only three permissible regions for the L-alanyl residue: those in the neighbourhood of (−60°, −60°), (−120°, +120°) and (+60°, +60°).

Figure 1.25 also shows (ϕ , ψ) positions that correspond to some regular conformations. Recall that regular conformations result when a series of dipeptide units in a chain all have the same ψ values and the same ϕ values. Notice that the α_R helix has ϕ and ψ values close to −60°.

Ramachandran plots can be constructed for polymers of each of the 20 amino acids. It is significant to note that the Ramachandran plots for most amino acid residues are generally very similar, having only three regions with favourable or tolerated conformations (labelled 1–3 in the plot for poly-L-alanine in Figure 1.25). Differences do occur, however. For instance, where the side chain is branched near C_α, as in the case of threonine it occupies more space close to the peptide backbone and restricts the approach of atoms in the neighbouring peptide groups. As a result, allowed conformations (ψ and ϕ angles) are more restricted for polypeptides of branched amino acids.

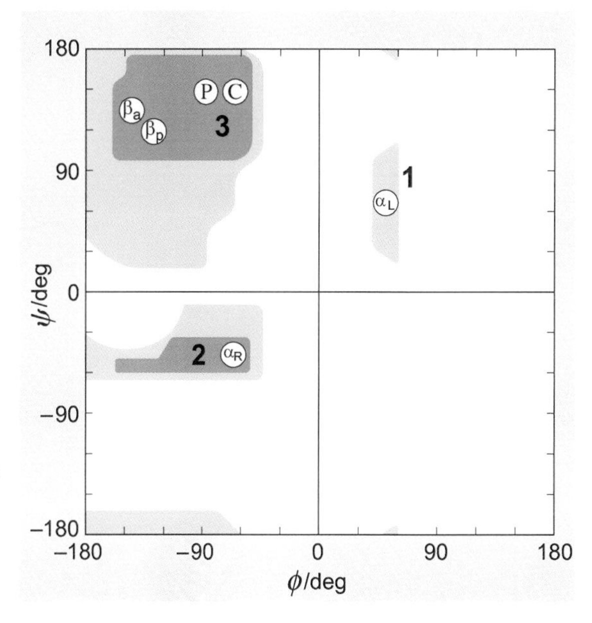

Figure 1.25 Ramachandran plot for the alanyl residue together with ψ and ϕ positions for some regular conformations. The blue areas indicate conformations where absolutely no overlap of atomic 'spheres' occurs, the green areas indicate the outer boundary where slight overlap occurs. The white areas indicate forbidden regions. Specific secondary structures are abbreviated on the figure as β_a = antiparallel β-sheet; β_p = parallel β-sheet; α_R and α_L = right- and left-handed α-helices; P = polyproline helix; C = helix found in collagen.

Figure 1.26 demonstrates very effectively what happens to the range of allowed conformations (ψ and ϕ values) as the side chain gets larger. For glycyl, alanyl, valyl and isoleucyl residues, the allowed region decreases respectively from 52% to 16% to 4.5% to about 2% of the total area of the map.

■ Proline, **1.10**, is also quite different from other amino acids in terms of allowed conformations and for polyproline only ϕ values from −85° to −35° are tolerated. Looking at the structure of proline, how can you explain this relatively narrow range of permitted ϕ values?

O
C–OH
HN

1.10

□ The side chain of proline is covalently bonded to the N of the amino group, so in polyproline, there will be less freedom of rotation about the C_α–N bond than with other amino acids. Consequently, allowed ϕ values will be relatively limited compared with other amino acids.

Ramachandran plots are *predictive* rather than actual conformational plots. We can, of course, use X-ray diffraction to determine experimentally the 'real' values of ψ and ϕ for residues in a polypeptide. In Figure 1.27, the ϕ and ψ values for all the residues (with the exception of glycine and proline) in a number of different structures have been determined by high-resolution X-ray diffraction and plotted on a Ramachandran plot. We can see that there is a striking correspondence between predicted and actual conformations. Notice, however, that there are some residues whose conformations map to the 'forbidden' areas. Most of these residues map in the region between 'allowed' regions 2 and 3, around $\psi = 0$. A limited number of 'forbidden' conformations of particular residues can be tolerated in a polypeptide if the conformation

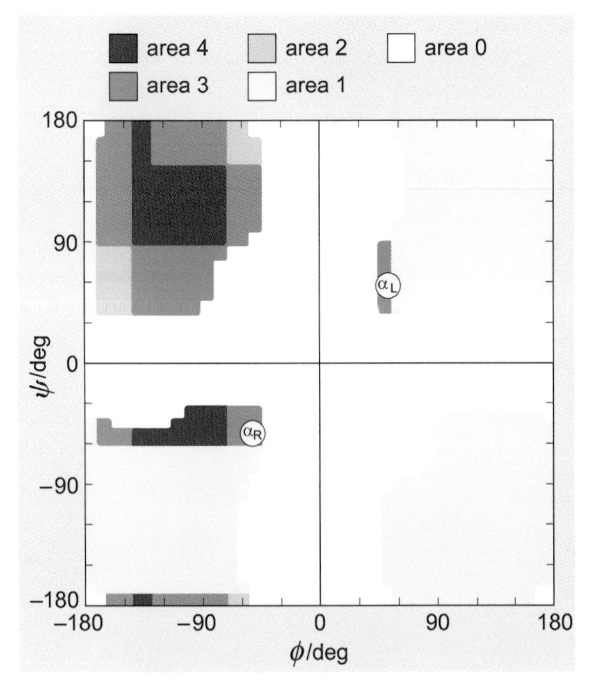

Figure 1.26 Ramachandran plots for various dipeptides. In the white area no conformations are allowed because of steric overlap. Conformations in areas 1–4 are allowed for glycylglycine: in areas 2–4, for glycyl-L-alanine: in areas 3 and 4, for higher straight-chain homologues. Only area 4 is allowed for glycyl-L-valine and glycyl-L-isoleucine, which have branched side chains. The circles marked α_R and α_L indicate the location of the standard right- and left-handed α-helices respectively.

adopted, as a whole, is energetically favourable. A polypeptide will tend to *fold* such that it adopts the most stable conformation.

Activity 1.9

You can use Discovery Studio to generate the Ramachandran plots of any proteins that you have loaded into the 3D window. Follow the instructions given in *Unit 2 Activities*.

1.5.3 Medium-range interactions

Although a particular pair of ϕ and ψ values has a direct effect on the conformation of only a single dipeptide unit, it is the sequence of such values in, say, a six-residue segment of chain that defines the overall conformation of that segment. Medium-range interactions, of which the hydrogen-bonding in the backbone of an α-helix is a clearly defined example, operate within short segments and these in turn could affect the ϕ and ψ values of individual residues. Thus, in a sense, the local conformation will reflect a compromise between the effect of medium-range interactions and the cumulative effect of short-range interactions in the constituent dipeptide units. This usually leads to a further reduction in allowed ϕ and ψ values for an individual unit. As discussed above, it could also lead to a particular residue being forced to accept ϕ and ψ values other than those allowed on the hard-sphere model. Clearly, hydrogen-bonding interactions along the backbone can be very important medium-range influences.

Can the same be said about other types of interactions, particularly interactions between the side chains of amino acid residues rather than the backbone? Think about this question for a minute or two and jot down any other types of medium-range interaction that could be important. You may find it helpful to use structure **1.11**, in which we show the fully extended form of a possible segment of a protein – focus on possible interactions between the side chains.

A segment of chain the size of that shown in **1.11** can adopt, in principle, shapes that range from the compactness of a β-turn to the fully stretched one shown. This means that it is possible for most of each side chain to reach most parts of the other side chains and the backbones. So, **hydrogen bonding** and **van der Waals repulsion**, between side chains and side chains, and between side chains and backbone, could be influential over the medium range. There are also other interactions that can operate over the medium range. As described in Unit 1, the distribution of electrons in a molecule can lead to a dipole where one part of the molecule is partially positively charged and another part negatively charged. When these dipoles line up in opposite directions (Figure 1.28), the positive end of one dipole is stabilised by the negative end of another and vice versa such that the two groups take up a particular arrangement next to each other. So the dipoles in particular side chains could align leading to **dipole–dipole interactions**.

Another medium-range interaction is the **ionic interaction**, also known as the salt bridge, where a negative charge on one part of the molecule is attracted to the positive charge on another part of the molecule, as shown in Figure 1.29, again leading to particular side chains 'linking up'.

Until now, we have overlooked the fact that not all **van der Waals forces** are repulsive forces. When two groups are separated by a distance that just exceeds the normal contact distance, weak non-bonding **attractive forces** exist between them which can become significant, particularly when groups containing polarisable electrons (for example, π and n electrons) are involved. For example, significant attractive forces would exist between the two π systems of the tryptophyl and tyrosyl residues in **1.11** at a particular distance between them (Figure 1.30a). Similarly, a **dipole-induced dipole attractive force** could result from the close proximity of the COO^- dipole of glutamyl (in red in Structure **1.11**) and the π system of tryptophyl (in blue in Structure **1.11**) (Figure 1.30d).

All of these medium-range interactions between side chains could lead to specific conformations of localised segments being favoured, including 'forbidden' ϕ and ψ values, such that a particular overall folding pattern can be achieved.

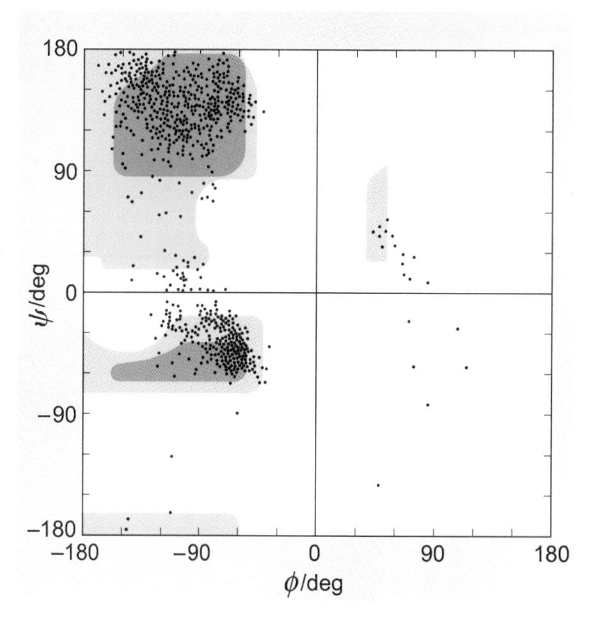

Figure 1.27 Based on X-ray diffraction data for a number of polypeptide structures, the ϕ and ψ values for all amino acid residues (with the exception of glycine and proline) have been superimposed on a predicted Ramachandran plot of 'allowed' and 'outer limit' conformations. Predictions were based on van der Waals distances for interatomic contacts as described in the text. Notice that the majority of actual values correspond to predicted permissible conformations.

1.11

1.5.4 Long-range interactions

The tertiary structure of a protein is responsible for bringing sequentially remote parts of the polypeptide chain close to each other. One of the key factors that lead to globular proteins, that work in an aqueous environment, taking up specific conformations is the hydrophobic effect. Most proteins contain 24–30% of amino acids with non-polar or hydrophobic side chains.

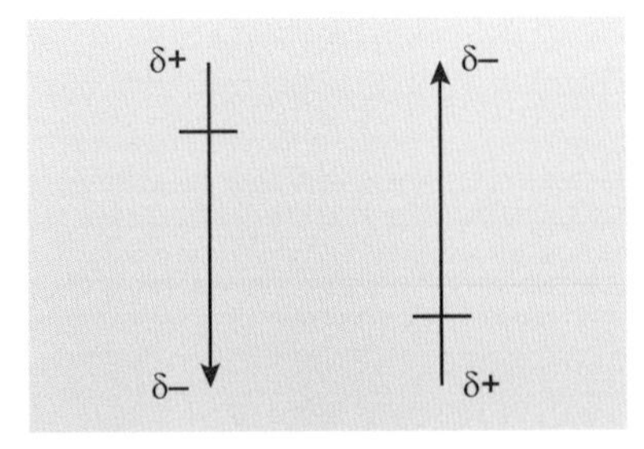

Figure 1.28 Dipoles line up in opposite directions so the positive part of one molecule is adjacent to the negative part of another.

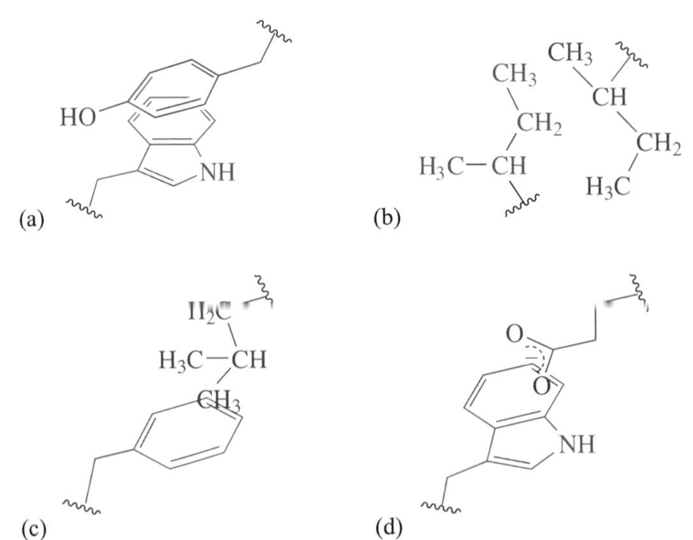

Figure 1.30 Examples of situations in which van der Waals attractive forces would operate: (a) tyrosyl and tryptophyl; (b) isoleucyl and isoleucyl; (c) leucyl and phenylalanyl; (d) glutamyl and tryptophyl.

~~~— $\overset{+}{N}H_3$ ^{-}OOC —~~~

Figure 1.29 Positive and negative charges tend to be adjacent to each other in space, thus 'linking' one part of the protein chain to another.

Groups such as methyl (alanine), 2-propyl (valine), 2-methylpropyl (leucine), 2-butyl (isoleucine) and benzyl (phenylalanine) are made up of hydrocarbon side chains that will not interact well with water – remember, like dissolves like – and are known as hydrophobic, *water-hating*, groups. X-ray structural analysis shows that the majority of these side chains are in the interior of such globular proteins, shielded from exposed water. About 45–50% of side chains in proteins are typically ionic or highly polar (hydrophilic: *water-loving*) and are concentrated on the surface of the structure. The rest of the side chains have little preference for being in or out of the aqueous environment. The preference of hydrophobic side chains for an interior position in contact with their own kind has become known as the **hydrophobic effect**, which has a major influence on the conformation of proteins that work in an aqueous environment.

The primary structure of a protein shows that hydrocarbon side chains are interspersed along the backbone with polar side chains, some of which are ionic such as arginine, lysine, glutamic acid and aspartic acid. These ionic side chains cannot easily be removed from an aqueous environment and so must remain at the surface of such globular structures. Since the ionic side chains cannot be physically separated from neighboring hydrophobic side chains, the limitations on possible stable structures are obvious. Chains containing normal proportions of the various kinds of amino acid, but in an arbitrary sequence may not be able to form stable globular structures at all in an aqueous environment. Indeed the sequences found in such globular proteins may represent a special group selected by the evolutionary process where the arrangement of hydrophobic and hydrophilic groups lead to a specific structure in which the hydrophobic residues can be segregated in internal regions without violating the requirement of ionic side chains for a surface location. Such sequences will also have a limited set of conformations that enable hydrophobic groups to gather together inside the protein with the ionic
~~~

groups on the outside. Of course, the polypeptide backbone is itself polar, but part of it must lie in the hydrophobic interior of a globular protein. When this happens, the stabilising influence of water molecules solvating the peptide groups is replaced by hydrogen bonding between the groups in both secondary and tertiary aspects of the structure. Thus highly hydrogen-bonded types of secondary structure, such as the α-helix and the β-sheet exist, in proteins partly for this reason.

The hydrophobic effect also brings non-polar side chains close enough for van der Waals attractive forces to have some effect. Although van der Waals attractive forces between saturated groups like the valyl and isoleucyl side chains are very weak, the cumulative effect of all such interactions in a protein is thought to be significant.

Now watch the following video clip which describes the secondary structure of barnase. This was recorded a number of years ago.

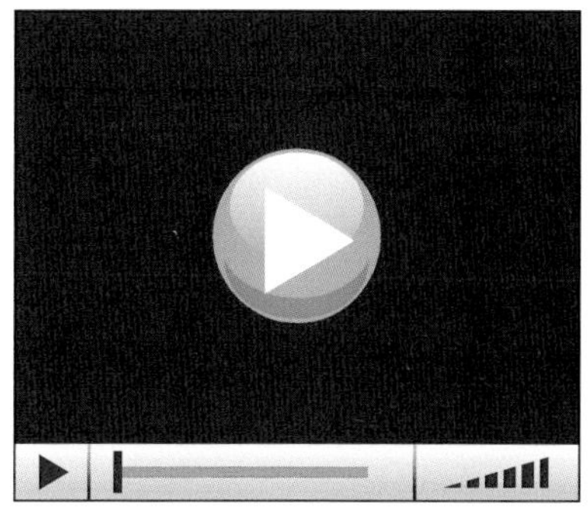

This sequence can be viewed from the online version of this text, or from Unit 2 resources – they are identical.

The secondary structure of barnase

1.6 Protein tertiary structure

The term 'tertiary structure' when applied to a protein refers to the 3D arrangement of the polypeptide as a whole, i.e. the spatial relationship between its elements of secondary structure. Though it may not be immediately obvious from the protein structures that you have already encountered in this module, proteins do follow certain recognisable folding patterns.

Examination of protein structures resolved by X-ray diffraction and NMR has revealed a variety of folding patterns common to many different proteins. However, even within these folds, distinct substructures or **structural motifs**, i.e. distinctive arrangements of elements of secondary structure, have been described. The term **supersecondary structure** has been coined to describe this level of organisation, which is intermediate between secondary and tertiary. The observation that these motifs and protein folds occur in many different proteins, with quite different amino acid sequences, indicates that they are not strictly sequence-dependent.

1.6.1 Motifs and supersecondary structures

Supersecondary structures or motifs are particular arrangements and combinations of two or three secondary structures, often with defined topology (or connectivity). Figure 1.31 describes some of the most common of these.

The coiled-coil structure, in which α-helices wrap around each other, is found in some structural proteins, such as myosin and α-keratin. The α helices have a strip of non polar side chains along one side, and formation of the coiled-coil is driven by interactions between these residues on the two α-helices, causing them to twist around each other. In this way, the hydrophobic residues are buried and the hydrophilic groups extend into the aqueous environment. Although the specific amino acid sequences of myosin and α-keratin are quite different, in each case we can identify patterns of hydrophobic and hydrophilic residues in the linear sequence, which specify the coiled-coil conformation.

Activity 1.10

In this activity you will investigate the RCSB Protein Data Bank (PDB) and look at some of the structures listed in Figure 1.31. Detailed instructions are given in *Unit 2 Activities*.

1.6.2 Protein domains

An important concept in protein structure is that of the **protein domain**. In many cases, a single polypeptide can be seen to contain two or more physically distinct substructures, known as domains. Often linked by a flexible hinge region, these domains are compact and stable, with a hydrophobic core. Domains fold independently of the rest of the polypeptide, satisfying most of their residue–residue contacts internally. A minimum size of 40–50 residues is required for a domain, though some domains can consist of up to 350 residues.

The physical resolution of different portions of a polypeptide is often indicative of distinct functions for these domains. For example, Src (pronounced 'sark'), a kinase that has a key role in intracellular signalling, has four domains: the catalytic activity of the protein resides in two domains (*kinase domains*) and the other two domains are important for the regulation of this activity (*regulatory domains*).

1.7 Protein quaternary structure

This level of protein structure applies only to those proteins that consist of more than one polypeptide chain, termed **subunits**. In such proteins, sometimes referred to as multisubunit proteins, the same kinds of non-covalent interaction that stabilise the folded polypeptides also specify the assembly of

Motif	Schematic	Description	Comments	Examples
$\beta\alpha\beta$	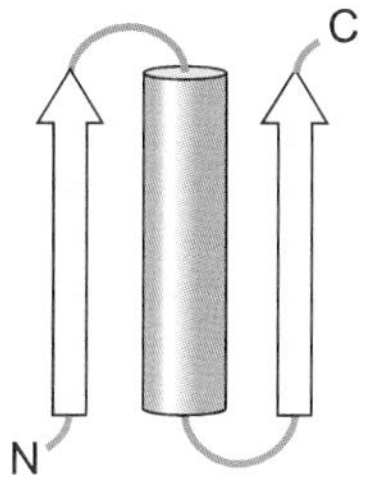	An α-helix connects parallel β-strands in β-sheets. Hydrophobic surfaces on the helix and β-sheet interact.	Residues in the first loop (C-terminal end of the β-strand) often contribute to the active site in enzymes.	Triose phosphate isomerase (a glycolytic enzyme) (pdb file 1tim)
β meander	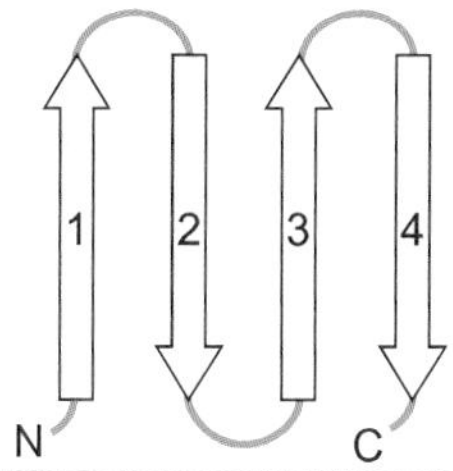	Antiparallel β-sheets are linked sequentially by short loops or hairpins consiting of two, three or four residues.	Basic antiparallel β-pleated sheet	
helix-turn-helix	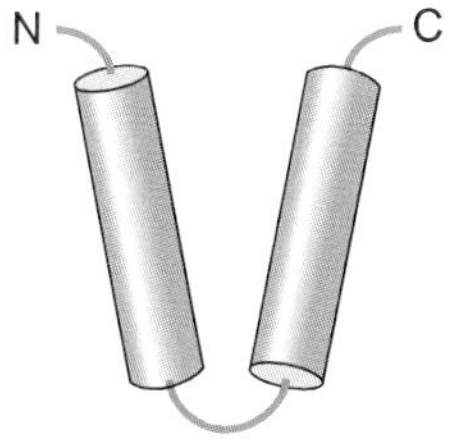	In the simplest arrangement, two helices lie antiparallel, connected by a short loop.	Energetically favourable interactions between side chains are accommodated by the relative positioning of the helices (usually at ~20° to each other).	Rop (an RNA binding protein) (pdb file 1rop)
Greek key	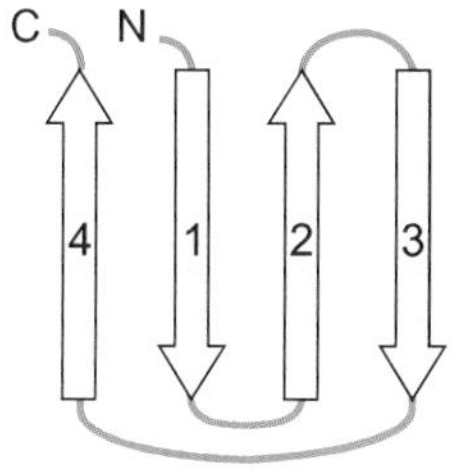	Antiparallel β-sheet with longer loop connections between some strands.		Gamma crystallin (a protein of the eye lens) (pdb file 1gcs)
coiled-coil		Two α-helices are wrapped around each other. Strips of hydrophobic side chains along the length of each helix interact with each other.		Myosin (a motor protein); α-keratin (a structural protein, e.g. in skin and hair)
zinc finger	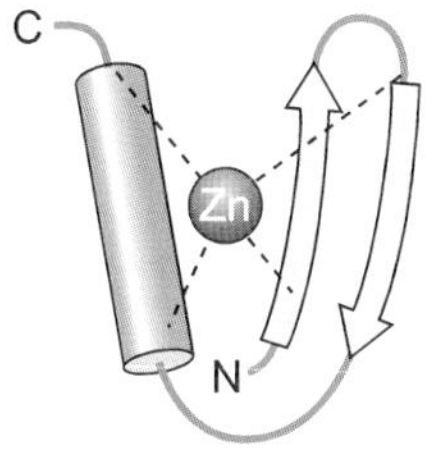	An α-helix and two short antiparallel β-strands are held together by a zinc ion, which forms coordinate bonds with side chains in the polypeptide.		Xfin (*Xenopus* DNA binding protein with a role in embryogenesis) (pdb file 1znf; single zinc finger from this protein)

Figure 1.31 Examples of common supersecondary structures/motifs.

complexes of subunits. Quaternary structure refers to the way in which the subunits of such proteins are assembled in the finished protein.

Multisubunit proteins can have a number of identical (**homomeric**) or non-identical (**heteromeric**) subunits. The simplest multisubunit proteins are homodimers – two identical polypeptide chains that are independently folded but held together by non-covalent interactions. An example of a homodimeric protein is the Cro repressor protein from bacteriophage lambda (Figure 1.32), which turns off expression of specific genes in its bacterial host.

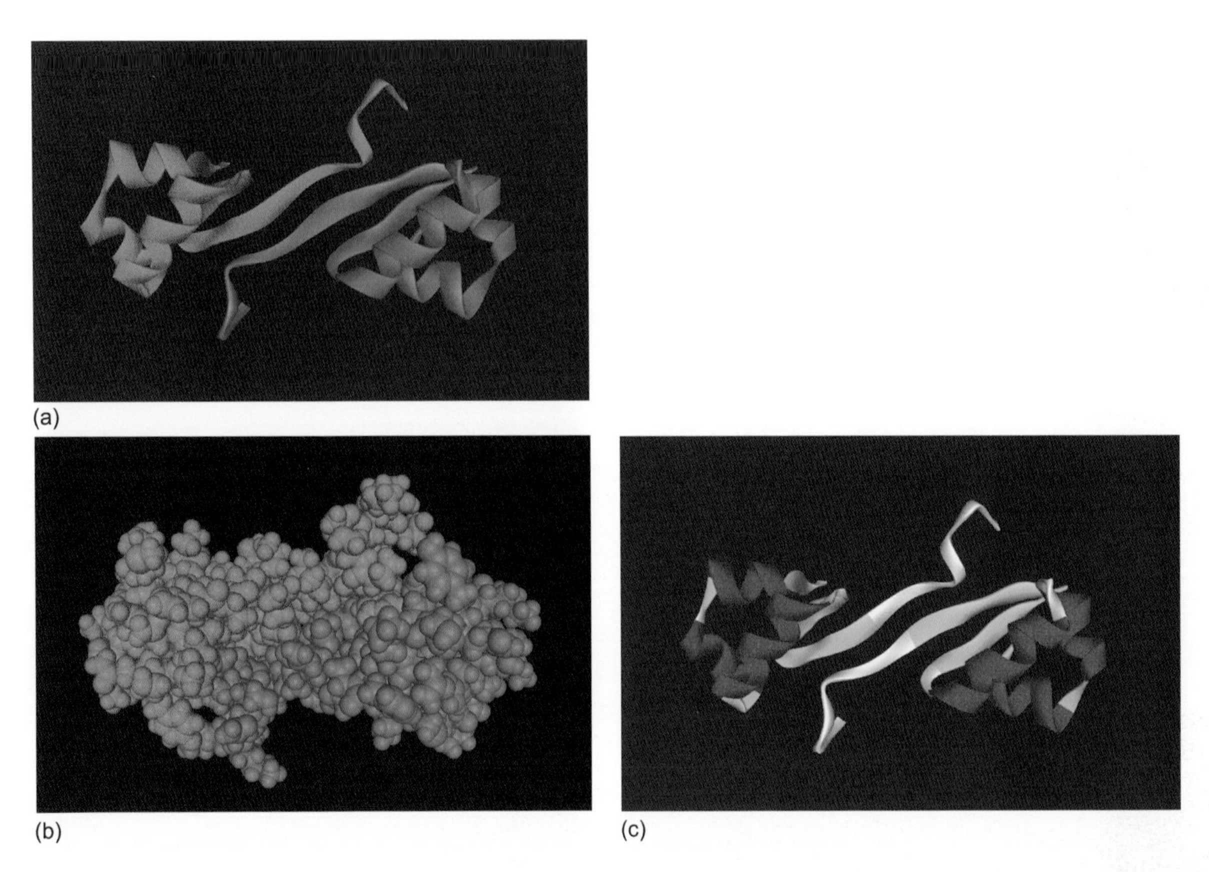

Figure 1.32 Bacteriophage lambda Cro repressor protein is a homodimer. It is represented here in three ways. (a) Ribbon format, with the subunits coloured differently; (b) Space-filling format with the subunits coloured as in (a); (c) Ribbon format with the polypeptide backbone coloured according to secondary structure: α-helix, red; β-sheet, cyan; turn, green; random coil, white. (Based on pdb file 1cop).

Activity 1.11

In this activity you will use Discovery Studio to explore the structure of the Cro repressor protein (Figure 1.32). The detailed instructions are given in *Unit 2 Activities*.

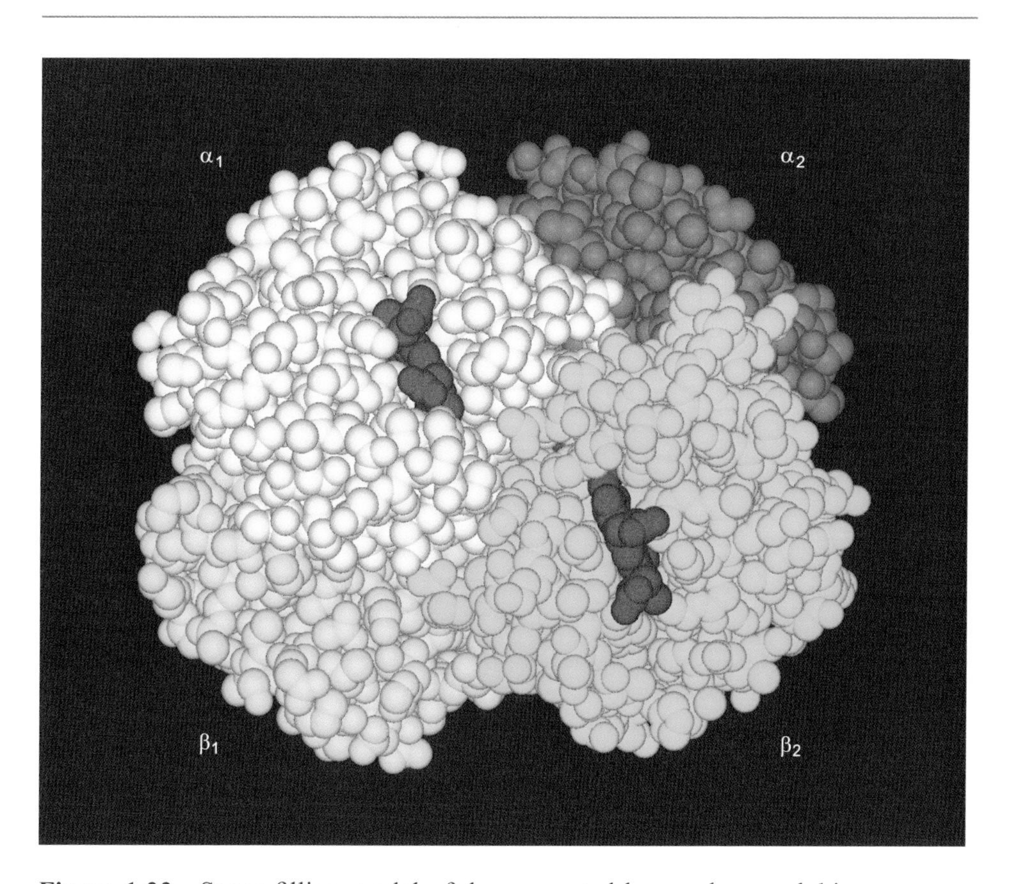

Figure 1.33 Space-filling model of deoxygenated human haemoglobin.

Haemoglobin, the red blood cell protein responsible for carrying molecular oxygen, contains two each of two different subunits, termed α and β globin (Figure 1.33). Note the symmetry of the two subunits in both these quaternary structures. The two α and the two β subunits are indicated and are coloured differently in Figure 1.33. The haem complexes associated with each unit are coloured red and only the front two can be seen in this representation. If you have time at the end of Activity 1.11 you may wish to carry out a similar analysis on haemoglobin – in particular, you should examine the haem that is part of each of the subunits.

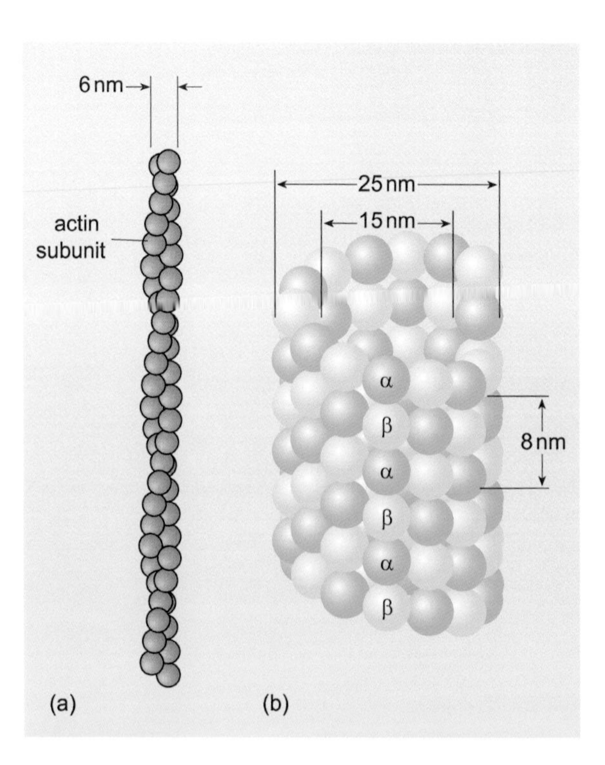

Figure 1.34 (a) Actin subunits can assemble into helical filaments called microfilaments. (b) Microtubules consist of repeating tubulin heterodimers (α and β subunits).

Some proteins can assemble to form long filaments. Two such proteins are actin and tubulin (Figure 1.34). These proteins exist in a soluble globular form that can assemble into long helical filaments called microfilaments (actin) and microtubules (tubulin). Both these proteins are important components of the cytoskeleton, and the filaments that they form can extend from one end of a cell to another.

Study note

Before moving on to Section 2, you should produce your own summary of this section and then compare it with ours. Go to Unit 2 summaries in Unit 2 resources on the module website.

1 Targets for drug design

In Unit 2 we studied the chemistry of proteins and in particular enzymes and receptors. The approach we took was to focus on the structure of the enzyme or receptor to understand how a related disease state could be treated. We start this unit with a slightly different approach and consider the following two questions:

- How can drugs make a difference?
- Where do we aim to deploy the 'magic bullet'?

1.1 Introduction

We focus on the small molecules that are used as drugs, examine how drug therapy has developed over the last 100 years or so and look at how drugs have been used to target specific common conditions. This will require us to understand their targets, but we will not be looking at the target structures.

The idea that small molecules can be deployed as 'magic bullets' to kill a pathogen really grew from the work of Paul Ehrlich (1854–1915), which concentrated on the use of the available synthetic dyes of the time to stain animal tissue. Ehrlich observed that some tissues showed much stronger affinities for particular dyes, compared with others (an early observation of selective protein binding). Towards the end of the 19th century, Ehrlich had realised that toxic dye-like molecules could be made to bind with some selectivity to pathogenic organisms and in doing this he had laid the basis of modern chemotherapy. It was Ehrlich who coined the term **magic bullet** to mean a molecule that would seek out and destroy a pathogen. This gives meaning to the modern term 'drug target', which refers to the particular site (in patient or pathogen) where a drug is intended to act. Refining and developing this choice of target, and the accuracy of the aim, is one of the major challenges of drug development.

1.1.1 The early drugs

Ehrlich (aided by the work of Béchamp, Hata and others) is particularly remembered for developing treatments for syphilis, caused by infection with the spirochetal bacterium *Treponema pallidum pallidum*. The drugs that he used were analogues of azo-dyes, for example **1.1**, taking advantage of the similarities between the chemistry of nitrogen and arsenic.

■ Why do you think the chemistry of nitrogen and arsenic might be similar?

□ The chemistry of nitrogen and arsenic are expected to be similar because arsenic is in the same group (V) as nitrogen in the Periodic Table.

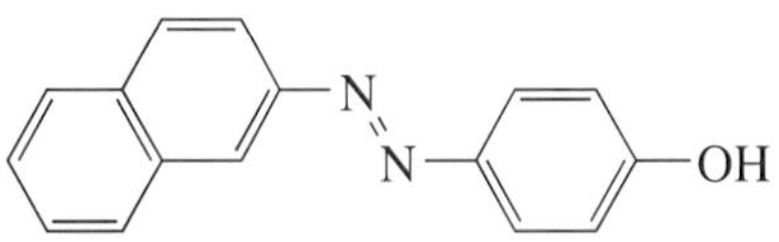

1.1 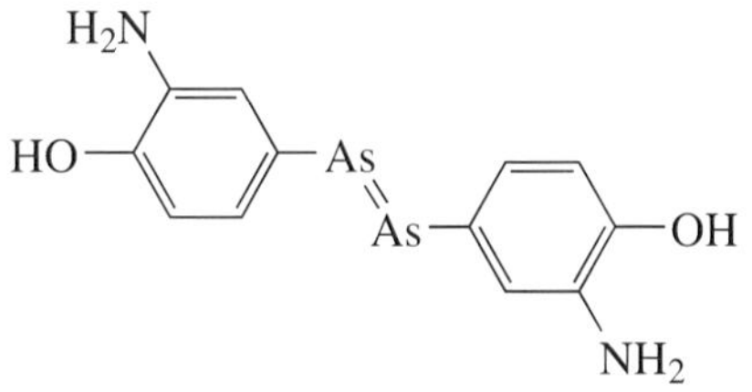 **1.2**

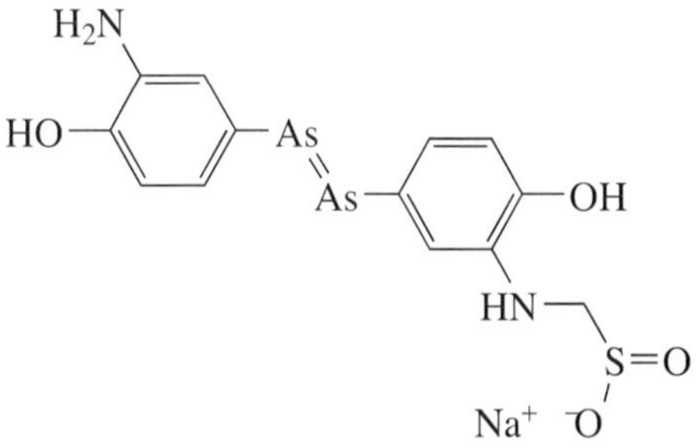

1.3

Although the two important drugs (salvarsan, **1.2**, and neo-salvarsan, **1.3**) had some quite serious side effects including deafness, these were still considered preferable to the worst symptoms of the disease itself. In the late (tertiary) stages of syphilis, these can include mental impairment, blindness, paralysis, extreme moods, severe organ damage and, in the absence of timely antibiotic treatment, death. It is hard to fully appreciate, in our post-antibiotic age, just what a huge contribution to the alleviation of suffering the arsenical drugs represented. Despite their magic 'grapeshot' (rather than bullet) reality, measured by today's standards, they gave a real alternative to death from the disease of syphilis, or the serious risk of it from the toxic effects of poisonous mercury compounds that were the only 19th-century treatment. For a long time the structure of salvarsan was thought to be structure **1.2**. However, in 2005, new crystallographic evidence revealed that salvarsan is actually a mixture of trimeric and pentameric molecules (**1.4** and **1.5**). Neo-salvarsan, a more soluble sequel to salvarsan, seems to conform to the conventional structure expected of an azo-dye analogue.

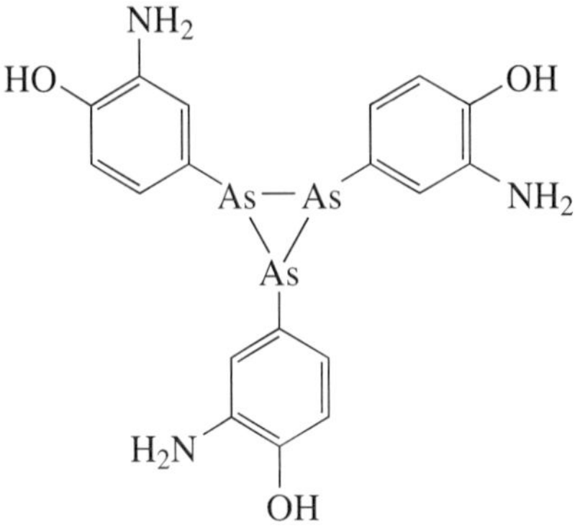

1.4 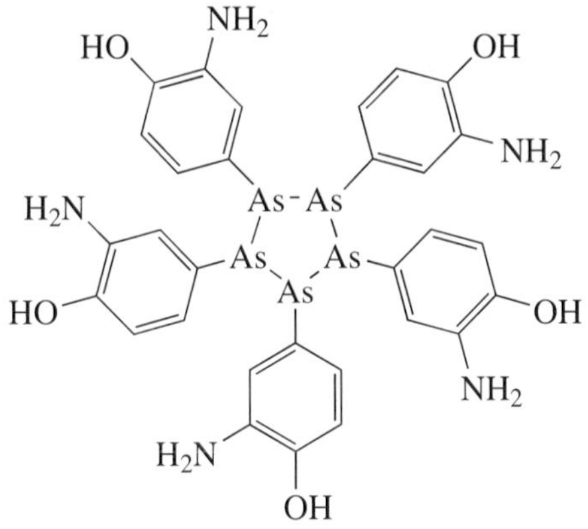 **1.5**

1.1.2 Penicillin

With the later discovery of prontosil (**1.6,** another azo-dye analogue) by Domagk in the 1930s, alternatives to Ehrlich's rather toxic, though effective, arsenicals (and the much more toxic mercury compounds that preceded them) began to emerge. **Penicillin** (**1.7**) was discovered by Fleming in 1928, but was not purified properly until 1940 (by Florey and Chain). By the early 1940s, penicillin was being used on patients with bacterial infections, and here the target turned out to be the cell walls of the bacteria, or more specifically the biosynthesis of cell wall constituents known as peptidoglycans. These molecules are composites of sugars and amino acids that strengthen the cell wall in, so-called Gram-positive, bacteria (Figure 1.1).

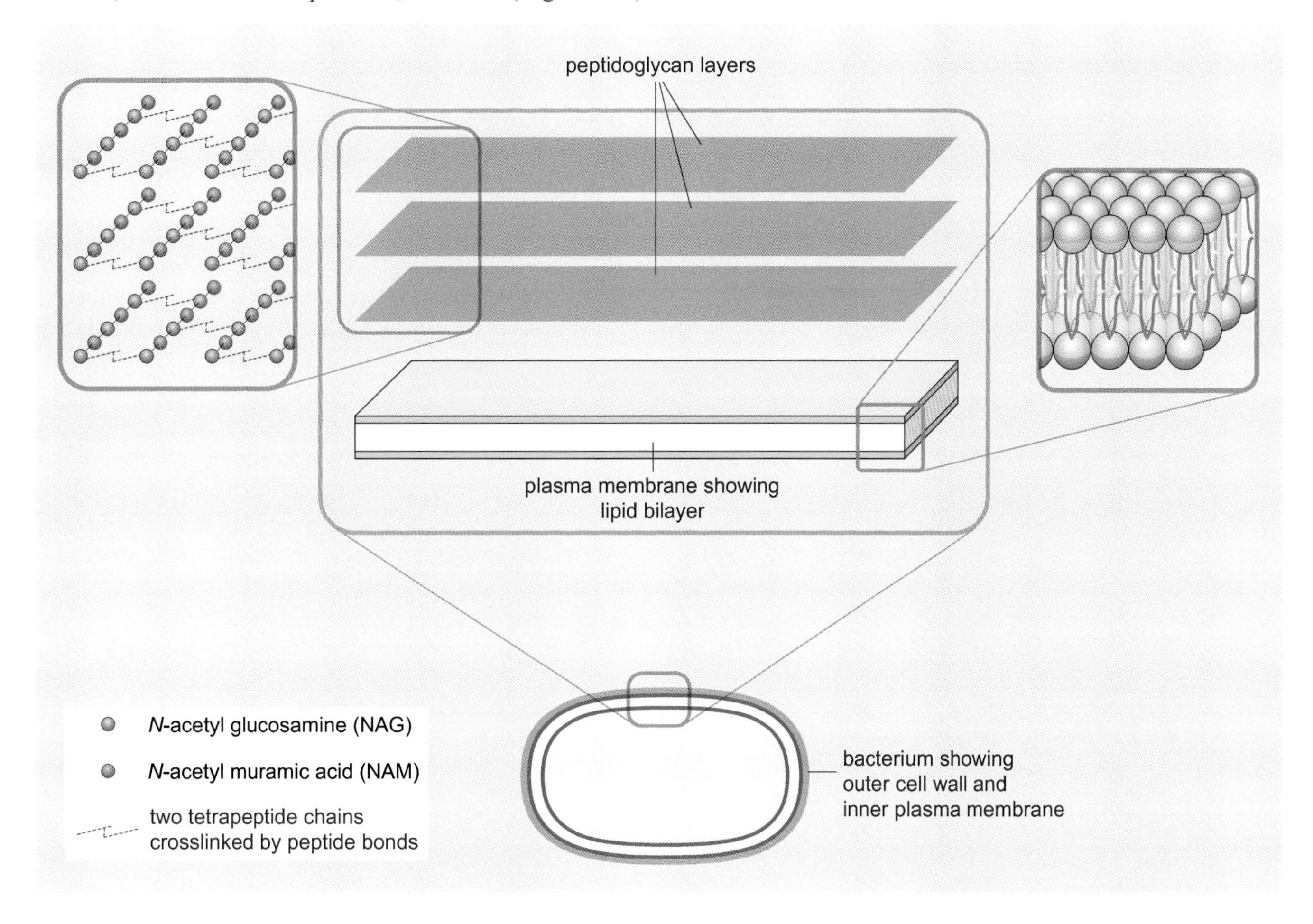

Figure 1.1 Schematic diagram of the structure of a Gram-positive bacterium highlighting the peptidoglycan wall. The polysaccharides are shown as a chain of pink and blue spheres (each being a different monosaccharide); the red chains are the tetrapeptide chains that are crosslinked to give the wall strength.

Note: Bacteria can be classified as **Gram-positive** or **Gram-negative** based on a staining technique. Bacteria with a thick cell wall (20–40 nm) absorb a purple dye thus turn purple and are classed as Gram-positive. Bacteria with a thin cell wall (2–7 nm) do not absorb the purple dye to any extent, although they can be stained by other dyes and are classed as Gram-negative. This difference in cell wall thickness and structure is important for how they respond to drugs.

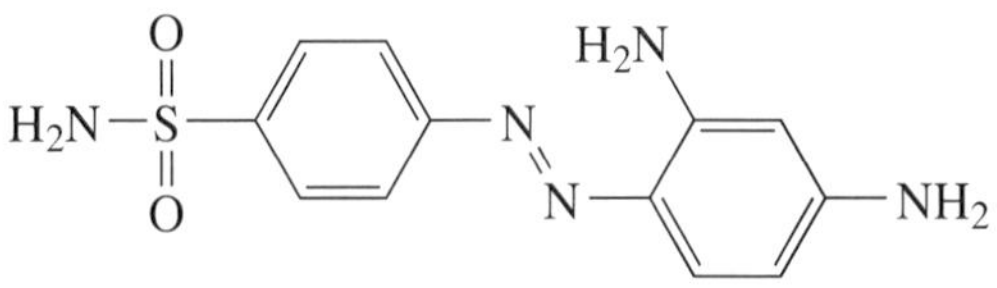

1.6 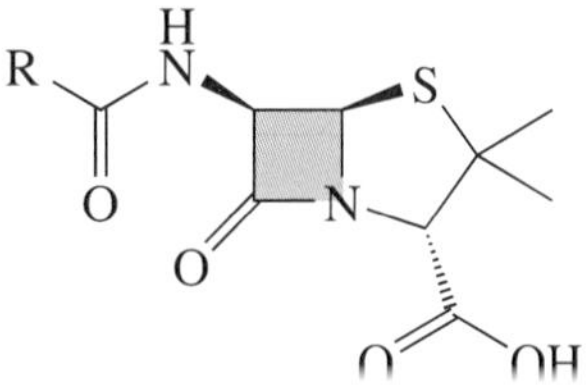 **1.7**

The Gram-stain process effectively dyes the peptidoglycan in the cell wall, which accounts for the relationship between a positive stain and susceptibility to penicillins. Enzymes (called transpeptidases) are involved in peptidoglycan synthesis and penicillin is capable of inhibiting these enzymes, through the chemistry of its four-membered β-lactam ring. Without a growing peptidoglycan 'net', bacterial cells cannot swell and are consequently burst by increasing osmotic pressure.

The chemical structure of penicillins varies depending on the precise nutrients available in the growth medium for the mould that produces them (*Penicillium chrysogenum* – formerly *notatum*); that is, R in structure **1.7** can vary. 'Normal' penicillin has a benzyl group for the R-group, but this can be altered by changing the compounds in the mould growth medium and/or carefully controlled synthetic reactions starting with a natural penicillin structure. This helps us to understand why such a large variety of so-called penicillins are available, and also why they are rotated in their use, by clinicians hoping to reduce the risk of pathogenic bacteria developing resistance to any particular one. Nevertheless, bacteria do fight back by producing enzymes known as β-lactamases; these hydrolyse the lactam ring rendering it ineffective. In the longer term, bacteria are also finding ways of modifying their transpeptidases to be less vulnerable to penicillin attack.

1.2 Vitamin C

With the advent of an improved understanding of nutrition, and the discovery of vitamins, which curiously was almost exactly concurrent with the development of chemotherapy and antibiotics, it became increasingly accepted that relatively small molecules can have health benefits but can also be used in therapies for the treatment of infectious and other diseases.

Scurvy became a real problem for early mariners, as vessels began spending longer and longer at sea. **Vitamin C** (or more accurately its deficiency) was eventually identified as the causal link. The process took a long time, however, as the disease of scurvy was noted in ancient times, but it was only in the 16th and 17th centuries that the prevention of scurvy with regular intake of fresh fruit and vegetables became common practice. The absence of acids in the diet was thought to be the true cause, but it was only much later, in the late 1920s and early 1930s, that 'antiscorbutic factor' (later to become known as vitamin C or ascorbic acid) was reported by a number of workers in the field. These include J. L. Svirbely and Albert Szent-Györgyi (Nobel Prize winner for medicine 1937) in Hungary, and Charles Glen King in the USA.

Today the way in which vitamin C prevents scurvy is much more clearly understood. The symptoms of scurvy arise from a malfunction of the biosynthesis of collagen, a widespread protein which you met in Unit 2 Section 1 and which, apart from being important to the structure of many connective tissues, is also a major component of the walls of blood vessels. Knowing that two major symptoms of scurvy are the loss of teeth and bleeding from the mouth, it isn't hard to see a physical explanation for how a shortage of collagen is responsible. Likewise, it is not hard to see how the disease can be fatal through the literal collapse of major blood vessels and other organs and tissues. How, though, can vitamin C play such an important chemical role in the production of collagen? What is its target?

It turns out that ascorbic acid, **1.8**, is needed by the enzyme proline hydroxylase. The role of this enzyme is to attach hydroxyl groups to the side chains of proline residues which are found in the individual peptide sequences of collagen fibres. Without these hydroxyl groups, the individual peptide chains cannot form the strong hydrogen bonds needed to coil up in a three-stranded rope arrangement (Figure 1.2).

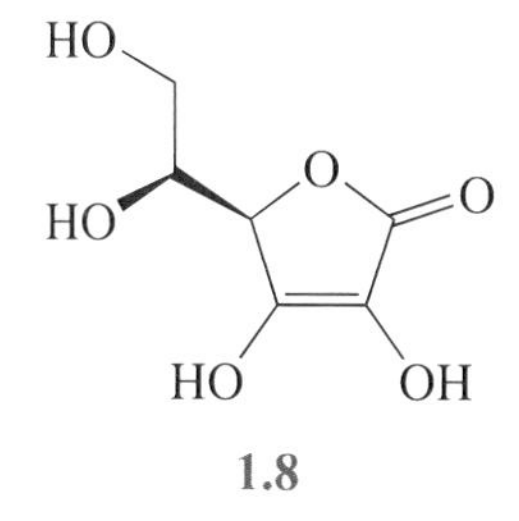

At the molecular level we can understand the role of vitamin C by appreciating the way it can be involved in redox reactions (Equation 1.1). Ascorbic acid is relatively easily oxidised to dehydroascorbic acid, and this occurs during the enzymatic oxidation of proline groups. The chemistry of the overall process is not fully understood, but it is believed that ascorbic acid is used 'sacrificially' to prevent the oxidation of the enzyme and, therefore, loss of activity during the proline oxidation. The overall reaction is summarised in Figure 1.3.

$$\mathbf{1.8} \rightleftharpoons \text{(structure)} + 2H^+ + 2e^- \qquad (1.1)$$

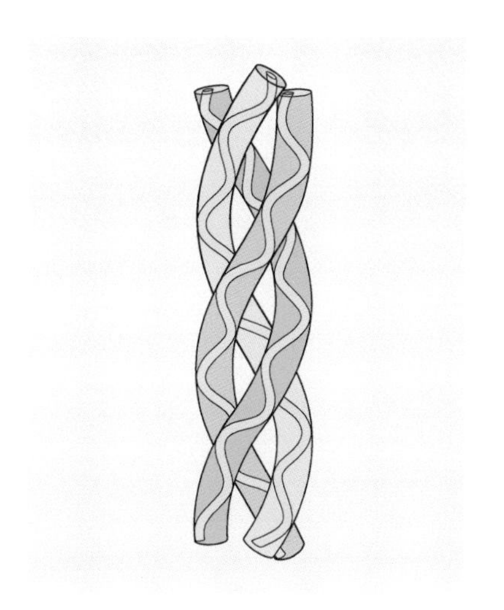

Figure 1.2 Collagen fibres are composed of three 'strands' of peptide chain held together by the hydrogen bonding between the hydroxylated proline side chain residues. These rope-like structures are covalently bonded to each other in the complete collagen structure.

Note the involvement of molecular oxygen as a reactant and Fe^{2+} as another co-factor. Since the equation could balance without the involvement of the ascorbic acid/dehydroascorbic acid system it seems reasonable that the ascorbic acid is maintaining the enzyme integrity by some kind of conditioning reaction that involves a reducing agent. Clearly the absence of ascorbic acid means the proline hydroxylase loses activity and proline residues are not hydroxylated and thus the collagen cannot form the strong rope-like structure.

■ Is ascorbic acid an oxidising agent or a reducing agent?

□ Ascorbic acid is a reducing agent in that it is itself oxidised (loses electrons) and another compound is reduced (gains electrons).

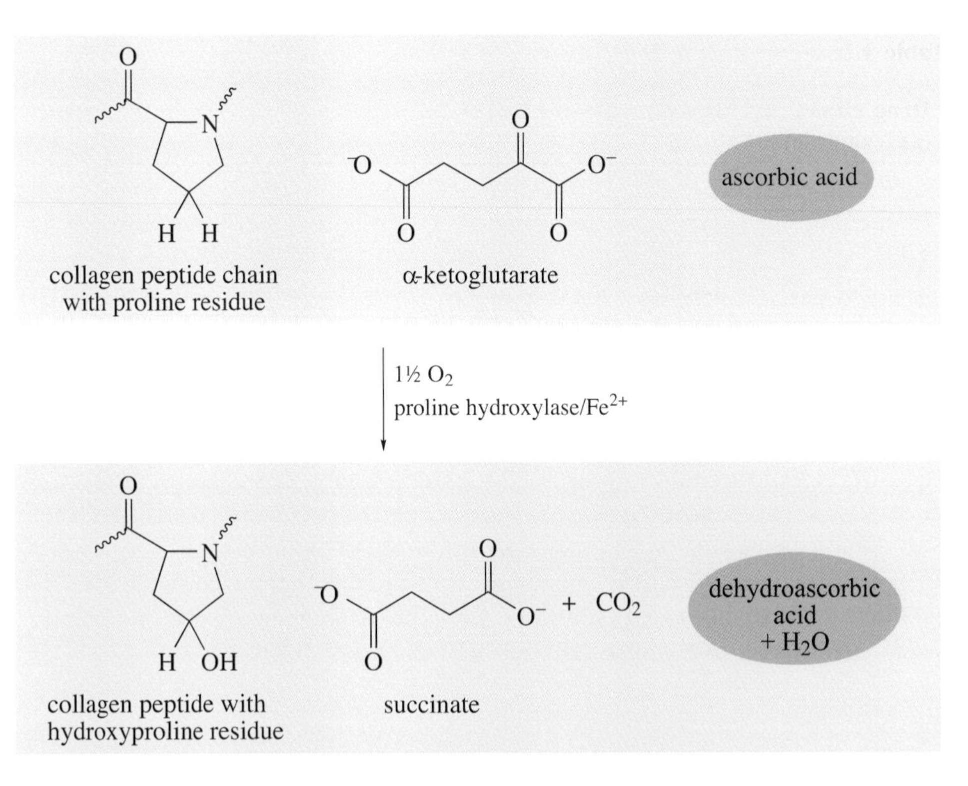

Figure 1.3 The oxidation of proline by proline hydroxylase.

There is another enzyme called lysine hydroxylase that functions in a very similar way to attach hydroxyl groups to the side chains of lysine residues. Once the hydroxyproline (and/or hydroxylysine) residues are formed, the full-strength collagen fibre and subsequently healthy collagen can be assembled. So here we have an example of a nutrient, in this case a vitamin, behaving in a remarkably drug-like way. The ascorbic acid molecule fixes the problem with collagen synthesis, which in turn rapidly alleviates the symptoms of the disease.

This idea of chemical intervention influencing the course of diseases is a cornerstone of modern drug therapy. The majority of diseases that are caused by a single pathogenic bacterium were, as we have seen, rendered treatable by chemical agents during the 20th century, while viral diseases have proven to be more problematic. We will look at the reasons for this later.

1.3 Other drugs and their targets

Aspirin, despite being in use for over 100 years, has been used to treat symptoms rather than as a cure for a specific disease and, in a way, has pre-empted a newer branch of drug treatments that is growing rapidly today. This includes treatments for metabolic and non-pathogenic disorders and represents one of the major achievements of modern medicine.

Table 1.1 illustrates the wide range of targets that we can now aim at in order to intervene in the progress of metabolic and related diseases. Many drugs today are categorised by the targets that they specifically interact with.

Table 1.1 Some drug types and their targets.

Drug class (an example)	Target	Specific effect	Disease(s) treated
ACE inhibitor (benazepril, **1.10**)	angiotensin converting enzyme	lowers blood pressure	hypertension
beta-blockers (atenolol)	β-adrenergic receptors	reduces heart-rate and contraction force	hypertension and anxiety
H_2 antagonists (ranitidine)	H_2 receptors in parietal cells in the stomach wall	reduces acid secretion in stomach	peptic ulcers
proton-pump inhibitors (PPIs) (omeprazole)	proton-pump system in parietal cells	prevents acid secretion in stomach	peptic ulcers

To gain a better understanding of the variety of modes of action that are encountered in different drugs, we will look (in Sections 1.3.1–1.3.4) in further detail at each of the examples in Table 1.1.

1.3.1 ACE inhibitors

ACE inhibitors act specifically on the angiotensin-converting enzyme (hence ACE), which is produced mainly in the capillaries of the lungs and has a very specific role as a protease (also termed peptidases, proteinases and proteolytic enzymes). The enzyme removes two amino acid residues from one end of the angiotensin I molecule, thereby generating a smaller peptide called angiotensin II. Specifically, a dipeptide consisting of a histidine and a leucine residue is removed from the C-terminal end.

Angiotensin I: Asp-Arg-Val-Tyr-Ile-His-Pro-Phe-His-Leu

Angiotensin II: Asp-Arg-Val-Tyr-Ile-His-Pro-Phe

Angiotensin I is a breakdown product of a much larger protein (angiotensinogen) produced mainly in the liver. Angiotensin I has no known biological function but after conversion, it becomes a potent hormone, producing a variety of effects that conspire to raise blood pressure. There are receptors for angiotensin II which, when activated, trigger vasoconstriction, significantly contributing to the rise in blood pressure associated with the molecule. Clearly, anything that either lowers the levels of angiotensin II or can block the receptors on which it acts is a potential treatment for raised blood pressure. The ACE inhibitors, as their name suggests, restrict the production of angiotensin II by inhibiting the enzyme that creates it from angiotensin I.

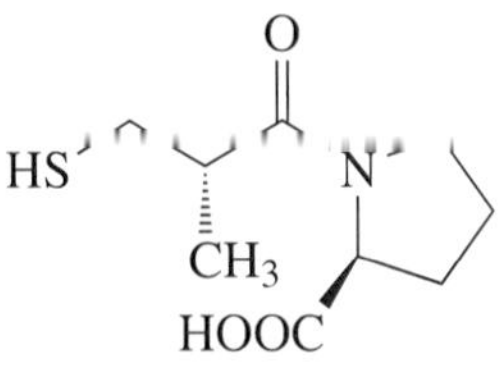

1.9

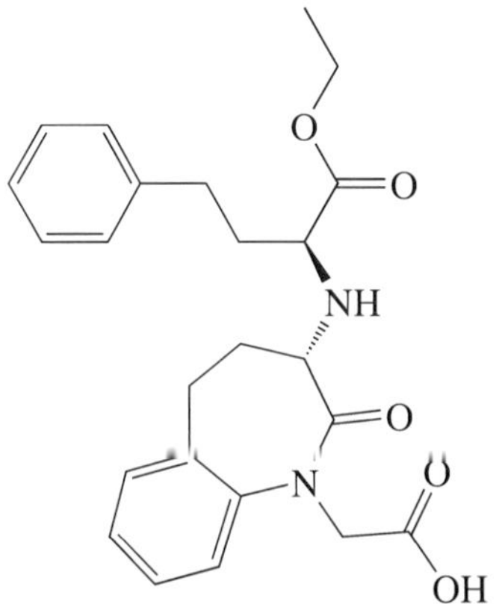

1.10

The first molecule of this type to be marketed was captopril (**1.9**), and a later example is benazepril (**1.10**).

■ What features do these two structures have in common?

□ They have at least one peptide (amide) linkage with a neighbouring carboxyl group.

■ What similarity is there with the natural substrate **1.11**?

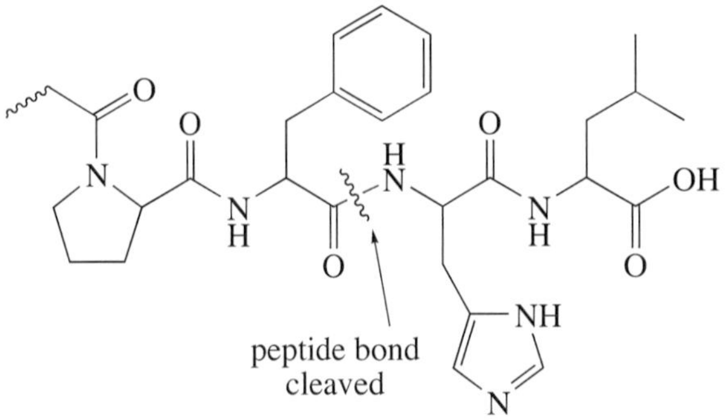

peptide bond cleaved

1.11

□ It is difficult to identify any similarity other than the presence of one peptide (amide) linkage with a neighbouring carbonyl group

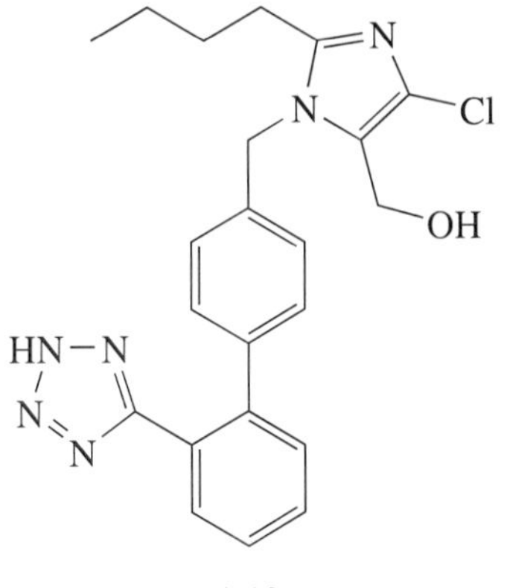

1.12

The more remote polar groups (–SH in captopril **1.9** and the amine function in benazepril **1.10**) are different, but both are capable of binding to some feature close to the enzyme active site. Although it may not seem like it, this analysis reinforces the common relationship that inhibitors often have with the natural substrate for the enzyme on which they act. More recently, a group of molecules has been developed to block the angiotensin receptors rather than moderating the levels of their agonist, angiotensin II. These are known as the angiotensin II receptor antagonists (or blockers); ARBs for short. The first of these is losartan (**1.12**).

Theoretically, the combination of the actions of ACE inhibitors and ARBs should give an even greater control over the blood pressure in patients. The general idea of combining agonist regulating drugs with **antagonist** drugs is growing in importance, and in the case of ACE inhibitors/ARB combinations there is growing evidence of multiple beneficial effects in the longer term.

This kind of approach, where more than one drug is used simultaneously to treat a single disease, is one example of a strategy known as **combination therapy**, which is quickly gaining recognition, particularly in the treatment of AIDS and cancer.

1.3.2 Beta blockers

As you saw in Unit 2 Section 3, **beta blockers** (β-blockers) are also used in the treatment of raised blood pressure (hypertension), but their mode of action is different from ACE inhibitors. These drugs are **antagonists** for the β-adrenergic receptors, which are normally stimulated by noradrenaline (**1.13**) and adrenaline (**1.14**), which are secreted by the adrenal glands situated above the kidneys.

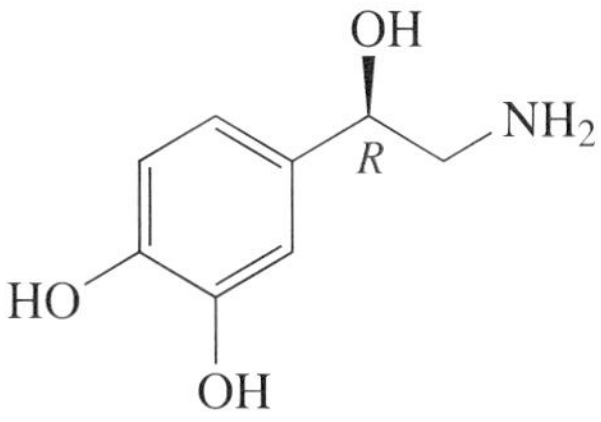

1.13 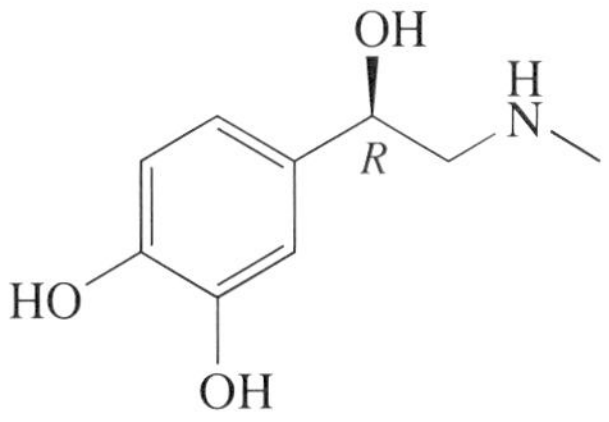 **1.14**

As you saw earlier in Unit 2, the β-adrenergic receptors fall into more than one category and the ones of interest to us here are the β_1 and β_2 types.

- ■ Where are the β_1- and β_2-type adrenergic receptors separately found in the body and what are their functions?

- □ Receptors of type β_1 are found in heart tissue and have the role of increasing the rate and force of the contractions of heart muscle. They play a role in the 'fight or flight' response that we are all familiar with following an unexpected exposure to danger.

  The β_2-type receptors are found in the smooth muscle of the lungs and when stimulated by the natural agonist, help to relax the airways (the trachea, bronchial tubes and bronchioles) assisting the normal response of the heart by providing improved ventilation and increased oxygen supply.

Modern β-blockers can act selectively, and atenolol, **1.15**, for example, shows a preference for β_1-receptors. It is therefore valuable in controlling elevated blood pressure by regulation of the heart without loss of the beneficial effects from the agonism of the β_2-receptors. Propranolol (**1.16**, an earlier example), on the other hand, is a non-selective antagonist and acts on both β_1- and β_2-receptor types. Note again, the structural similarities between noradrenline (**1.13**), adrenaline (**1.14**) and the β-blockers propranolol (**1.16**) and atenolol (**1.15**). The NH–CH_2–C–OH motif is common to all four molecules, as is the presence of at least one aromatic ring, not too distant from the alcohol function. Another point to observe here is that, although the natural agonists are single stereoisomers, the drugs are racemic mixtures, possibly reflecting the expense of marketing a single enantiomer in these cases. For atenolol, the most active isomer is the *S*-enantiomer, and it has been suggested that the *R*-enantiomer is responsible for some of the side effects of the drug. Atenolol is also too polar to cross the blood–brain barrier, and this may explain the absence of nightmares as one of its side effects, which is something that is observed as a side effect with propranolol.

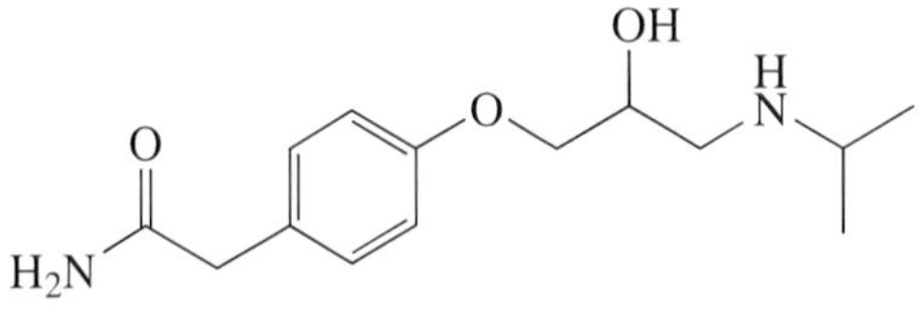

1.15

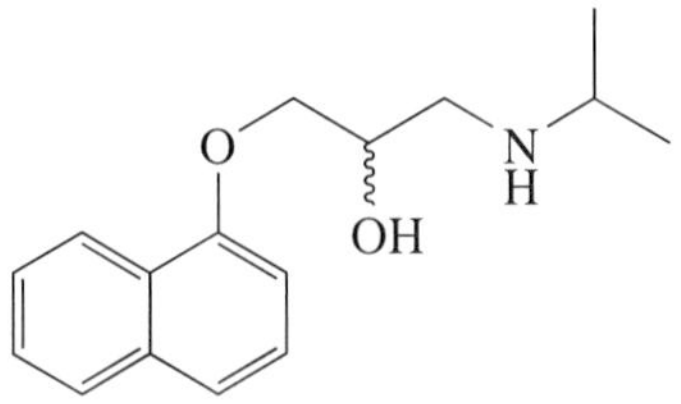

1.16

Clearly, from a clinical perspective, there are choices to be made as to which drug is best suited to a patient's individual condition. There are more than 20 β-blockers available today. Some are non-selective, others are β_1-selective and some are even active at both β-receptors and so-called α_1-receptors, which are responsible for certain types of smooth muscle contraction. Antagonism of these α_1-receptors has an added bonus of blood vessel dilation, which may be beneficial to some individuals.

1.3.3 H_2 antagonists

Our next category of drug, the **H_2 antagonists**, is another we met in Unit 2 Section 3. These drugs are interesting because they represent the results from one of the first coordinated efforts to design a drug from a rational development of the structure of a natural agonist. In the early 1960s, when work began, the H_2 histamine receptor was only speculation and it was observed that the anti-histamine drugs of the time (used to treat inflammation from insect venom and symptoms of hay fever) had no effect on the secretion of stomach acid. This suggested that the molecule histamine, **1.17** (the natural agonist released by trauma to the tissues), was binding to a different receptor when causing classic inflammation responses, compared with the receptor responsible for the release of acid from the parietal cells in the stomach wall.

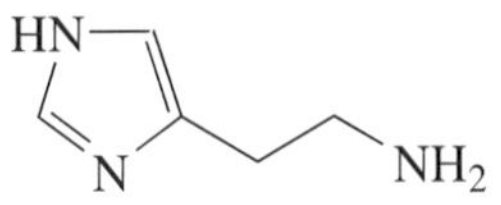

1.17

It had been demonstrated that histamine was one of three agents that could trigger acid release, the other two being acetylcholine and the hormone gastrin. The inflammation response receptor was named H_1 and found to have different agonist requirements to the acid-release receptor (later coined H_2). An extensive search revealed that changing the histamine structure in a number of very precise ways resulted in an effective antagonist that could dramatically reduce the acid concentration in the stomach, and the first effective treatment for peptic ulcers was therefore realised.

Figure 1.4 shows how it is possible for one molecule (histamine) to activate two different receptors.

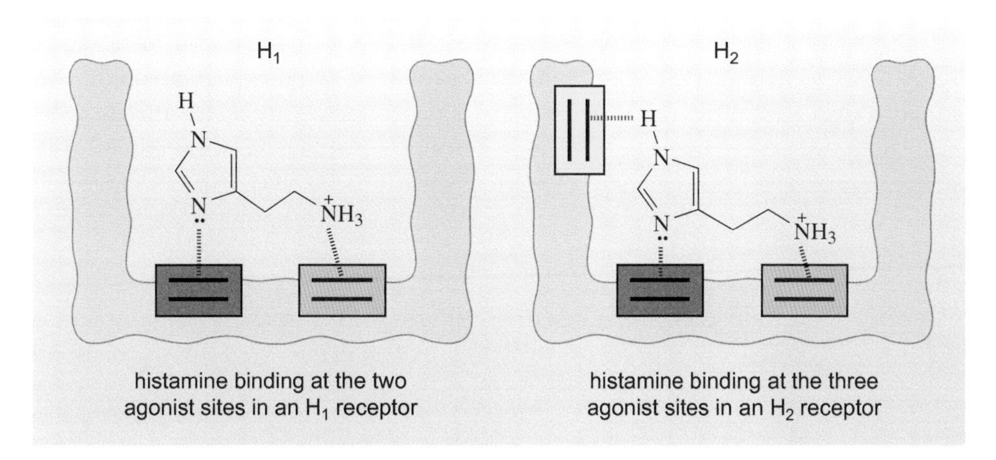

Figure 1.4 Histamine binding to stylised H_1 and H_2 receptors.

Figure 1.5 highlights the way a cimetidine molecule is designed to act as an antagonist by binding in a different way to the H_2 receptor than histamine does.

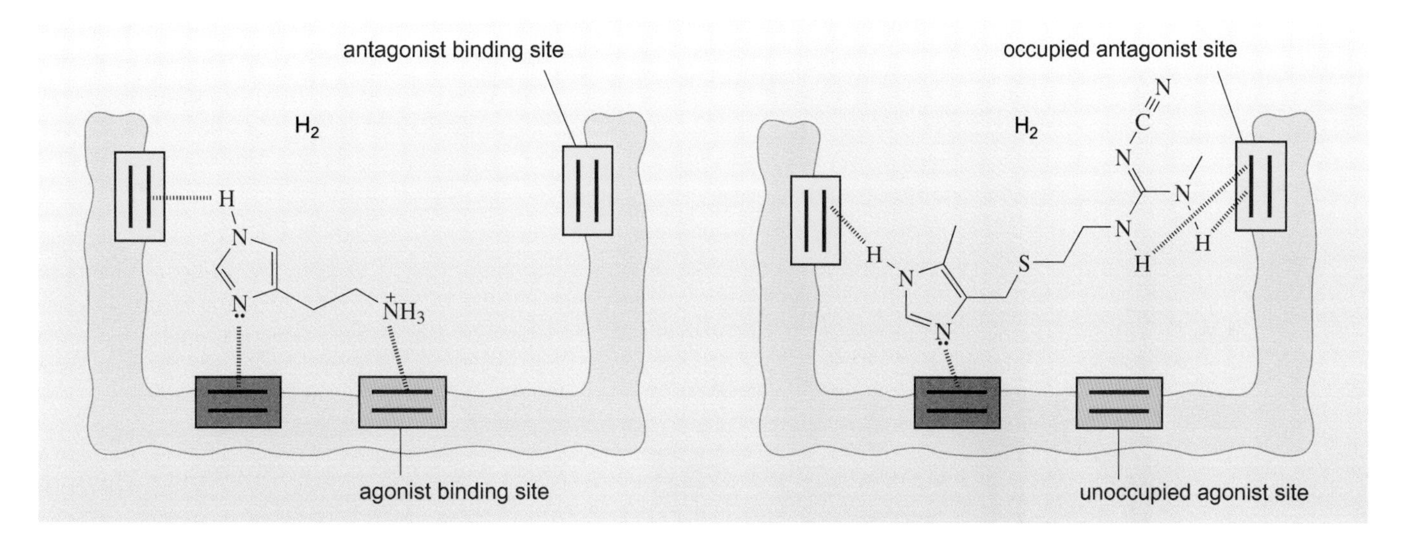

Figure 1.5 The more remote antagonist binding site (left) and a cimetidine molecule showing antagonist binding (right).

In histamine, the terminal amino function is sufficiently basic to be protonated at stomach pH (about 2) and, therefore, can bind to one of the agonist sites through an ionic interaction to a negatively charged group at the surface of the receptor. The tail group of cimetidine (a cyanoguanidine group), however, has a very electron-withdrawing cyano group which prevents protonation by lowering the basicity of the surrounding nitrogen atoms. This is important as the group is still polar and, therefore, able to bind at the antagonist site through dipole–dipole interactions. The absence of a full positive charge, however, prevents cimetidine from binding at the ionic site. This effect is enhanced by the extended chain length in cimetidine, which reaches out to the remote antagonist site. The addition of the methyl group and the sulfur atom are subtle changes to ensure that the ring NH in the position shown is the dominant form of the drug. Following cimetidine, several other H_2 antagonists were developed, with perhaps the most well known being ranitidine (**1.18**), better known as Zantac.

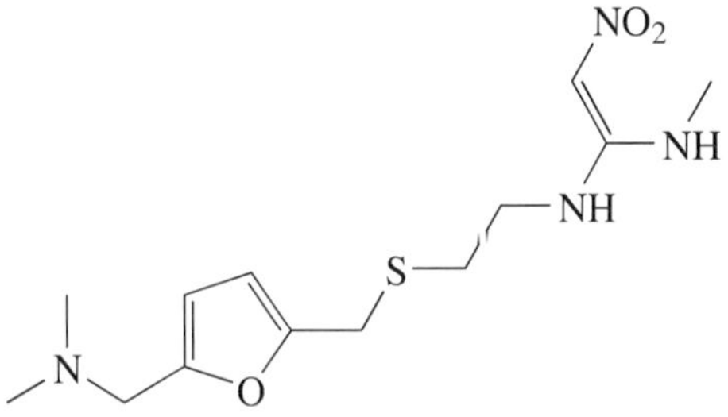

1.18

Note that in ranitidine, the $-NO_2$ replaces the cyano group and the ring system is significantly altered.

- ■ Do you think that the nitro group will have a similar electron-withdrawing effect to the cyano group?
- □ As you may remember if you have done the Level 2 module, the nitro group is an electron-withdrawing group deactivating benzene rings to electrophilic attack and causing the substituent to go in the *meta* position.

There are close similarities in the rest of the structure, though, which retain the H_2 antagonist properties found in cimetidine. Ranitidine is noted for being longer acting, more potent and having fewer side effects than cimetidine. It was introduced to the market in 1981 and for a time was the world's highest earning drug as a popular treatment for peptic ulcers and acid reflux symptoms.

1.3.4 Proton-pump inhibitors

Since the success of the H_2 antagonists, there have been a number of important developments in the treatment of peptic ulcers. First, the discovery that some ulcers are caused by an infection of the stomach with the bacterium *Helicobacter pylori* has meant that many cases can be treated with antibiotics and do not recur. Second, the **proton-pump inhibitors** (PPIs) have been introduced. These act directly on the system that generates the acid, rather than on the regulatory systems that control parietal cell activity. These pumps involve ion channels (Unit 2 Section 4) that pump protons through the membrane, against the pH gradient. Acid (HCl) is 'pumped' into the stomach by an energy (ATP)-consuming protein complex known as an H^+/K^+ ATPase. (ATP is adenosine triphosphate.) This works rather like a revolving door in the cell wall, pulling K^+ ions into the parietal cell and pushing out H^+ into the stomach. The net result can be a stomach pH lower than 2, which can cause irritation to ulcers or the lining of the oesophagus.

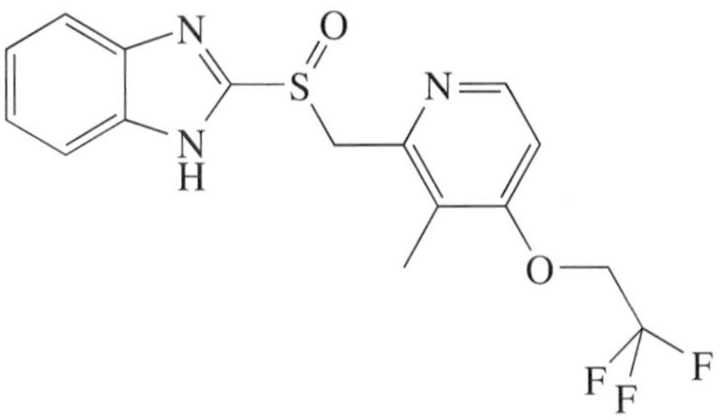

1.19

The PPI drugs, such as lansoprazole (**1.19**), inhibit acid production by undergoing acid-catalysed breakdown to the active component sulfenamides which bind irreversibly to the protein of the proton-pump.

This family of drugs is very effective, since they stop acid secretion completely and the process cannot be resumed until new H^+/K^+ ATPase is expressed by the cell. Another subtle aspect of the operation of PPIs is, that as they begin to take effect, drug hydrolysis slows as the pH rises, meaning that one moderate dose can last up to 24 hours.

1.3.5 Non-steroidal anti-inflammatory drugs

Some **non-steroidal anti-inflammatory drugs** (NSAIDs), such as aspirin (**1.20**), have been known for over 100 years.

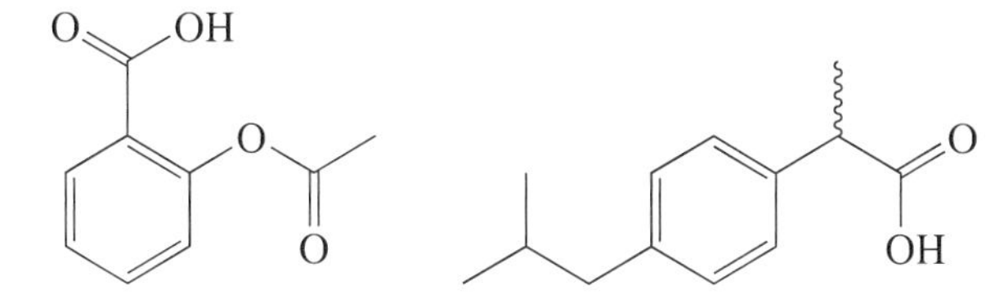

O OH O O

1.20

O OH

1.21

Their modes of action have only relatively recently become clear and there are still some aspects that are not completely understood. Aspirin and other NSAIDs, such as ibuprofen (**1.21**), appear to act by inhibition of the cyclooxygenase (COX) enzyme, responsible for a crucial step in the synthesis of **prostaglandins**.

O 5 7 OH 11 14

arachidonic acid

$2O_2$ fatty acid cyclooxygenase

O OH 7 5 O O 11 14 OOH

PGG_2

peroxidase

O OH 7 5 O O 11 14 OH

PGH_2

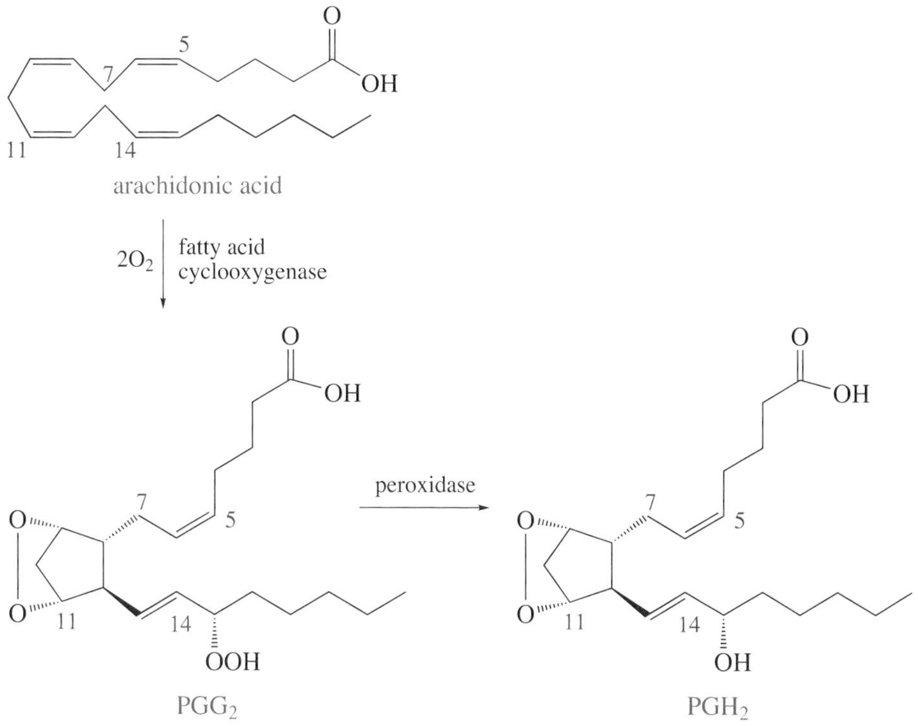

Figure 1.6 The early steps in the synthesis of prostaglandins.

Figure 1.6 shows how arachidonic acid (from the diet) reacts with oxygen in the presence of the COX enzyme to give the five-membered ring and two side chains that are an essential feature of the prostaglandin family of molecules.

PGH_2 is modified further to give several more related structures shown in Figure 1.7.

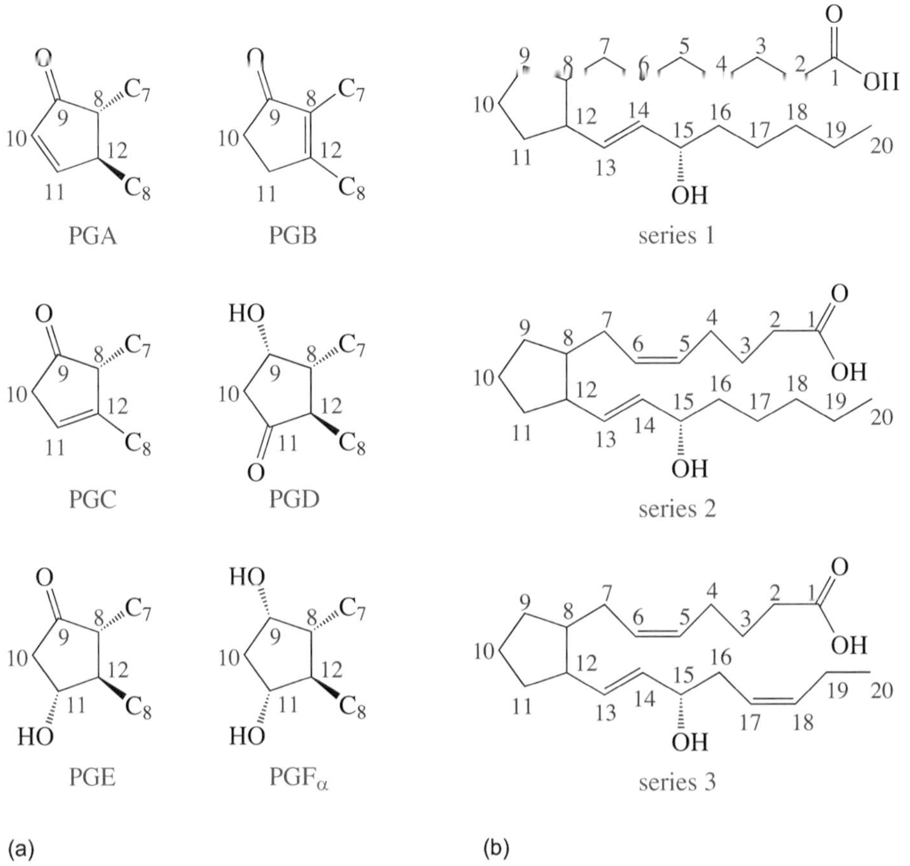

Figure 1.7 The family of prostaglandins. Each ring pattern in part (a) can have one of three associated side-chain patterns in (b) (PGE_1, PGE_2, etc.).

The role of the prostaglandins is to act as short-lived hormone-like molecules that trigger processes associated with inflammation. Their synthesis is prompted by the normal causes of inflammation such as physical trauma, burns and infection. The COX enzyme has three known variants (called iso-enzymes, COX-1, COX-2 and COX-3) and these are expressed in different proportions depending on the tissue type. NSAIDs can be general inhibitors of the COX enzyme or may show specificity for one or more of the iso-enzymes, and this may account for the variation in efficacy with choice of drug and type of inflammation. Overall, though, inhibiting the COX enzyme suppresses prostaglandin synthesis and reduces temperature, swelling and other associated effects of inflammation and fever. Thromboxanes are structurally very similar to prostaglandins and also require COX in their synthesis. As thromboxanes encourage clotting of the blood, giving aspirin at low dose is a very effective long-term treatment for people at risk from stroke or heart attack.

1.3.6 Statins

Our last two drug types, **statins** and cholesterol uptake inhibitors, both help to regulate blood cholesterol levels, but they have very different modes of action. We will consider statins first, as they have been in use for much longer. Statins act by competitive inhibition of an enzyme in the liver called HMG-CoA reductase. The role of the enzyme is to reduce 3-hydroxy-3-methylglutaryl-coenzyme A (HMG-CoA) to mevalonic acid and coenzyme A, as shown in Figure 1.8.

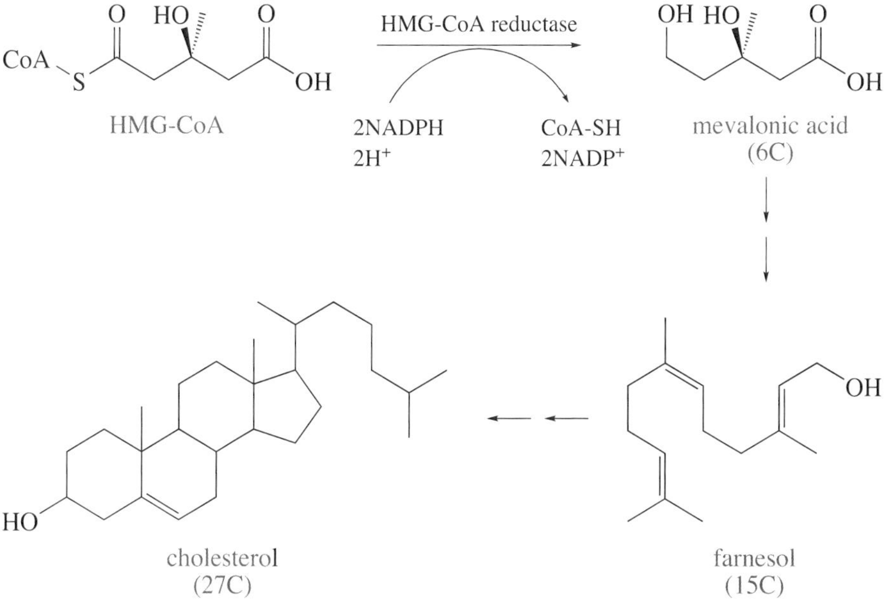

Figure 1.8 The biosynthesis of cholesterol (simplified). Carbon numbers for each molecule are indicated as 6C, etc.

Mevalonic acid is the key to terpene biosynthesis and goes on through many steps involving the addition and removal of phosphate groups to give farnesol, which is a trimer of mevalonic acid that has lost three CO_2 and five H_2O molecules. Farnesol goes on to become cholesterol after several further steps. Cholesterol is synthesised in this way by the liver, and so inhibition of HMG-CoA reductase, preventing the synthesis of the mevalonic acid starting material, has the effect of lowering the levels of blood cholesterol. The earliest statin was lovastatin (**1.22**), first launched in 1987. Since then many new statins have been introduced, such as simvastatin (**1.23**), which, like lovastatin is a synthetically modified natural product, and atorvastatin (**1.24**), which is completely synthetic. All of them are HMG-CoA reductase inhibitors, but comparison of the structures shows that, in some cases, molecules with very different structures can still have similarities in their protein binding properties.

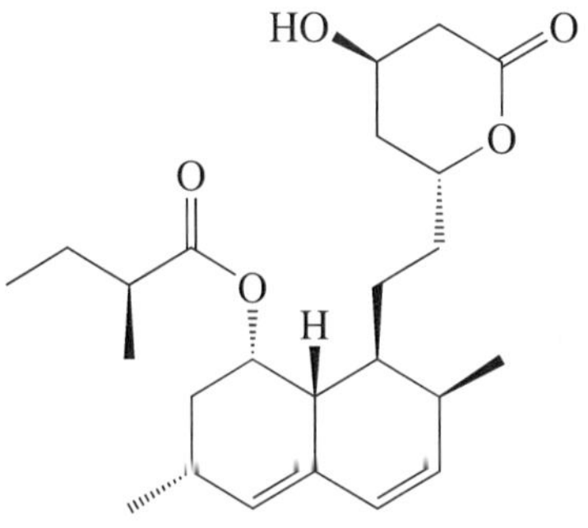

1.22

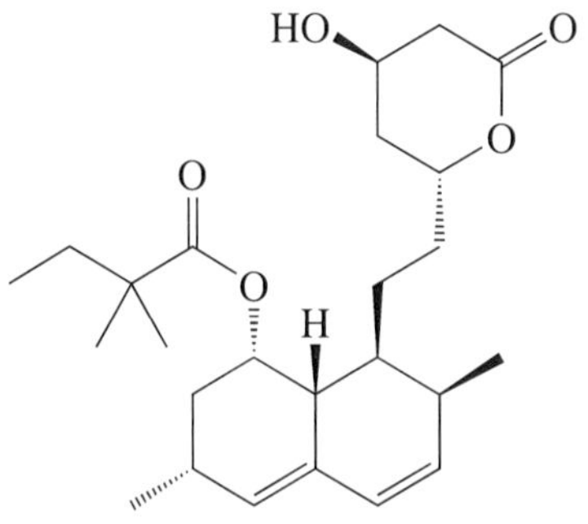

1.23

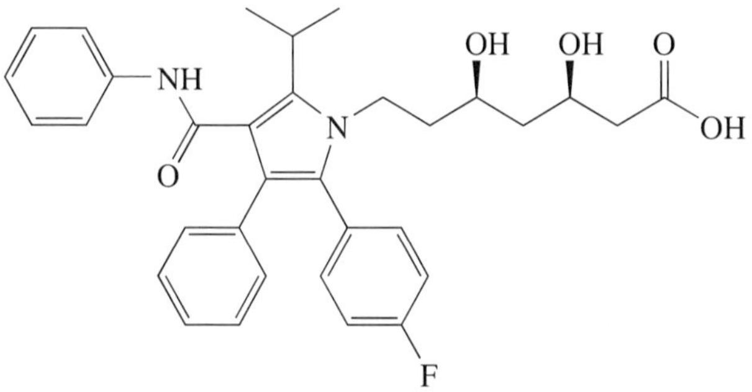

1.24

1.3.7 Cholesterol uptake inhibitors

Cholesterol uptake inhibitors, on the other hand, reduce levels of blood cholesterol by blocking the uptake of dietary cholesterol in the small intestine. They are a very recent development, and the only one marketed so far (ezetimibe, **1.25**) appeared early in the new millennium.

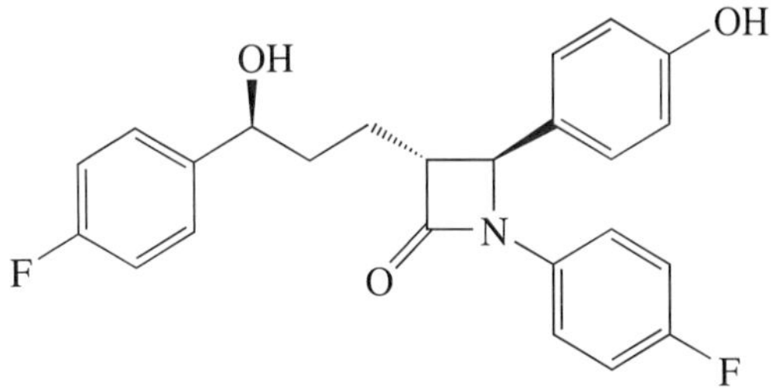

1.25

Ezetimibe is believed to work by binding to a protein called Niemann-Pick C1-like 1 (NPC1L1), which is named after the gene that codes for the protein in question. It is an intestinal cholesterol transporter, and the protein is no longer able to carry out its normal role when ezetimibe binds to it. There are some recent suggestions that the extent to which ezetimibe is successful is dependent upon individual genetic variation within the NPC1L1 gene and, therefore, the protein. Efficacy trials are still being undertaken for ezetimibe and, although there is great optimism about its effectiveness, some recent results appear to suggest only a slowing of cholesterol deposition in arteries rather than the expected reversal of the process. It is also currently being prescribed as part of a combination therapy with statins, in order to maximise its effects.

All of the drug targets we have considered so far are proteins, and there are strong parallels between active sites and receptors, between agonists and substrates and between antagonists and inhibitors, as we have seen in the examples so far. So, is it the case that all targets are necessarily proteins?

1.4 Other drug targets

There are two other kinds of target, which we will briefly consider here, namely DNA and protein biosynthesis (specifically ribosome function). We mentioned earlier that viral diseases have resisted effective treatments much more than other pathogenic illnesses that are largely caused by bacteria, fungi or parasites. Curiously, for example, Louis Pasteur and Emil Roux had some dramatic early successes in the 19th century with the development of a vaccine for rabies (a viral disease) cultured in the spinal cords of rabbits. The weakened virus obtained resulted in the transmission of immunity to humans without the harmful damage to nerve tissue that causes the well-known symptoms of the disease.

Slowly, other viral vaccines were developed, but antiviral drugs that treat the disease after it has been contracted have not really kept pace with the dramatic changes that antibiotics have brought in.

1.4.1 Targeting DNA replication

One way of attacking viral disease is to interfere with the usually rapid DNA replication that viruses depend upon to replicate and disperse. This approach has been exploited in the treatment of the *herpes simplex*, and other viruses with the drug aciclovir (**1.26**, or acyclovir), marketed as Zovirax.

How does it work? Drugs such as aciclovir are often termed nucleoside analogues or mimics. To understand this we need to remind ourselves of the structure of DNA, as shown in Figure 1.9.

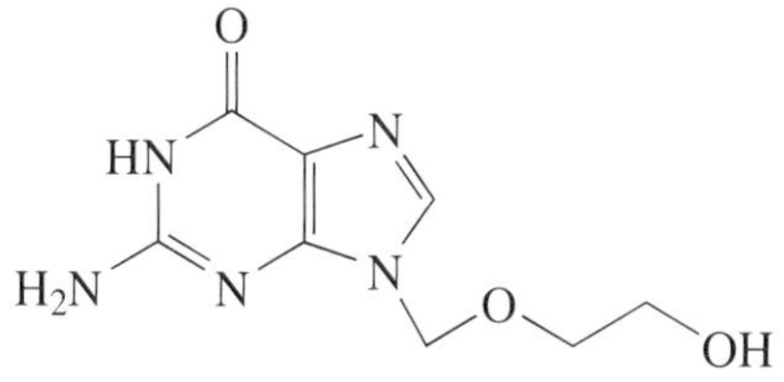

O HN N H_2N N N O OH

1.26

The aciclovir molecule has a structural resemblance to the purine bases adenine and guanine, but on its own is not the active drug. By being sufficiently similar to adenine and guanine it enters the DNA replication process and becomes phoshorylated (phosphate groups are added to the OH group) by the appropriate enzymes. In the next stage, the viral DNA polymerase enzyme picks up the now active drug, but the absence of a complete ribose sugar makes the drug a potent inhibitor for the enzyme rather than just the next base to be added to the sequence. This arrests the viral DNA replication and effectively prevents the virus from reproducing. Aciclovir is able to selectively target the viral DNA, because the host cell DNA is protected in the nucleus, with a larger timescale necessary for its own reproduction.

Many other antiviral drugs have been developed. AZT (**1.27**), for example, was the first drug to be effective against the HIV virus. In the case of AZT, the enzyme targeted is the reverse transcriptase that the virus employs to make a DNA copy of its RNA code. AZT most closely resembles thymine, one of the pyrimidine bases.

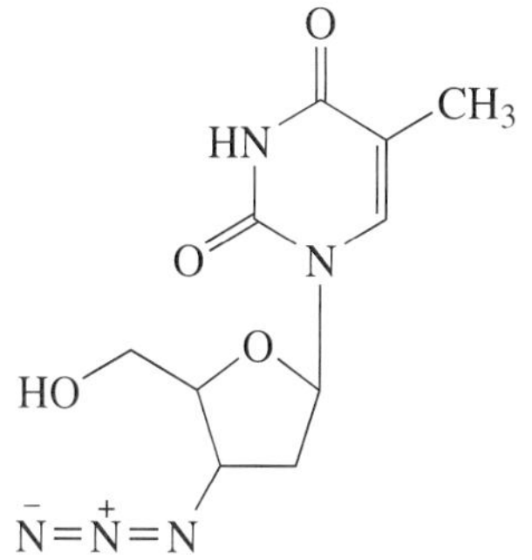

O CH_3 HN O N O HO $\bar{N}=\overset{+}{N}=N$

1.27

1.4.2 Targeting protein biosynthesis

Our final drug target is the process of protein biosynthesis. All cells need to synthesise protein as part of their life cycle, so the actual process of gathering the amino acid building blocks, reading the required sequence code from

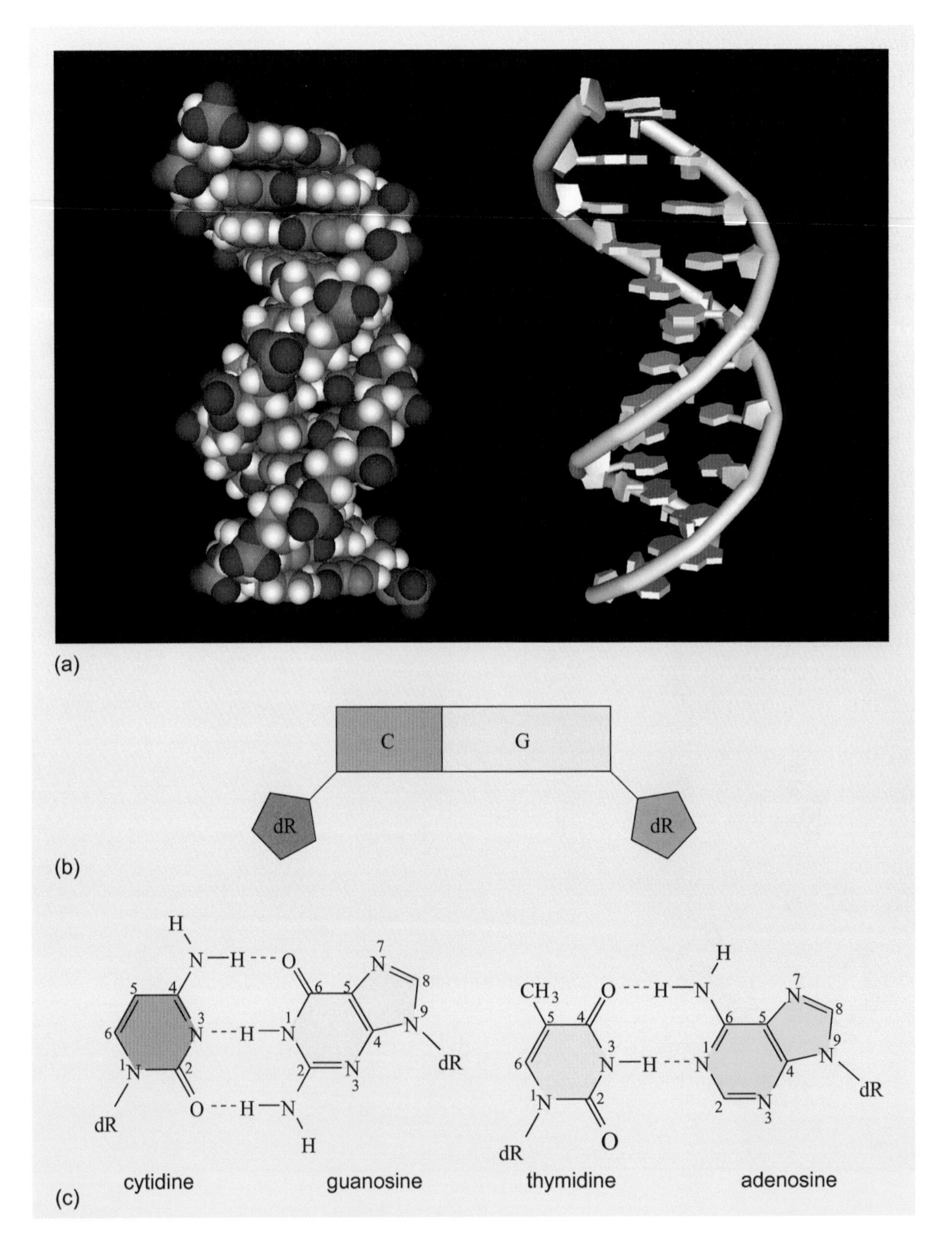

Figure 1.9 DNA consists of two strands, each being a polymer of nucleotides. Each nucleotide consists of a phosphorylated sugar molecule linked to a base, either thymine, adenine, cytosine or guanine. In the DNA polymer the sugars are linked by phosphate groups. The bases in the two strands are complementary – thymine hydrogen bonds with adenine and cytosine hydrogen bonds with guanine. (dR is deoxyribose)

DNA and assembling the finished protein is a complex but vital part of a cell's function. Even prevention of synthesis for just a few vital enzyme proteins can be sufficient to arrest a pathogen. The drug chloramphenicol (**1.28**) has been known and used for 60 years as an antibiotic, but its mode of action is very different from that of the β-lactam antibiotics. It is still used to treat conjunctivitis, but for many other uses it has been replaced by less toxic alternatives.

Chloramphenicol belongs to the group of **bacteriostatic** drugs that prevent bacteria from growing normally. Protein synthesis takes place in organelles called ribosomes, which are highly organised structures of protein and RNA. They are in essence a protein synthesis unit, equipped to read genetic code and assemble proteins in accordance with the instructions contained therein. The details are complex, but we need to know that in assembling the protein chain an 'enzyme' called peptidyl transferase is involved. The role of peptidyl transferase is to form the amide bond between the incoming amino acid chosen from the genetic information and the growing peptide chain.

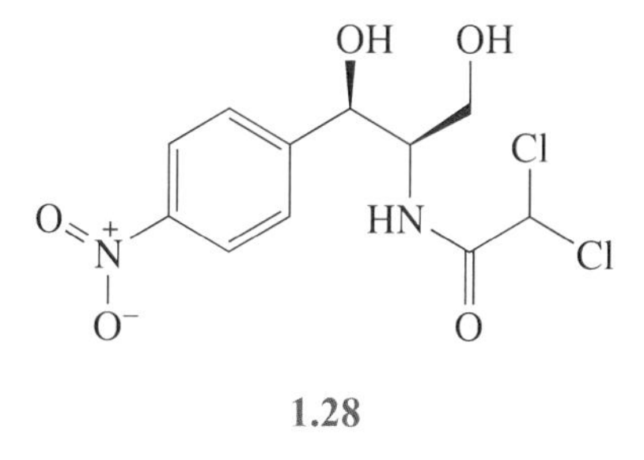

1.28

The interesting point here is that, although peptidyl transferase is behaving as an enzyme, a large part of it is composed of RNA and not protein, so we can argue that it is not a protein drug target. The name sometimes used in place of enzyme when RNA is involved is **ribozyme**. Chloramphenicol inhibits the function of the peptidyl transferase, and in doing so arrests the growth of the bacterium. Chloramphenicol has a peptide bond within its structure and, therefore, resembles the substrate for peptidyl transferase. Binding to the ribozyme occurs by interaction with RNA bases, rather than protein side chains, as shown in Figure 1.10.

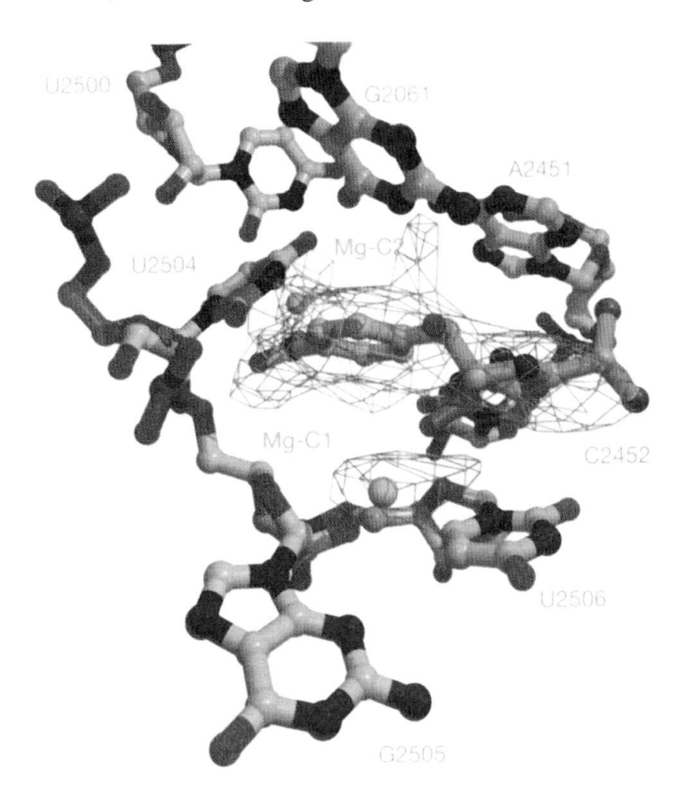

Figure 1.10 Chloramphenicol (in green) binding to bacterial peptidyl transferase. The letters G, U, A and C refer to the RNA bases (guanine, uracil. adenine and cytosine). Note that the thymine in DNA is replaced by uracil in RNA.

Since chloramphenicol, other bacteriostatic drugs have been discovered that bind to the peptidyl transferase centre in bacterial ribosomes. These include clindamycin (**1.29**) and the well-known erythromycin (**1.30**). Both are prescribed as antibiotics. Clindamycin is a semi-synthetic structure, based on a naturally occurring molecule from *Streptomyces lincolnensis*, whereas erythromycin is wholly derived from the bacterium *Streptomyces griseus*.

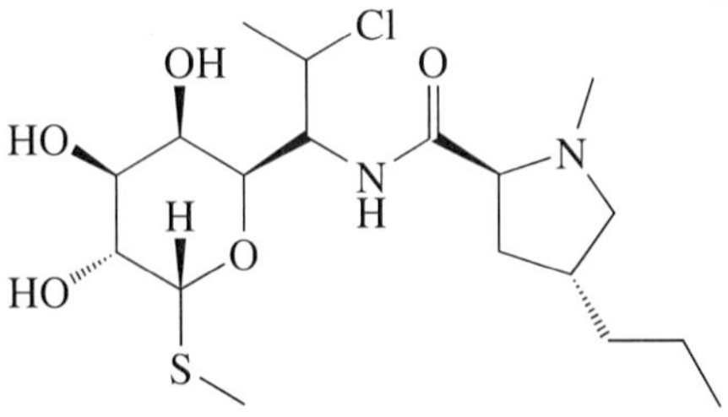

1.29 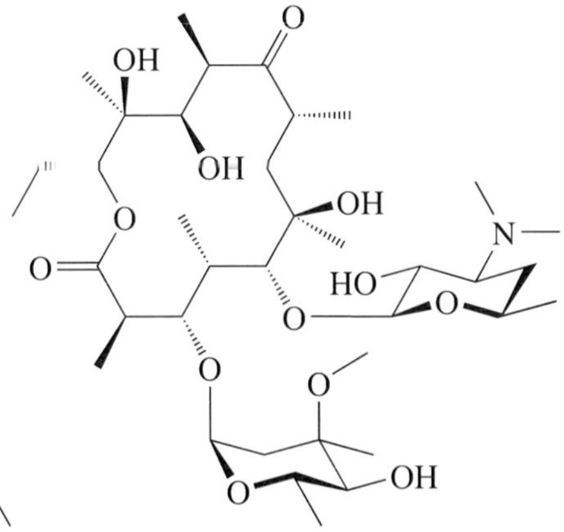 **1.30**

Interestingly clindamycin has some structural similarity with chloramphenicol (in particular the amide function) but erythromycin bears virtually no resemblance.

Study note

Having looked at the various drug targets, we will now return to examine the properties of organic molecules. This will not only help us understand how drugs work at their target but also how drugs can be synthesised. We will consider first the electronic effects (in Sections 2 and 3) before looking at the steric effects in Section 5 and Unit 4.

However, before moving on to Section 2, you should produce your own summary of this section and then compare it with ours. Go to Unit 3 summaries in Unit 3 resources on the module website.

2 Electronic effect of structure on equilibria

So far in the module we have examined the structure and properties of proteins and looked at how small molecules such as drugs interact with the active sites of enzymes and the binding sites of receptors. Before we can progress much further we need to spend some time looking at the reactions of small molecules. First, we need to appreciate how enzymes can transform small molecules into other molecules. An understanding of the chemistry involved provides insight into the catalytic mechanism of a particular enzyme. This in turn helps in the design of enzyme inhibitors – drug molecules. Secondly, the latter half of the module is concerned with how we synthesise drugs and for this we need to develop our understanding of what influences organic reactions. So we will halt our study of biomolecules for a while and investigate some of the organic chemistry behind reactivity.

So often, organic chemistry appears to be just a collection of isolated facts, but this is far from the truth. In reality, the subject has an underlying logical structure and is unified by a number of fundamental concepts. A basic principle is the functional group approach: in general, organic molecules can be separated conceptually into an inert carbon backbone to which is attached a variety of reactive functional groups. It is these functional groups that are directly involved in much of the interesting chemistry that takes place. In general, a functional group has the same pattern of reactivity irrespective of its environment, and so knowing the reactions of a particular functional group allows one to predict the reactivity of a whole range of compounds. But we were still left with the problem of having to memorise the chemistry of a number of different functional groups. However, this can be simplified by learning to classify organic reactions according to type: for example, as substitution or elimination. By examining the polarity of a bond we could identify electrophilic and nucleophilic parts of molecules. Finally, by using curly arrows we can keep track of electron movement during a reaction. This enables us to understand the mechanisms of reactions and thereby account for the particular products that are formed. Here, we go one step further and examine how the molecular environment influences the properties of a functional group, attenuating or accentuating its reactivity. In particular, we shall examine how:

- the distribution of electronic charge within a molecule can affect its reactivity, both in terms of equilibria, particularly acidity, and of rates of reaction
- mathematical models can be used to predict the reactivity of substituted aromatic compounds
- the shape of a molecule can affect its reactivity, both in terms of equilibria and of rates of reaction.

As you will see, this kind of approach allows us to rationalise many observations within both chemistry and biochemistry.

2.1 Setting the scene

When an organic chemist has to prepare a new compound a number of decisions have to be made regarding reagent, catalyst, solvent and conditions. Take a look at the following examples and think about the questions posed.

Example A The sweetener 5-nitro-2-propoxyaniline (**2.1**) is 4000 times as sweet as sugar and has no bitter aftertaste. It can be prepared in the following way:

$$\text{2-amino-4-nitrophenol (OH, NH}_2\text{, NO}_2\text{)} \xrightarrow[\text{ii, } CH_3CH_2CH_2Br]{\text{i, } NaOCH_2CH_3} \text{5-nitro-2-propoxyaniline (O–}CH_2CH_2CH_3\text{, NH}_2\text{, NO}_2\text{)} \quad \mathbf{2.1} \qquad (2.1)$$

Normally amino groups are considered to be more nucleophilic than alcohols. How has the chemist controlled the reaction to ensure alkylation of the oxygen rather than the amino nitrogen?

Example B The muscle relaxant decamethonium (**2.2**) can be prepared in the following way:

$$N{\equiv}C{-}(CH_2)_8{-}C{\equiv}N \xrightarrow{\text{reduction}} H_2N{-}(CH_2)_{10}{-}NH_2$$

$$\xrightarrow{\text{methylation}} (CH_3)_3\overset{+}{N}{-}(CH_2)_{10}{-}\overset{+}{N}(CH_3)_3 + 2Cl^- \quad \mathbf{2.2} \qquad (2.2)$$

After the reduction step, the organic reaction mixture is washed with dilute acid to isolate and purify the amine. The acid protonates the amine making it soluble in the water layer, while the unwanted side products and unreacted starting material remain in the organic phase. Separation of the two layers followed by neutralisation of the aqueous layer regenerates the amine. Why is the amine protonated but not the nitrile?

Example C The *tert*-butyloxycarbonyl (BOC) group (see **2.3**) is used as a protecting group for the amine function of amino acids.

$$\underbrace{CH_3{-}\underset{CH_3}{\overset{CH_3}{C}}{-}O{-}\overset{O}{\overset{\|}{C}}}_{\text{BOC group}}{-}\overset{H}{N}{-}\overset{R}{CH}{-}COOH \quad \mathbf{2.3}$$

At an appropriate point in the synthesis, this protecting group is removed by treatment with trifluoroacetic acid, CF_3COOH. Why does the chemist choose this acid rather than (say) acetic acid?

Each of these three questions relates to a subtle change of acidity or basicity of the groups involved. We shall be able to answer them once we have an idea of what determines the acidity or basicity of the substrate or reagent. We shall need to examine how the Gibbs energy change for the acid dissociation equilibrium is affected by the structure of the molecule. So let's begin by reviewing how acidity and basicity are defined and then revising Gibbs energy and Gibbs energy diagrams.

2.2 Acids and bases

In earlier chemistry modules you may have come across a number of definitions of acids and bases. Three common definitions with different levels of sophistication are:

- *Arrhenius definition* – an **acid** is a substance that produces hydrogen ions, proton, H^+, in water and a **base** is a substance that produces hydroxide ions, OH^-, in water
- *Brønsted–Lowry definition* – an acid is a substance that donates a hydrogen ion, and a base is a substance that accepts a hydrogen ion
- *Lewis definition* – a Lewis acid is a substance that accepts a pair of electrons and a base is a substance that donates a pair of electrons.

It is the latter two definitions that we will discuss in more detail.

2.2.1 Conjugate acids, conjugate bases and pK_a values

Hydrogen bromide, HBr, is a gas that ionises in water according to the equation

$$HBr(aq) + H_2O(l) = H_3O^+(aq) + Br^-(aq) \tag{2.3}$$

According to the Brønsted–Lowry definition, hydrogen bromide is an acid because it donates a hydrogen ion to water, which is acting as a base. The hydronium ion, H_3O^+, that is formed is known as the **conjugate acid** and the bromide ion, Br^- is known as the **conjugate base**. This is because in the back reaction the hydronium ion, H_3O^+ (conjugate acid), donates a proton to the bromide ion, Br^- (conjugate base). So we can write the general equation

$$\begin{array}{ccccc} \mathrm{H{-}A} \; + & \mathrm{:B} & \rightleftharpoons & \mathrm{A:^-} \quad + & \mathrm{H{-}B^+} \\ \text{acid} & \text{base} & & \text{conjugate base} & \text{conjugate acid} \end{array} \tag{2.4}$$

■ Identify the acid, base, conjugate acid and conjugate base in the following reaction:

$$NH_3(aq) + H_2O(l) \rightleftharpoons NH_4^+(aq) + HO^-(aq) \tag{2.5}$$

□ In this reaction water donates a hydrogen ion to ammonia, NH_3, and so the water is acting as an acid and ammonia as a base. The ammonium ion, NH_4^+, is the conjugate acid and the hydroxide ion, OH^-, is the conjugate base.

Equations 2.3 and 2.5 show that water can act as an acid or a base depending upon the acidity or basicity of the other reactant – hydrogen bromide is a stronger acid than water and so donates a hydrogen ion to water, which acts as a base, whereas ammonia is a stronger base than water and so water acts as an acid, donating a hydrogen ion to the ammonia. We can get a measure of the relative acidity and basicity of a substance by examining the equilibrium constant for the reaction of the substance HA with water.

$$HA(aq) + H_2O(l) \rightleftharpoons H_3O^+(aq) + A^-(aq) \tag{2.6}$$

■ Write out the equation for the equilibrium constant, K, for this acid dissociation.

□ $$K = \frac{[H_3O^+][A^-]}{[HA][H_2O]}$$

For a strong acid the position of the equilibrium in Equation 2.6 will lie far to the right, leading to a large value of K, whereas the equilibrium position for a weak acid will lie to the left giving a small K value.

Since dilute solutions are used to measure the equilibrium constants of these reactions, the concentration of water $[H_2O]$ remains effectively constant at 55.5 mol dm^{-3}, so the acidity constant K_a can be defined as:

$$K_a = K[H_2O] = \frac{[H_3O^+][A^-]}{[HA]} \tag{2.7}$$

Figure 2.1 shows that the range of acidity constants, K_a, is enormous ranging from methane which has a value of K_a around 10^{-50} to strong inorganic acids that have K_a values of 10^{15}.

In order to compare compounds easily with such a wide range of acidities, we use the **p*K*a**, which is the negative logarithm of the acidity constant.

$$pK_a = -\log K_a \tag{2.8}$$

This is the acidity constant equivalent of pH (pH = $-\log[H^+]$) and provides an easy way of handling such a wide range of powers of ten. Strong acids will have large values of K and so the negative logarithm will have a large magnitude but be negative, whereas a weak acid will have a very small acidity constant and so its pK_a will be large and positive, as shown in Figure 2.2.

■ Order the following compounds, starting with the most acidic and finishing with the least acidic compound: phenol, C_6H_5OH, pK_a = 10; nitric acid, pK_a = −1; acetic acid, pK_a = 5; ethanol, pK_a = 16; hydrofluoric acid, pK_a = 3.

□ The pK_a of the most acidic compound will be negative with the highest magnitude and the least acidic compound will be positive with the highest magnitude. So the order of acidity will follow the sizes of the pK_a values as we go from more negative to more positive. The most acidic compound is nitric acid with a pK_a of −1. Next comes hydrofluoric acid, then acetic acid, then phenol and lastly, with the largest positive pK_a, ethanol.

	Acid	Name	K_a	pK_a	Conjugate base	Name	
WEAKER ACID	CH_4	methane	10^{-50}	~50	CH_3^-	methyl carbanion	STRONGER BASE
	NH_3	ammonia	10^{-30}	~30	NH_2^-	amide ion	
	HC≡CH	ethyne	10^{-25}	25	HC≡C$^-$	ethynide ion	
	CH_3CH_2OH	ethanol	10^{-16}	16	$CH_3CH_2O^-$	ethoxide ion	
	H_2O	water	10^{-16}	16	HO^-	hydroxide ion	
	HCN	hydrocyanic acid	10^{-9}	9	CN^-	cyanide ion	
	CH_3COOH	acetic acid	10^{-5}	5	CH_3COO^-	acetate ion	
	HF	hydrofluoric acid	10^{-3}	3	F^-	fluoride ion	
	HNO_3	nitric acid	10	–1	NO_3^-	nitrate ion	
	HCl	hydrochloric acid	10^{7}	–7	Cl^-	chloride ion	
STRONGER ACID	HI	hydroiodic acid	10^{10}	–10	I^-	iodide ion	WEAKER BASE

Figure 2.1 K_a and pK_a values of a range of compounds. Going down the table, the acids get stronger and the bases get weaker.

Figure 2.1 shows that there is an opposing relationship between the acidity of an acid and the basicity of its conjugate base: the stronger the acidity of an acid is, the weaker is the basicity of its conjugate base. In order for the equilibrium in Equation 2.6 to lie to the right, a strong acid HA will want to donate a hydrogen ion to a water molecule and the conjugate base A^- will not want to accept a hydrogen ion from the hydronium ion H_3O^+. This means that the stronger conjugate bases will be associated with weak acids, as shown in Figure 2.2.

Knowing the pK_a values of acids enables us to determine whether a particular acid/base reaction will occur or not, for example, the reaction of acetic acid with sodium hydroxide, Equation 2.9.

$$CH_3COOH + HO^- \rightleftharpoons CH_3COO^- + H_2O \qquad (2.9)$$

Figure 2.1 shows the pK_a value of acetic acid, 5, to be smaller than the pK_a of water, 16, meaning that acetic acid is a stronger acid than water. On the other hand, the order in Figure 2.1 suggests that the hydroxide ion is a stronger base than the acetate ion, CH_3COO^-. Thus, Equation 2.9 involves the reaction of the stronger acid with the stronger base, leading to the conclusion that the reaction in Equation 2.9 will proceed to a reasonable extent.

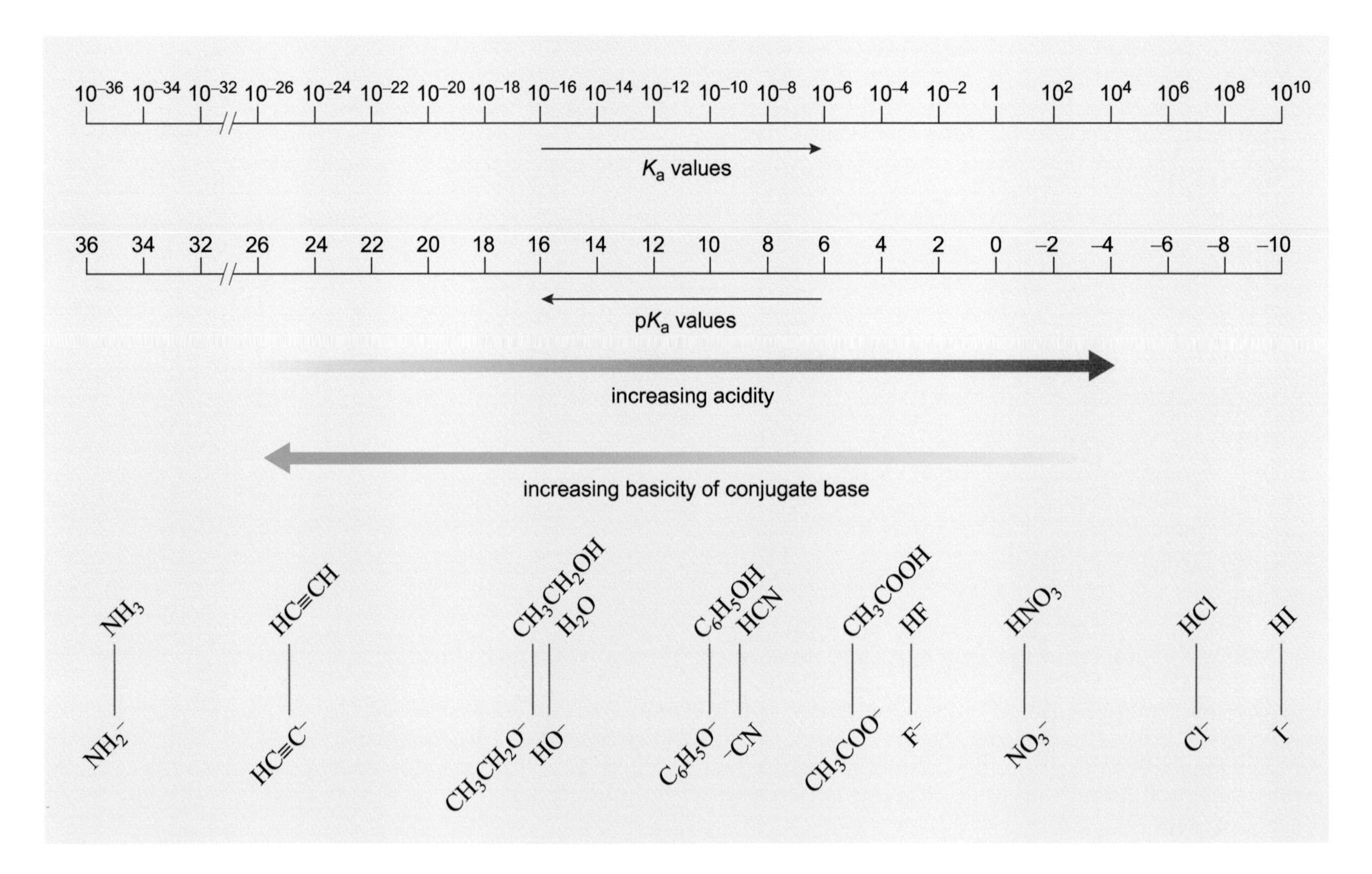

Figure 2.2 pK_a number line showing the position of weak and strong acids. (pK_a are high on the left and low on the right.)

In fact, we can say that the reaction of an acid with a base will occur if the pK_a of the acid is less than the pK_a of the conjugate acid of the base. In Equation 2.9 the pK_a of the acid, CH_3COOH, 5, is less than the pK_a of the conjugate acid of the base, 16, which is H_2O (from the base HO^-).

■ Look again at Figure 2.2; providing the pK_a of the acid lies to the right of the pK_a of the conjugate acid of the base, the reaction will occur. For example, will the reaction between ethanol and sodium amide occur to any large extent?

$$CH_3CH_2OH + NH_2^- \rightleftharpoons CH_3CH_2O^- + NH_3 \qquad (2.10)$$

□ The pK_a of ethanol is 16 whereas the pK_a of ammonia, NH_3, which is the conjugate acid of the base NH_2^-, is 30. Since the pK_a of ethanol is smaller than that of ammonia this reaction is favoured. Looking at Figure 2.2, the pK_a of ethanol lies to the right of the pK_a of ammonia.

■ Identify which of the following reactions is favourable and which is not.

$$CH_3CH_2OH + Cl^- \rightleftharpoons CH_3CH_2O^- + HCl \qquad (2.11)$$

$$CH_3COOH + CH_3CH_2O^- \rightleftharpoons CH_3COO^- + CH_3CH_2OH \quad (2.12)$$

□ For the first reaction the pK_a of ethanol is greater (more positive) than the pK_a of HCl, the conjugate acid of the base Cl^-, so the reaction will not occur.

For the second reaction the pK_a of acetic acid is smaller than the pK_a of ethanol, the conjugate acid of the base $CH_3CH_2O^-$ and so we predict the reaction will occur.

As we saw earlier, water can both accept a hydrogen ion and donate a hydrogen ion and so if we are investigating an acid–base reaction in water as the solvent we need to consider whether it is more acidic or basic than the reactants. For example, if we carried out the reaction of ethyne with sodium amide in water, then we would expect to observe the formation of OH^- in preference to $HC{\equiv}C^-$, because water is more acidic than ethyne, thus we would need to find an alternative solvent that is not so acidic.

2.2.2 Lewis acids and bases

A **Lewis acid** is defined as a compound that can accept a pair of electrons. This means it must have an empty low-energy orbital which can accept the electrons. For example, boron trifluoride, BF_3, is a typical Lewis acid. If we draw its Lewis structure, the first thing we notice is that it only has six electrons in its outer shell and so will accept two more to make a complete octet.

Other Lewis acids are aluminium trichloride, $AlCl_3$, iron trichloride, $FeCl_3$, titanium tetrachloride, $TiCl_4$, zinc chloride, $ZnCl_2$, and tin chloride, $SnCl_2$.

F
F B
F

■ Can the hydrogen ion, H^+, be classed as a Lewis acid?

□ Yes, the hydrogen ion has no electrons in its outer, 1s, orbital and accepts two electrons when it forms a bond with a base.

$$H^+ + Cl^- \longrightarrow HCl \quad (2.13)$$

■ A **Lewis base** can donate a pair of electrons. Identify two common Lewis bases?

□ One common Lewis base is water, which can donate a pair of electrons to a hydrogen ion to form the hydronium ion.

$$H^+ + H_2O \rightleftharpoons H_3O^+ \quad (2.14)$$

A second Lewis base is ammonia, NH_3, which again has a non-bonded pair which it can donate to a Lewis acid.

$$\mathrm{F_3B} + \mathrm{:NH_3} \longrightarrow \mathrm{F_3B^{-}{-}N^{+}H_3} \qquad (2.15)$$

In fact, any nitrogen or oxygen compound with a non-bonded electron pair can act as a Lewis base.

2.3 Gibbs energy and Gibbs energy diagrams

The **Gibbs energy** (free energy) changes during a reaction. If the Gibbs energy of the product is lower than that of the reactant, the reaction is thermodynamically favourable. However, if the Gibbs energy of the product is the higher, the reaction is thermodynamically unfavourable. This is best represented using a **Gibbs energy diagram** (Figure 2.3). The change in Gibbs energy during a reaction is often given the symbol $\Delta G^{\ominus}$ and is defined by Equation 2.16.

$$\Delta G^{\ominus} = \text{Gibbs energy of products} - \text{Gibbs energy of reactants} \qquad (2.16)$$

■ What will be the sign of $\Delta G^{\ominus}$ for (a) thermodynamically favourable and (b) thermodynamically unfavourable reactions?

□ $\Delta G^{\ominus}$ is negative for a thermodynamically favourable reaction and positive for a thermodynamically unfavourable reaction.

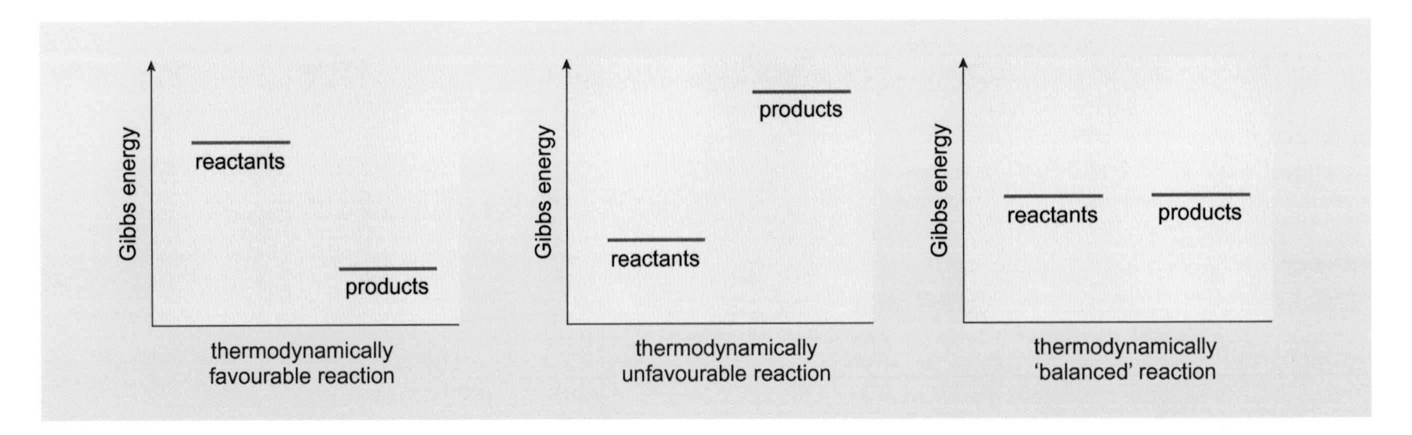

Figure 2.3 Possible comparisons of the Gibbs energy of the products and the reactants for a chemical reaction.

Unfortunately Gibbs energy data are not available for the majority of organic substances so organic chemists, rather than viewing reactivity in absolute terms, tend to look for trends in a series of related compounds. For example, any factor that tends to lower the Gibbs energy of the product compared with a reactant will decrease (or make more negative) the value of $\Delta G^{\ominus}$, favouring the formation of more product. In other words the equilibrium constant for that reaction will be larger. This effect is demonstrated in Figure 2.4 and can be expressed mathematically using Equation 2.17, where R is the gas constant and T is the temperature:

$$\Delta G^{\ominus} = -RT \ln K \quad (2.17)$$

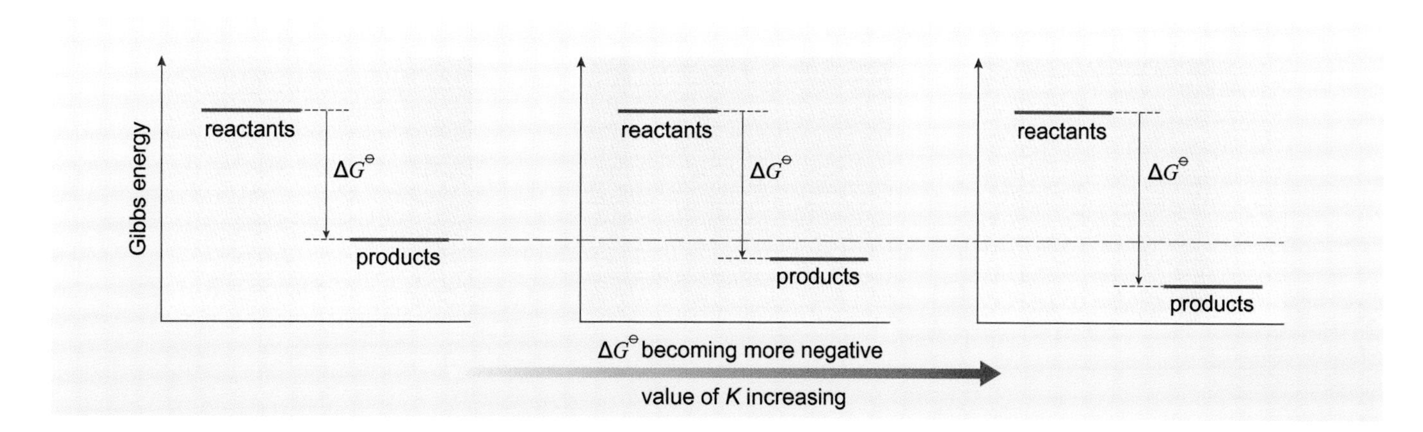

Figure 2.4 The effect on the value of the equilibrium constant of decreasing (making more negative) the value of the Gibbs energy of the product compared with that of the reactants.

Now let's look at a real example based on our theme of acidity, the acidity of the hydrides of carbon, nitrogen, oxygen and fluorine (Equations 2.18–2.21).

$$H_2O + CH_4 \rightleftharpoons H_3O^+ + CH_3^- \quad (2.18)$$

$$H_2O + NH_3 \rightleftharpoons H_3O^+ + NH_2^- \quad (2.19)$$

$$H_2O + H_2O \rightleftharpoons H_3O^+ + OH^- \quad (2.20)$$

$$H_2O + HF \rightleftharpoons H_3O^+ + F^- \quad (2.21)$$

Or, generally,

$$H_2O + HX \overset{K_a}{\rightleftharpoons} H_3O^+ + X^- \quad (2.22)$$

Electronegativity increases as we progress across the Periodic Table from carbon to fluorine.

■ What effect will this increase in electronegativity have on the stability of the anion X^-?

□ The most electronegative element fluorine will attract electrons the most strongly, stabilising the extra electron that causes the negative charge.

Whilst the stability of the X^- ion increases with electronegativity, the stability of the acid HX can be assumed not to vary a great deal; we'll comment on this assumption later. This means that on going from reaction in Equation 2.18 to reaction in Equation 2.21 the Gibbs energy of the products relative to that of the reactants decreases (gets more negative) and thus, as shown in Figure 2.4, the equilibrium constant, K_a, increases.

■ Figures 2.1 and 2.2 lists the pK_a values of CH_4, NH_3, H_2O and HF. Do these values agree with the predicted trend?

□ Yes. Remembering pK_a = −log K_a, then (because of the negative sign) the reaction with the largest equilibrium constant will have the smallest or most negative value of pK_a. This is HF, as we predicted above.

Throughout this section we shall be examining again and again how such changes in a species alter its energy.

■ Using Equation 2.16 and Figure 2.4, determine how the following trends alter $\Delta G^\ominus$ and hence the equilibrium constant.

(a) Setting $G^\ominus$ of the reactants constant and decreasing $G^\ominus$ of the products.
(b) Setting $G^\ominus$ of the reactants constant and increasing $G^\ominus$ of the products.
(c) Setting $G^\ominus$ of the products constant and decreasing $G^\ominus$ of the reactants.
(d) Setting $G^\ominus$ of the products constant and increasing $G^\ominus$ of the reactants.

□ Equation 2.16 shows that if we set $G^\ominus$ (reactants) constant and decrease $G^\ominus$ (products) then $\Delta G^\ominus$ will also decrease (or become more negative). Figure 2.4 shows that this leads to a larger equilibrium constant. If, on the other hand, we increase $G^\ominus$ (products), then $\Delta G^\ominus$ will increase (or become less negative) and the equilibrium constant gets smaller. Similarly if we set $G^\ominus$ (products) constant and decrease $G^\ominus$ (reactants), Equation 2.16 shows that $\Delta G^\ominus$ will increase (become less negative), leading to a reduction in the equilibrium constant. Conversely, increasing $G^\ominus$ (reactants) decreases $\Delta G^\ominus$ (it becomes more negative), with a consequent increase in the equilibrium constant.

The results you obtained above are summarised below. Before moving on to examine other effects on equilibria, it is important that you are familiar with these relationships.

relative lowering of energy of products or raising energy of reactants	≡	decrease in $\Delta G^\ominus$ (i.e. more negative)	≡	increase in value of K	≡	decrease in value of pK_a (i.e. more negative for an acid–base equilibrium)
relative raising of energy of products or lowering energy of reactants	≡	increase in $\Delta G^\ominus$ (i.e. more positive)	≡	decrease in value of K	≡	increase in value of pK_a (i.e. more positive for an acid–base equilibrium)

Of course, in real systems it is not possible to vary the structure such that $G^\ominus$ of say the product changes whilst that of the reactant is kept constant. Any structural variation must alter $G^\ominus$ of both species. However, in some ways this doesn't matter because, as we stated at the beginning of this section, $G^\ominus$ is not known for most organic compounds. Since it is the change in Gibbs energy, $\Delta G^\ominus$, that is important, organic chemists try to identify factors that will increase or decrease the stability of one species (reactant or product) more than the other. To highlight the main source of the variation in $\Delta G^{\ominus}$ we then arbitrarily equalise the Gibbs energy of the species which shows the smaller variation (Figure 2.5). The plot of relative Gibbs energy now clearly shows that it is the variation in the Gibbs energy of the product that is mainly responsible for the observed trend in the equilibrium constant.

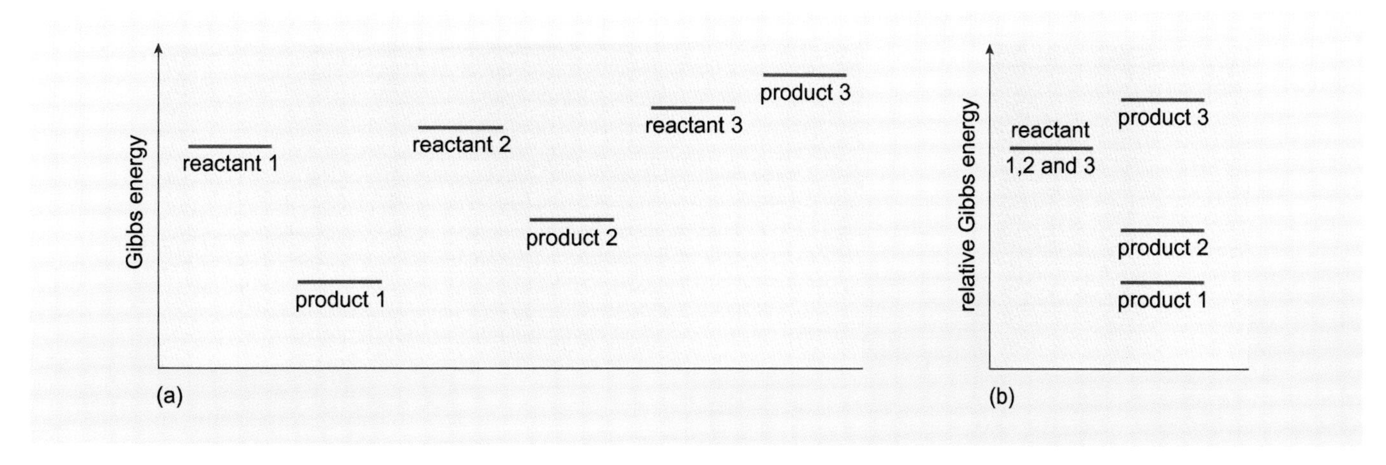

Figure 2.5 (a) Absolute and (b) relative variation of Gibbs energy for three structurally different reactants and products.

We are now in a position to answer the first question, posed in Example A at the beginning of Section 2.1. The use of the base sodium ethoxide ensures that the substrate **2.4** exists predominantly as the anion **2.5**. The negatively charged oxygen atom is a much better nucleophile than the neutral amino nitrogen atom so it is not surprising that under these conditions the oxygen is alkylated (Equation 2.23).

OH, NH_2, NO_2 (**2.4**) $\xrightarrow{^{-}OCH_2CH_3}$ O^-, NH_2, NO_2 (**2.5**) $\xrightarrow{CH_3CH_2CH_2Br}$ $O{-}CH_2CH_2CH_3$, NH_2, NO_2 (**2.1**) (2.23)

- ■ But this only raises another question: Why is the proton removed from the hydroxyl group to give **2.5** rather than from the amino group to give **2.6**?

- □ As we have just seen the greater electronegativity of oxygen ensures that the OH is more acidic than the NH_2 – as we saw in Figure 2.1 water is more acidic than ammonia. Put another way, relative to the reactants, **2.5** has a lower Gibbs energy than **2.6**.

OH, NH^-, NO_2

2.6

Having seen how equilibria can vary between analogous reactions of different elements, let's now examine how, with the same element, equilibria can be affected by molecular structure. This will enable us to answer the second question, posed in Example B.

2.4 The effect of hybridisation on acidity and basicity

In this section we shall examine how the acidity or basicity of a compound changes with the hybridisation of the hydrogen-bearing atom. Take, for example, the acidity of alkanes, alkenes and alkynes (Equations 2.24–2.26).

$$\underset{\textbf{2.7}}{\mathrm{H_3C{-}CH_3}} + \mathrm{H_2O} \rightleftharpoons \underset{\textbf{2.8}}{\mathrm{H_3C{-}CH_2{:}^-}} + \mathrm{H_3O^+} \qquad (2.24)$$

$$\underset{\textbf{2.9}}{\mathrm{H_2C{=}CH_2}} + \mathrm{H_2O} \rightleftharpoons \underset{\textbf{2.10}}{\mathrm{H_2C{=}CH{:}^-}} + \mathrm{H_3O^+} \qquad (2.25)$$

$$\underset{\textbf{2.11}}{\mathrm{H{-}C{\equiv}C{-}H}} + \mathrm{H_2O} \rightleftharpoons \underset{\textbf{2.12}}{\mathrm{H{-}C{\equiv}C{:}^-}} + \mathrm{H_3O^+} \qquad (2.26)$$

■ What is the hybridisation of the carbon atoms in ethane, ethene and ethyne?

□ Ethane, sp^3; ethene, sp^2; ethyne, sp. Remember, the non-bonded electron pair of the carbanion will also have this hybridisation.

Note: In structures **2.8**, **2.10** and **2.12** we have indicated the presence of a non-bonded pair of electrons by two dots. We will only do this when we want to emphasise their existence, as in some resonance structures. In other cases where they are not drawn in you must not forget they are there!

In general, s orbitals are nearer the positively charged nucleus than are p orbitals. So, a negative charge can be stabilised to a greater extent in an orbital with a high s character, such as an sp, with 50% s character, than in an orbital with a lower s character, such as sp^3, with 25% s character. It follows that a non-bonded pair of electrons on an sp^3 carbon (as in **2.8**) will have a higher energy than a non-bonded pair of electrons on an sp^2 carbon (as in **2.10**) which, in turn, will have a higher energy than those on an sp carbon (as in **2.12**). In a C–H bond the presence of a proton (hydrogen nucleus) ensures that the energy of the electron pair is not so dependent upon the distance of the electrons from the carbon nucleus, so the reactants **2.7**, **2.9** and **2.11** can be collected together as shown in Figure 2.6. Thus, as we go from Equations 2.24 to 2.25 to 2.26, the Gibbs energy of the product decreases relative to that of the reactant, so $\Delta G^{\ominus}$ for the reaction decreases, hence K increases (pK_a

decreases). This is consistent with the pK_a values estimated for ethane, ethene and ethyne (Table 2.1).

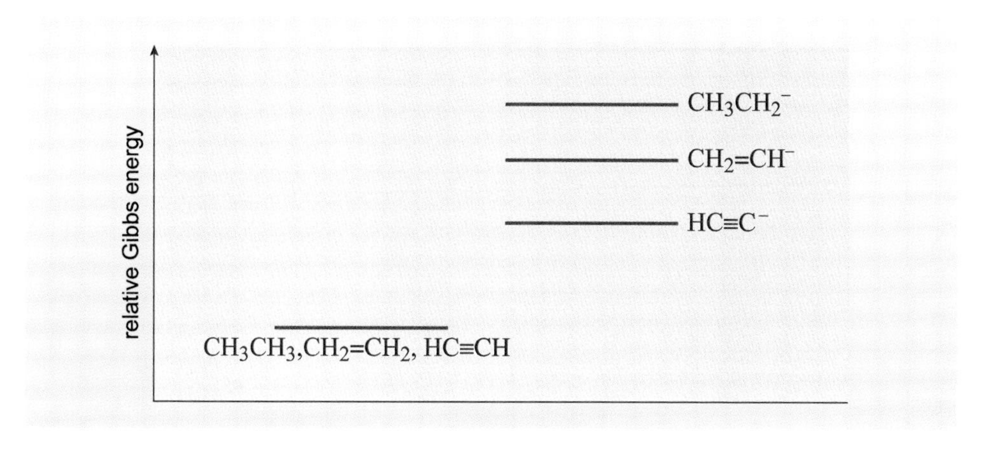

Figure 2.6 Variation in the relative Gibbs energy with hybridisation for ethane, ethene and ethyne. (Such diagrams are pictorial representations – actual values of $\Delta G^{\ominus}$ should not be inferred from them.)

Table 2.1 Estimated pK_a values of ethane, ethene and ethyne in aqueous solution at 25 °C.

Hydrocarbon	pK_a
$CH_3{-}CH_3$	50
$CH_2{=}CH_2$	44
$CH{\equiv}CH$	24

- ■ The acidity of an acid and the basicity of its conjugate base are interrelated. Which of the conjugate bases **2.8**, **2.10** or **2.12** is the most basic?

- □ As shown in Figures 2.1 and 2.2, the conjugate base of the weakest acid is the strongest base. The pK_a values in Table 2.1 show that ethane is the weakest acid (the equilibrium in Equation 2.24 lies farthest to the left) so the ethyl carbanion is the strongest base.

Let's now look at the second question posed at the beginning of Section 2.1, in Example B: Why is the amine protonated by the aqueous acid but the nitrile not? Clearly the amine must be more basic than the nitrile. This difference again arises from hybridisation. Take a look at Equations 2.27–2.29. In this instance, to highlight the basicity, we have simply reversed the equation for the acid dissociation equilibrium. In each case the basicity arises from the ability of the nitrogen atom to donate a non-bonded electron pair to form an $^{+}$N–H bond.

$$\underset{\mathbf{2.13}}{CH_3{-}CH_2{-}\ddot{N}H_2} + H_3O^+ \rightleftharpoons CH_3{-}CH_2{-}\overset{+}{N}H_3 + H_2O \qquad (2.27)$$

$$\mathrm{CH_3{-}CH{=}\ddot{N}H \;+\; H_3O^+ \;\rightleftharpoons\; CH_3{-}CH{=}\overset{+}{N}H_2 \;+\; H_2O} \qquad (2.28)$$

2.14

$$\mathrm{CH_3{-}C{\equiv}\ddot{N} \;+\; H_3O^+ \;\rightleftharpoons\; CH_3{-}C{\equiv}\overset{+}{N}H \;+\; H_2O} \qquad (2.29)$$

2.15

Using the same rationale as for the hydrocarbon example above, as with the C–H bond the energy of the $^{+}$N–H bond will vary very little with hybridisation. However, the stabilisation of the non-bonded pair of electrons on the nitrogen atom of the reactants will depend upon the s character of the orbital. The unshared pair on the amine (**2.13**) will be sp^3 hybridised so it will have a higher energy than the non-bonded pair on the imine (**2.14**) which is sp^2. This in turn will be higher in energy than the non-bonded pair on the nitrile (**2.15**) which is sp and so has the highest s character, and thus the greatest stabilisation, as shown in Figure 2.7. Thus as we go from Reaction 2.27 to 2.28 to 2.29 there is a decrease in the energy of the reactant relative to that of the product. This leads to an increase in $\Delta G^{\ominus}$ (less negative) and a consequent decrease in the equilibrium constant. This again is in agreement with experiment – the amine is more basic than the imine, which is more basic than the nitrile.

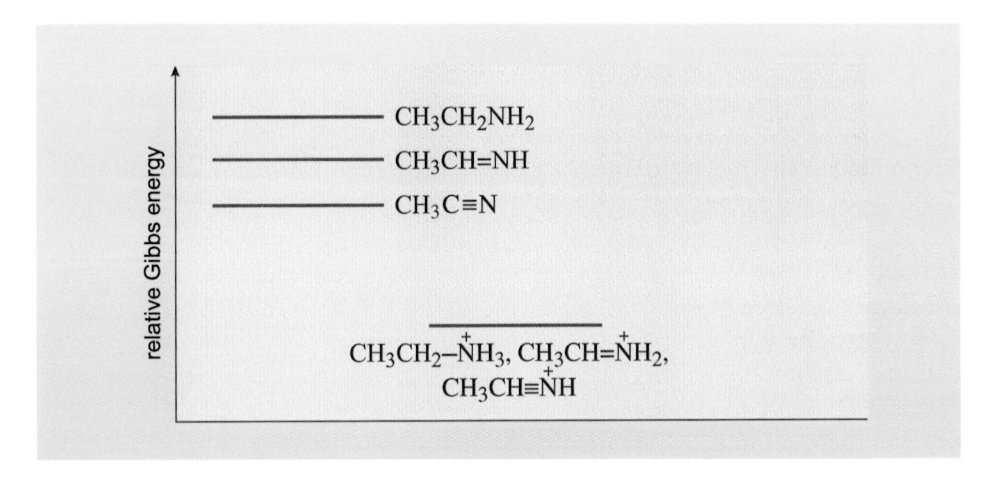

Figure 2.7 Variation in the relative Gibbs energy with hybridisation for ethylamine, ethanimine and ethanenitrile.

Activity 2.1

Look back at the list of amino acids in Figure 1.1 of Unit 2 Section 1 and the pK_a data given in Table 2.2 and answer the following questions.

(a) Are the pK_a values of aspartic acid and glutamic acid as expected?

(b) Why is the pK_a of the conjugate acid of lysine greater than that of histidine? (*Hint*: in Histidine both the nitrogen atoms are sp^2 hybridised.)

Table 2.2 pK_a of the side groups of acidic and basic amino acids.

Amino acid	Side chain	Acidic or basic	pK_a of acid	pK_a of conjugate acid of base
aspartic acid	$-CH_2-COOH$	acidic	3.8	–
glutamic acid	$-CH_2-CH_2-COOH$	acidic	4.3	–
tyrosine	$-CH_2-C_6H_4-OH$	weakly acidic	10.1	–
histidine	$-CH_2-$(imidazole ring, N–H, N)	weakly basic	–	6.1
lysine	$-(CH_2)_4-NH_2$	basic	–	10.5
arginine	$-(CH_2)_4-NH-C(=NH)-NH_2$	basic	–	12.5

Answer

(a) Aspartic acid and glutamic acid both contain a carboxylic acid in their side chain so they are classed as acidic amino acids. Their pK_a values are similar to that of acetic acid (pK_a = 5 from Figure 2.1).

(b) Lysine and histidine both contain nitrogen atoms in their side chains that have non-bonded pairs of electrons that can be readily donated, so are basic amino acids. The pK_a of the conjugate acid of lysine is greater than that of histidine which suggests that lysine is a stronger base (if you are unsure about this look back at how the basicity of the conjugate base changed with pK_a of the acid in Figure 2.1). In lysine, the nitrogen of the amino group is sp^3 hybridised, whereas in histidine the nitrogen atoms are sp^2 hybridised – see **2.16** where the non-bonded pair of the N–H occupies a p orbital that overlaps with the two double bonds creating an aromatic six-electron π system as in benzene. A non-bonded pair is available on the other nitrogen – they occupy an sp^2 orbital pointing away from the ring. The sp^3 nitrogen is more basic than the sp^2 nitrogen in agreement with the pK_a values observed in Equations 2.27 and 2.28.

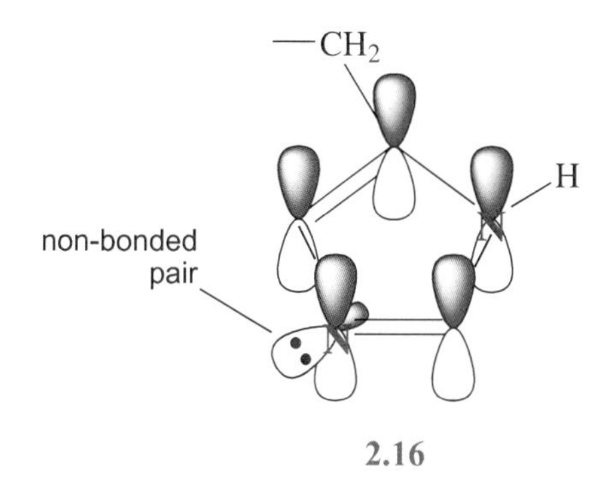

2.16

Notice (in Unit 2 Figure 1.1) that tryptophan contains a nitrogen atom but is not classed as a basic amino acid. This is because, as in histidine, the non-bonded pair occupies a p orbital which is part of an aromatic six-electron π system as in benzene. These electrons are not available for donation without destroying the aromaticity of the ring. Notice also that tyrosine is weakly acidic and arginine is quite basic and asparagine and glutamine both contain nitrogen atoms but are classed as neutral amino acids. We will come back to these observations in Section 2.6.

2.5 Dipole moments and the inductive effect

To answer the last of our three questions from Section 2.1, in Example C, we need to examine how atoms remote from the functional group can influence a reaction. This involves examining bond dipoles and how they perturb the electronic structure of a molecule.

As you saw in Unit 1, the experimental value for the dipole moment of a polyatomic molecule requires careful interpretation, for it is made up of the vector sum of all the individual bond dipoles and dipoles associated with non-bonded pairs of electrons. Nevertheless, we are able to calculate the dipole using Discovery Studio as described in Activity 2.2.

Activity 2.2

The experimental dipole moments in debyes (D) are given below for toluene (**2.17**), fluorobenzene (**2.18**), and nitrobenzene (**2.19**).

CH_3	F	NO_2
0.37	1.61	4.19
2.17	**2.18**	**2.19**

Draw the structures in separate 3D windows of Discovery Studio and use the Dreiding force field to minimise their energy.

Use the molecular properties tool to calculate the dipole moment. How well do the results match the experimental values?

The calculation also gives the direction of the dipole, which is not available experimentally. Are the dipoles in the same direction relative to the point of substitution?

What does this say about the electron-donating or -withdrawing effect of the substituents on the benzene ring?

Answer

The values we calculated for **2.17**, **2.18** and **2.19** are 0.13 D, 1.9 D and 5.5 D respectively. Whilst the calculations aren't perfect they are close and do predict the relative sizes of the dipoles. The directions of the dipoles are shown below – it may have been difficult to identify the direction with toluene, **2.17**, because the dipole is so small.

CH_3	F	NO_2
0.37	1.61	4.19
2.17	**2.18**	**2.19**

The fluoro group and nitro group are both electron withdrawing, leading to a buildup of negative charge in the vicinity of the substituent and a buildup of positive charge on the aromatic ring and so the dipole points towards the substituent. The methyl group is electron donating and so in this case the direction of the dipole is reversed.

Dipole moments, then, provide experimental confirmation of bond polarisations. In turn, bond polarisations allow us to explain how remote substituents can affect reactions of a functional group. For example, bond polarisation deduced from electronegativities would suggest a bond dipole in fluoroethane as shown in **2.20**. This, in turn, means that the electrons of other bonds attached to C-1 would be drawn towards it, producing secondary displacements and so on, even as far away as the C–H bonds of the methyl group. This is shown in **2.21**, the number of arrowheads indicating the degree of polarisation brought about in each bond by the electronegativity difference between C and F.

H H
H–$_2$C–$_1$C–F (δ+ on C-1, δ– on F)
H H

2.20

H H
H→C→→C→→→F
H H

2.21

- Table 2.3 lists the pK_a values of some carboxylic acids. To what extent do these data accord with the above arguments?

Table 2.3 pK_a values of selected carboxylic acids in aqueous solution at 25 °C.

Carboxylic acid	pK_a	Carboxylic acid	pK_a
CH_3COOH	4.67	$CH_3CH_2CH_2COOH$	4.82
CH_2FCOOH	2.66	$CF_3CH_2CH_2COOH$	4.15
CHF_2COOH	1.24	CF_3CH_2COOH	3.04
CF_3COOH	0.23	CF_3COOH	0.23

□ The acidity, and thus the stability of the anion **2.22**, seems to increase as electron-withdrawing atoms are introduced successively on the carbon next to the COOH group. Furthermore this effect diminishes as the number of bonds between the halogen atom and the COOH group increases.

$$H_2O + R{-}C(=O)OH \rightleftharpoons H_3O^+ + R{-}C(=O)O^- \qquad (2.30)$$

2.22

In effect, the fluorine 'pulls' at the electrons of the nearby bonds. This creates a slight negative charge on fluorine and a slight positive charge on the carbon adjacent to the oxygen atoms. The slight positive charge interacts favourably with the negative charge on oxygen, as shown in **2.23**, thus lowering its energy, with a resulting increase in acidity of the carboxylic acid. Clearly the size of the positive charge on the carbon of the carboxylate anion will depend upon how many electron-withdrawing groups are present and how close they are. Electron-withdrawing groups like halogens are said to exert a **negative inductive effect, −I**, on the reaction centre. As you can see from the right-hand column of Table 2.3 the inductive effect falls off rapidly along a chain of bonds.

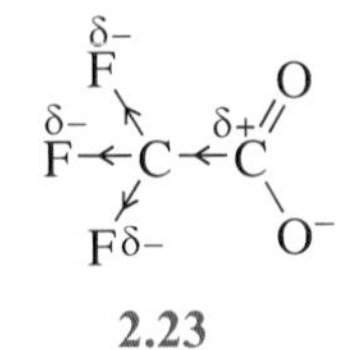

2.23

Now the answer to the question in Example C becomes clear. Removal of the protecting group is similar to an amide hydrolysis and is an acid-catalysed process. As we have seen, trifluoroacetic acid is a far stronger acid than acetic acid and is therefore chosen because it catalyses the deprotection more efficiently.

Though we have now answered our three initial questions we shall continue to survey the effect of structure on equilibrium since this will help us to understand the arguments involved regarding selectivity, or the choice of reagents, that are presented later in the module when we discuss how drugs are synthesised.

■ You may already know that tertiary carbocations are more stable than secondary carbocations which are more stable than primary carbocations. What does this tell us about the inductive effect of alkyl substituents?

□ This observation implies that alkyl groups exert an **electron-donating effect, +I**, that is, they are electron-donating relative to hydrogen.

To be precise, only when an alkyl group is attached to an unsaturated or trivalent carbon is its behaviour best explained by assuming it is +I. When it is connected to a saturated atom, the results are not as clear and alkyl groups seem to be +I in some cases and −I in others. However, in all the examples you will meet in this module, you can assume an alkyl group is +I.

$$R_3C^+ > R_2HC^+ > RH_2C^+ > H_3C^+$$

increasing stability ←

The latter explanation is based upon a very important 'empirical hypothesis' which, perhaps more than any other single factor, is responsible for the success of an electronic theory of organic chemistry. On the basis of a vast mass of accumulated experimental data, organic chemists believe:

Any effect that tends to spread charge in a molecular species will lower its internal energy.

So we can say that, in a tertiary carbocation, the positive charge is largely spread over four carbon atoms through the electron-donating, +I, effect of the three alkyl groups.

Alkyl groups are one of the few common groups that can show a +I effect. Others include groups carrying a negative charge, such as O^- and COO^-. Most groups involving heteroatoms show −I effects, in line with expectations from electronegativities relative to carbon. The inductive effects of various groups are shown in Figure 2.8.

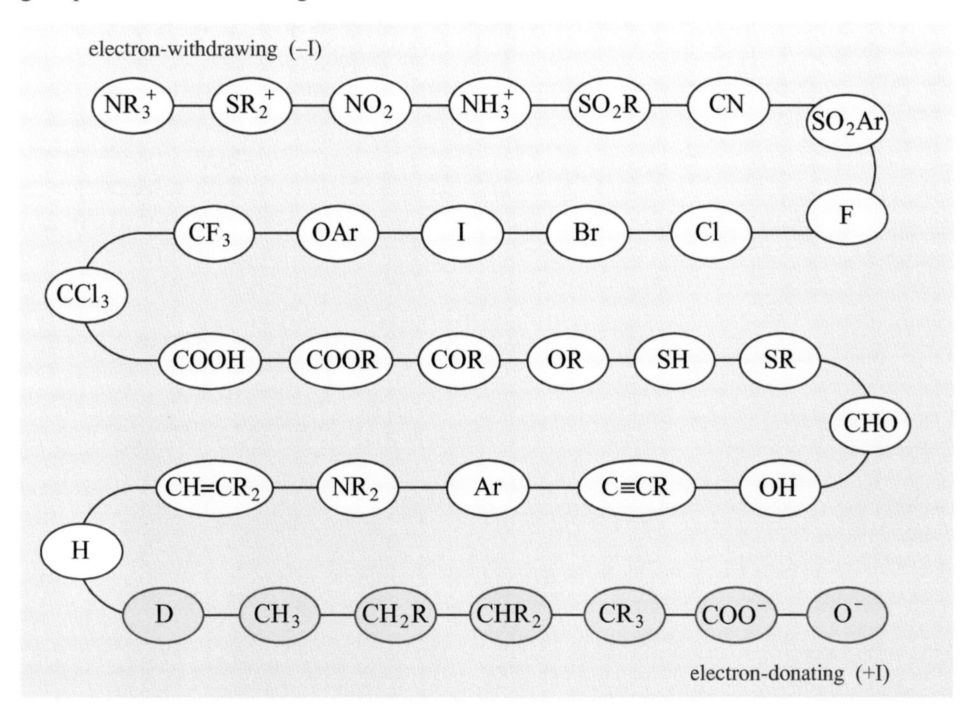

Figure 2.8 Inductive effects of various groups relative to hydrogen. Starting from NR_3^+ the groups are arranged in descending order of electron-withdrawing ability.

To complete this section, we shall examine how the transmission of inductive effects is affected by unsaturation. We have seen how a permanent dipole in, say, a C–F bond induces a dipole in the electron cloud of a neighbouring bond and this is similarly relayed through the bonds of the molecule to the reaction centre. The extent to which nearby electron clouds are polarised depends on their **polarisability**, or 'willingness to be deformed'. The polarisability of an electron pair in turn depends on the nature of its molecular orbital; electrons in double bonds are more polarisable than those in single bonds. Hence polar effects in molecules are much more easily relayed through double bonds. For example the CF_3 group increases the acidity of the corresponding carboxylic acids to a greater extent in **2.25** than in **2.24**.

$CH_3CH_2CH_2COOH$ $pK_a = 4.82$ $CH_3CH{=}CHCOOH$ $pK_a = 4.70$

$CF_3CH_2CH_2COOH$ $pK_a = 4.15$ $CF_3CH{=}CHCOOH$ $pK_a = 3.48$

2.24 **2.25**

2.6 Resonance effects

In Section 2.4, we examined the acidity of carboxylic acids, but made no comment about their acidity relative to other hydroxy compounds. For example why is the pK_a of ethanoic acid (acetic acid) (**2.26**) so much smaller than that of ethanol (**2.28**)?

$$\underset{\textbf{2.26}}{CH_3COOH} + H_2O \rightleftharpoons \underset{\textbf{2.27}}{CH_3COO^-} + H_3O^+ \qquad pK_a = 4.8 \qquad (2.31)$$

$$\underset{\textbf{2.28}}{CH_3CH_2OH} + H_2O \rightleftharpoons CH_3CH_2O^- + H_3O^+ \qquad pK_a = 16 \qquad (2.32)$$

The inductive effect of the extra oxygen in **2.26** is too small to account for such a large difference in acidity of the two hydroxyl groups – a factor of approximately 10^{11}! To answer the question we must examine the structure of the ethanoate anion (**2.27**). Spectral data show the two carbon–oxygen bonds to be equivalent. The ethanoate ion has a structure intermediate between the two major resonance structures, often written as **2.29** where the negative charge is shared. The resonance stabilisation incurred by having two equivalent structures and the spreading of the negative charge in **2.27** lowers the energy of the anion such that ethanoic acid is much more acidic than ethanol. This is an example of the **resonance effect**.

$$\left[CH_3{-}C({=}O)O^- \longleftrightarrow CH_3{-}C(O^-){=}O \right] \equiv CH_3{-}C(\cdots O)_2^{-}$$

2.29

One word of warning about the meaning of resonance: we are *not* implying that resonance is in any way a dynamic effect where bonding is changing all the time. The double-headed arrow ↔ is used to indicate that the true structure, the resonance hybrid, has a fixed structure which is intermediate between the various resonance structures. The curly arrows are only used to show how one resonance form can be *conceptually* transformed into another. This can be confirmed by examining the structure of the ethanoate ion, **2.29**, using Discovery Studio.

Activity 2.3

Open the pdb file ethanoate_ion from Unit 3 resources on the module website and examine the carbon–oxygen bond lengths and charges on the oxygen atoms. You should see that they are identical to each other – the bonds are midway between a single carbon–oxygen bond (1.44 Å) and a double carbon–oxygen bond (1.23 Å). The charge on each oxygen atom is about 0.5.

■ Table 2.2 suggests the side chain of tyrosine is slightly acidic with a pK_a of 10.1 compared with serine (–CH_2–OH) which has a pK_a of around 15. This is because the negative charge on the oxygen of the conjugate base can be spread more in tyrosine than in serine. How is this possible?

□ The negative charge on the oxygen of the conjugate base can be spread via resonance with the adjacent benzene ring in tyrosine. This is not possible in serine.

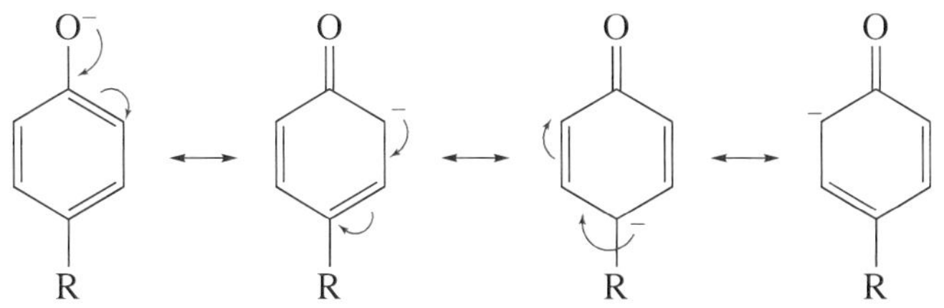

■ Example A at the beginning of Section 2.1 involved the reaction between a phenol and sodium ethoxide (Equation 2.33).

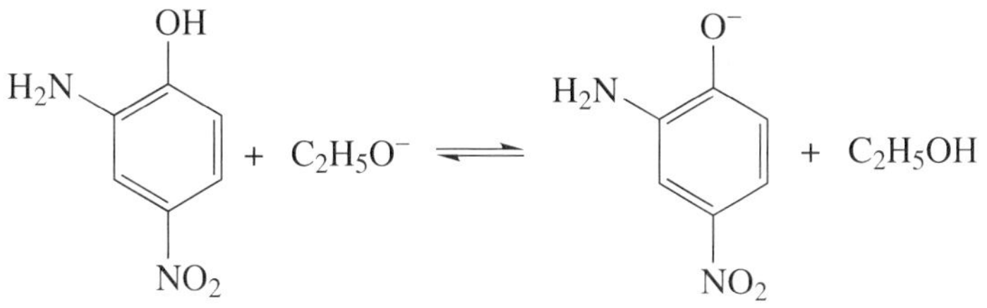

$$\text{H}_2\text{N-C}_6\text{H}_3(\text{OH})\text{-NO}_2 + C_2H_5O^- \rightleftharpoons \text{H}_2\text{N-C}_6\text{H}_3(\text{O}^-)\text{-NO}_2 + C_2H_5OH \qquad (2.33)$$

Why do you think the equilibrium of this reaction lies to the right?

□ It lies to the right because, with respect to the alcohols, the phenoxide ion **2.5** has a lower energy than the alkoxide ion. This is because it is resonance stabilised.

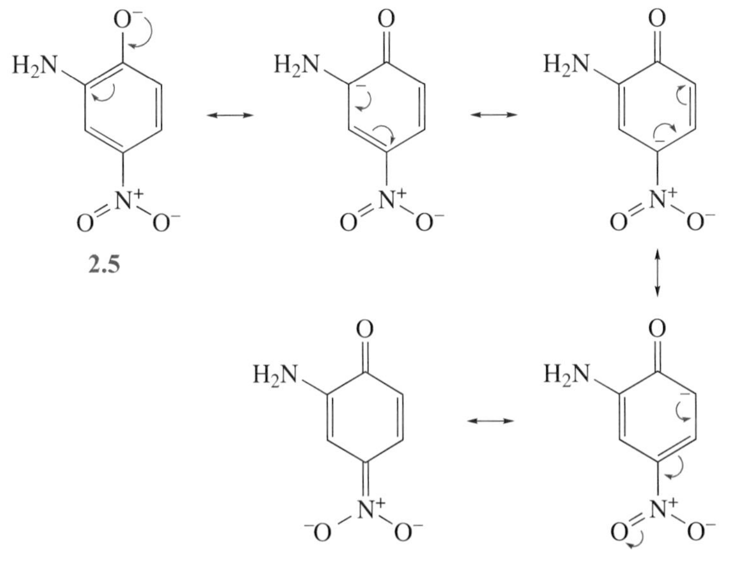

H_2N O$^-$ O=N$^+$ O$^-$ ⟷ H_2N O O=N$^+$ O$^-$ ⟷ H_2N O O=N$^+$ O$^-$

2.5

H_2N O $^-$O N$^+$ O$^-$ ⟷ H_2N O O=N$^+$ O$^-$

Notice that the nitro group is also involved in the resonance stabilisation even though it is quite remote from the reaction centre. As well as aiding the resonance stabilisation of the phenoxide ion, the nitro group also withdraws electrons by the inductive effect, thereby spreading the charge. These two factors stabilise the anion a great deal more than the neutral phenol, such that a *para* nitro group increases the acidity of a phenol by a factor of 600.

- ■ Arginine has a particularly basic side chain, the $\mathrm{p}K_\mathrm{a}$ of its conjugate acid is 12.5 (Table 2.2). This is because of resonance stabilisation of the conjugate acid formed from protonation of the sp^2 nitrogen. Draw out the resonance forms of this conjugate acid.

- □ The positive charge is shared equally between the three nitrogen atoms and thus the conjugate acid formed on protonation of arginine is particularly stable. The conjugate acid is thus a weak acid and so the side chain of arginine must be a relatively strong base.

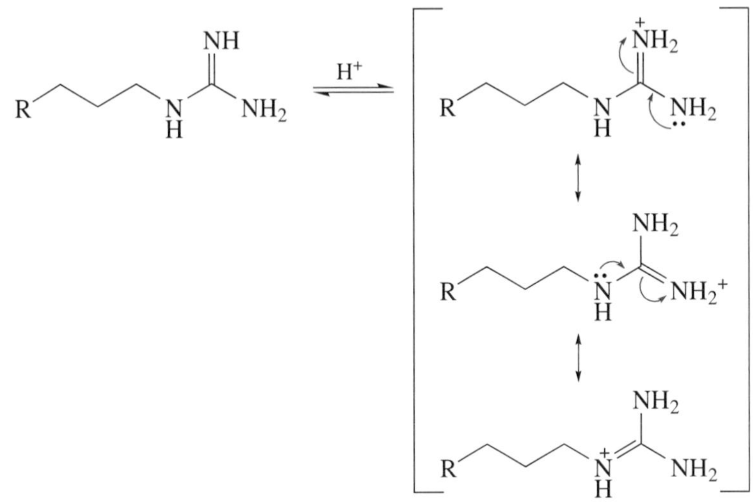

R N H NH NH_2 $\xrightleftharpoons{H^+}$ [R N H $\overset{+}{N}H_2$ NH_2 ⟷ R N H NH_2 NH_2^+ ⟷ R $\overset{+}{N}$ H NH_2 NH_2]

Whereas Table 2.3 showed the inductive effect to fall off rapidly along a chain of bonds, the resonance effect, because it operates through the π framework, can operate over many bonds. Transmission of electronic effects over long conjugated systems is an important result of the resonance effect.

In the last few examples resonance stabilisation of the charged species has been important but this isn't always the case. Take a look at the following equilibria. (The acid dissociation reaction is reversed to emphasise basicity.)

$$\underset{\textbf{2.30}}{C_2H_5NH_2} + H_3O^+ \rightleftharpoons \underset{\textbf{2.31}}{C_2H_5\overset{+}{N}H_3} + H_2O \qquad (2.34)$$

$$\underset{\textbf{2.32}}{C_6H_5NH_2} + H_3O^+ \rightleftharpoons \underset{\textbf{2.33}}{C_6H_5\overset{+}{N}H_3} + H_2O \qquad (2.35)$$

Aniline (**2.32**) is 10^6 times less basic than ethylamine (**2.30**). This is because aniline (**2.32**) is stabilised by resonance which is not possible in the anilinium ion (**2.33**).

:NH$_2$ ⟷ $\overset{+}{N}H_2$ ⟷ $\overset{+}{N}H_2$ ⟷ $\overset{+}{N}H_2$

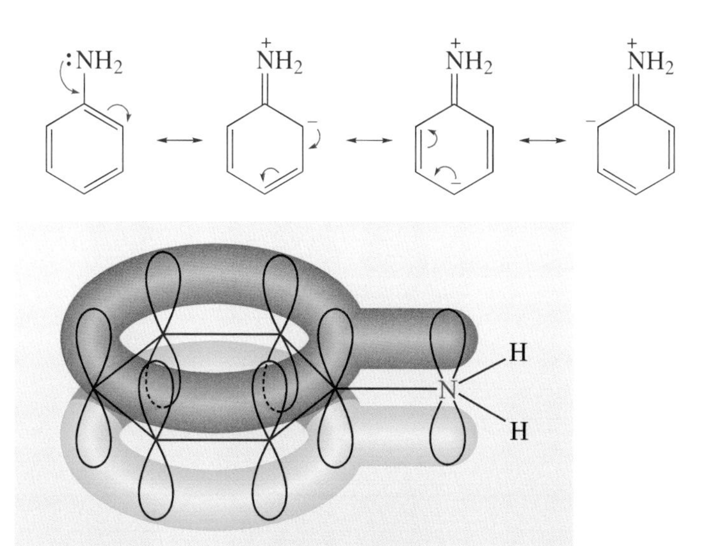

Figure 2.9 The π molecular orbitals in aniline.

In effect the non-bonded electron pair which is in a p orbital overlaps with the π system of the benzene ring as shown in Figure 2.9. This is not possible with the anilinium ion since the unshared pair has been donated to a proton to form an N–H bond.

Since the reactant is stabilised relative to the product, $\Delta G^{\ominus}$ for Reaction 2.35 is less negative and thus protonation is less favourable, and so aniline is less basic than alkylamines where resonance stabilisation of the base or conjugate acid is not possible.

■ The amides asparagine and glutamine did not have very basic side groups despite containing nitrogen atoms. Why do you think amides are not very basic?

$$R{-}C({=}O)NH_2 \overset{H^+}{\rightleftharpoons} R{-}C({=}OH^+)NH_2 \qquad (2.36)$$

□ This is quite a tricky question. Resonance stabilisation of the conjugate acid leads to spreading of the positive charge, but there is substantial resonance stabilisation of the unprotonated amide as well, such that the non-bonded pair on the nitrogen atom is no longer available for protonation as it is tied up with the π system of the carbonyl. This is why oxygen protonation is observed. Resonance stabilisation of the reactant is more significant than resonance stabilisation of the product such that the amide is less basic.

$$\begin{array}{ccc} R{-}C({=}O)\ddot{N}H_2 & \overset{H^+}{\rightleftharpoons} & R{-}C({=}OH^+)\ddot{N}H_2 \\ \updownarrow & & \updownarrow \\ R{-}C(O^-){=}NH_2^+ & & R{-}C(OH){=}NH_2^+ \end{array} \qquad (2.37)$$

Now try the following question – it introduces you to an important class of compounds.

■ Explain why acetone (**2.34**) is a stronger acid than ethane (**2.36**).

$$\underset{\mathbf{2.34}}{CH_3{-}C({=}O){-}CH_3} + H_2O \rightleftharpoons \underset{\mathbf{2.35}}{CH_3{-}C({=}O){-}CH_2^-} + H_3O^+ \qquad pK_a = 20 \qquad (2.38)$$

$$\underset{\mathbf{2.36}}{CH_3{-}CH_3} + H_2O \rightleftharpoons \underset{\mathbf{2.37}}{CH_3{-}CH_2^-} + H_3O^+ \qquad pK_a = 50 \qquad (2.39)$$

□ In the acetone anion the non-bonded electron pair is not localised on a single carbon atom, as shown in structure **2.35**, but part of an extended π system:

$$\left[\underset{\mathbf{2.35}}{CH_3{-}C({=}O){-}CH_2^-} \longleftrightarrow CH_3{-}C(O^-){=}CH_2\right] \equiv \underset{\mathbf{2.38}}{CH_3{-}C(\overset{\delta-}{\cdots}O)\overset{-}{\cdots}CH_2}$$

Moreover you can see that some of the negative charge is on the oxygen atom which, being more electronegative than carbon, can accommodate negative charge more easily. Again resonance stabilisation and spreading of the negative charge (especially onto oxygen) lowers the energy of the product acetone anion such that the acidity of acetone is much greater than that of ethane where no such effects are possible.

Carbanions adjacent to carbonyls which are stabilised by resonance, as shown in the anion **2.38,** are called enolate ions and are important throughout many areas of organic synthesis, as we shall see in Unit 6 of this module.

To complete this section we shall examine the stabilisation of a special kind of compound. As you saw in Unit 2, molecules such as amino acids (**2.39**) which contain both a negative and positive charge are known as zwitterions. A special type of **zwitterion** where the carbanion is adjacent to a positive charge, as in **2.40**, is called an **ylide** (pronounced illid). Here, inductive and/or resonance effects can lead to a stable carbanion.

$$H_3\overset{+}{N}-\underset{R}{\overset{|}{C}}H-COO^-$$

2.39

$$\overset{+}{X}-\overset{-}{C}$$

2.40

Nitrogen ylides (e.g. **2.42**) are formed by removing a proton from a tetraalkylammonium ion (Equation 2.40).

$$\underset{\textbf{2.41}}{(CH_3)_3\overset{+}{N}-CH_3} + H_2O \rightleftharpoons \underset{\textbf{2.42}}{(CH_3)_3\overset{+}{N}-\overset{-}{C}H_2} + H_3O^+ \qquad (2.40)$$

The tetramethylammonium ion is more acidic than an ordinary hydrocarbon or amine because the stability of the carbanion (**2.42**) is enhanced by the adjacent N^+. The N^+-substituent is electron-withdrawing, spreading the charge by the inductive effect, and the adjacent positive and negative charges are stabilised through the electrostatic effect – they tend to balance each other.

Phosphorus and sulfur ylides are even more stable:

$$(CH_3)_3\overset{+}{P}-CH_3 + H_2O \rightleftharpoons (CH_3)_3\overset{+}{P}-\overset{-}{C}H_2 + H_3O^+ \qquad (2.41)$$

$$(CH_3)_2\overset{+}{S}-CH_3 + H_2O \rightleftharpoons (CH_3)_2\overset{+}{S}-\overset{-}{C}H_2 + H_3O^+ \qquad (2.42)$$

Unlike nitrogen, phosphorus and sulfur can accommodate more than eight valence electrons, so they both have a neutral resonance structure:

$$(CH_3)_3\overset{+}{P}-\overset{-}{C}H_2 \longleftrightarrow (CH_3)_3P=CH_2$$

$$(CH_3)_2\overset{+}{S}-\overset{-}{C}H_2 \longleftrightarrow (CH_3)_2S=CH_2$$

Whilst the actual structures are usually closer to the charged form than the neutral form, the presence of an extra resonance structure leads to resonance stabilisation of the ylide. As you will see in the second half of this module when we discuss drug synthesis, phosphorus ylides are important stabilised carbanions that are used extensively in carbon–carbon bond forming reactions.

2.7 The pK_a of amino acid side chains and the isoelectric point of proteins

As we saw in Section 2 of Unit 2, the side chains of amino acid residues are important for binding molecules into receptors and for creating the catalytic sites of enzymes. Thus, acidic side chains can donate a hydrogen to protonate a particular group of the substrate, leading to ionic interactions in the binding site. Similarly, basic side chains can accept a proton. Proton donors and acceptors are also important in forming hydrogen bonds to substrate molecules. Acid–base reactions are often the source of catalytic activity, as in the catalytic triad of serine proteases.

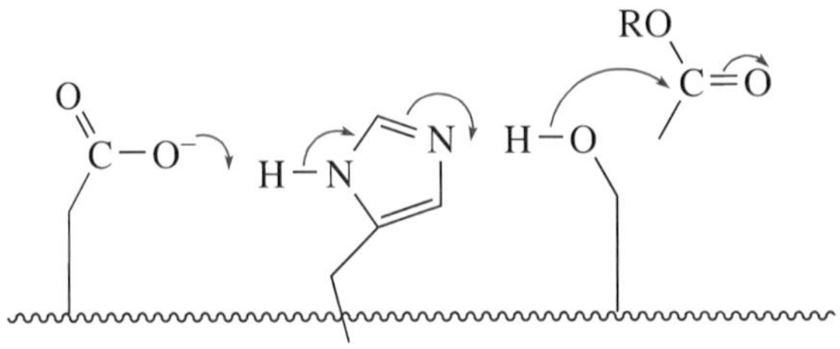

One important property of a protein is its **isoelectric point** (pI). Most proteins consist of both acidic and basic amino acids in varying proportions. If a protein were largely made up of acidic amino acids then they would be mainly ionised at neutral pH and so the protein would carry a net negative charge. On the other hand, if a protein were largely made up of basic amino acids then they would be mainly protonated at neutral pH and so the protein would carry a net positive charge. Most proteins have a mix of acidic and basic amino acid residues, but they rarely balance each other out. So, at neutral pH, most proteins will be negatively or positively charged. If we were to decrease the pH from neutral, then more basic groups would be protonated and acid dissociation would occur to a smaller extent; thus, the protein would become more positive. If we were to increase the pH from neutral, then more acidic groups would be ionised and protonation would occur to a smaller extent; thus the protein would become more negative.

The isoelectric point is the pH at which the extent of ionisation of acidic groups matches the extent of protonation of basic groups such that the molecule carries no net positive or negative charge. At pH values below the isoelectric point the protein carries a positive charge and at pH values above the isoelectric point the protein carries a negative charge. The isoelectric point is important for protein purification since proteins usually have their lowest solubility in water at the pI. The technique of isoelectric focusing involves creating a pH gradient across a gel. An electric charge is placed across the gel with the negative cathode on the high pH side and the positive anode at the low pH side. The sample is usually placed at the low pH side so that it is positively charged and attracted to the cathode. As the protein migrates to the cathode the gel environment becomes increasingly less acidic and so the positive charge on the protein decreases. Eventually it reaches the pH zone corresponding to its pI, where it is neutral and, therefore, ceases to migrate to the cathode. If it overshoots, then the protein becomes negatively charged and, therefore, is attracted back to the anode until it reaches its pI again, giving a narrow band of pure protein. Thus, a mixture of proteins can be separated based on their different pI values.

Study note

Before moving on to Section 3, you should produce your own summary of this section and then compare it with ours. Go to Unit 3 summaries in Unit 3 resources.

3 Electronic effect of structure on the rate of reaction

So far we have considered only the effect of structure on the equilibrium constant of a reaction, that is, how far the reaction will go. To get a complete picture of whether a reaction will work or not and how selective it will be, we must also consider the rates of reactions.

One step in a preparation of the heart-active steroid digitoxigenin involves addition of bromine in the presence of water across a double bond (Equation 3.1).

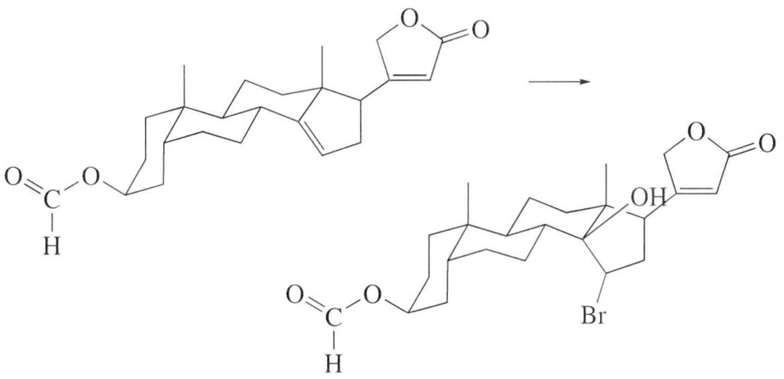

O C O H O O OH Br (3.1)

Notice that only one of the double bonds is attacked and the Br and OH end up at specific sites. This selectivity arises not because of the relative stability of the various products but as a result of how fast addition occurs to give each of the possible addition products. So in order to explain the selectivity we need to consider the mechanism of the reaction. We start this section with a general review of how reactivity – in terms of kinetics – and mechanism are interlinked. Then we examine, as a typical example, how structure can affect the rate and orientation of an addition. From this, the basis of the selectivity observed in Equation 3.1 will become clear.

3.1 Reactivity and mechanism

The term 'rate' implies that some quantity is changing with time. The rate of a reaction, J, is a measure of how quickly the concentration of the product increases or the concentration of the reactant decreases. As you may remember, we can write a rate equation which relates the rate of a reaction to the concentration of the reactants. So for the S_N2 reaction:

$$HO^- + CH_3I \longrightarrow CH_3OH + I^- \qquad (3.2)$$

where the rate depends upon the concentration of both reactants, the rate, J, is defined as

$$J = k[HO^-][CH_3I] \qquad (3.3)$$

k is known as the rate constant and is a constant at a particular temperature but generally increases with temperature.

- ■ We have mentioned two ways of making a reaction go faster: one is to increase the concentration of reactants and the other is to heat the reaction up. Can you think of a third way in which a reaction which may be too slow to be at all useful can be speeded up?
- □ We can add a catalyst (such as an enzyme) to the reaction, which speeds up the reaction but does not alter the position of equilibrium. It does this by taking part in the reaction and changing the mechanism – but whilst being consumed in one part of the mechanism it is regenerated in another, such that overall its concentration does not change.

Just as we used Gibbs energy diagrams to represent equilibria pictorially, so we use reaction-coordinate diagrams when dealing with rates of reaction. Figure 3.1 shows the reaction-coordinate diagram for the addition of HBr to 2-methylpropene (Equation 3.4).

$$(CH_3)_2C{=}CH_2 + H^+ \longrightarrow (CH_3)_2\overset{+}{C}{-}CH_3 \ (\mathbf{3.1}) \xrightarrow{Br^-} (CH_3)_2CBr{-}CH_3 \qquad (3.4)$$

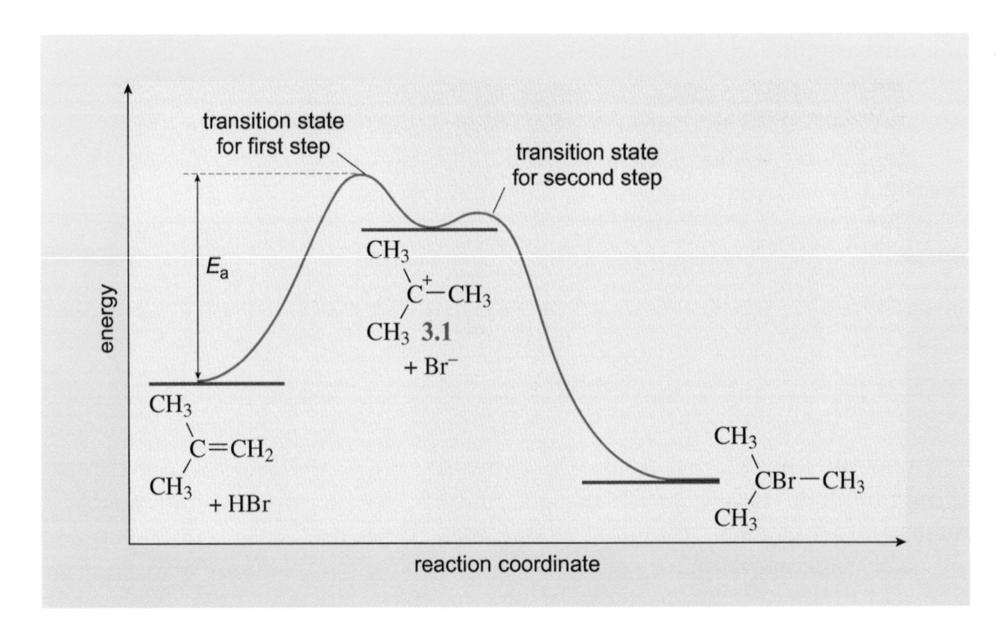

Figure 3.1 Reaction coordinate diagram for the addition of HBr to 2-methylpropene (Equation 3.4).

The energies of the reactants and products are shown on the left and right respectively. The energy of the intermediate (**3.1**) is represented by a minimum, whereas the transition states for the two steps occur at energy maxima. Notice that the energy of the first transition state is higher than that of the second step, which means that the first step is rate-limiting. Since this is the highest energy barrier that the reaction has to go over, the height of this transition state represents the activation energy E_a.

The reverse of addition is elimination, as shown in Equation 3.5.

$$(CH_3)_2CBr{-}CH_3 \longrightarrow (CH_3)_2C{=}CH_2 + HBr \qquad (3.5)$$

Since we know the mechanism of the forward reaction (Equation 3.4), then, provided the reaction is carried out under the same conditions, we automatically know the mechanism of the reverse reaction; it is simply Equation 3.4 written backwards (Equation 3.6).

$$Br{-}C(CH_3)_2{-}CH_3 \rightleftharpoons (CH_3)_2\overset{+}{C}{-}CH_3 + Br^- \longrightarrow (CH_3)_2C{=}CH_2 + HBr \qquad (3.6)$$

This follows from an empirical law known as the **principle of microscopic reversibility** which, as well as saying that forward and reverse reactions proceed along the same pathway though in opposite directions, also points out that forward and reverse reactions have the same rate-limiting step.

■ Using Figure 3.1, decide which is the rate-limiting step in Equation 3.6.

□ Since the first step in Figure 3.1 – the reaction concerning 2-methylpropene and H^+ – is rate-limiting in the forward direction (Equation 3.4), it is this step which is also rate-limiting in the elimination reaction (as shown in Equation 3.7). Figure 3.1 shows that the transition state on the left is the highest barrier to surmount, irrespective of direction.

$$Br{-}C(CH_3)_2{-}CH_3 \rightleftharpoons (CH_3)_2\overset{+}{C}{-}CH_3 + Br^- \xrightarrow{\text{rate-limiting step}} (CH_3)_2C{=}CH_2 + HBr \qquad (3.7)$$

You may think that this elimination is an E1 process so the first step should be rate-limiting. This brings us on to an important point: which step is rate-limiting often depends upon the conditions under which the reaction is carried out, such as temperature, nature of solvent, concentration of reactants and nature of catalyst. It so happens that the second step of Equation 3.6 is rate-limiting under the conditions employed for the corresponding addition reaction, but under the conditions normally employed for elimination reactions, which ensure that elimination is the thermodynamically favourable process, it is the first step that is rate-limiting.

3.2 The effect of structure on the direction and rate of addition

We will now examine the factors that affect the direction and rate of addition starting with simple model compounds before moving on to explain the behaviour observed in Equation 3.1.

3.2.1 Effect of structure on the direction of addition

When dealing with equilibria in Section 2 we concentrated on the Gibbs energy difference $\Delta G^{\ominus}$ between reactants and products. When discussing rates we must focus on the activation energy. In other words, to account for changes in the rate on varying the structure of a molecule we must consider how the structure affects (1) the energy of the reactants and (2) the energy of the transition state of the rate-limiting step. We have already been through this exercise for reactants in Section 2, but transition states are trickier because, by their nature, we cannot clearly define their structure. For example, **3.2** is a possible transition state for the rate-limiting first step of Equation 3.4.

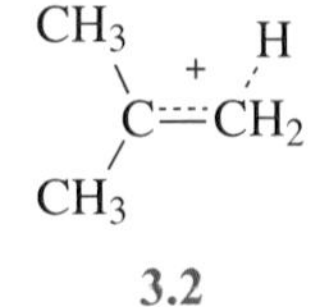

3.2

The C–H bond is partially made and some positive charge is building up on the tertiary carbon. But, without making certain assumptions about the extent of bond formation, etc., it is difficult to predict how the structure will affect the energy of such species. The solution to this problem can be found in the **Hammond postulate** which states:

If a transition state lies close in energy to a real molecule (or ion or radical) then the two will have similar structures.

Put another way, the geometry of the transition state for a step will resemble the side (i.e. reactant or product) to which it is closer in energy.

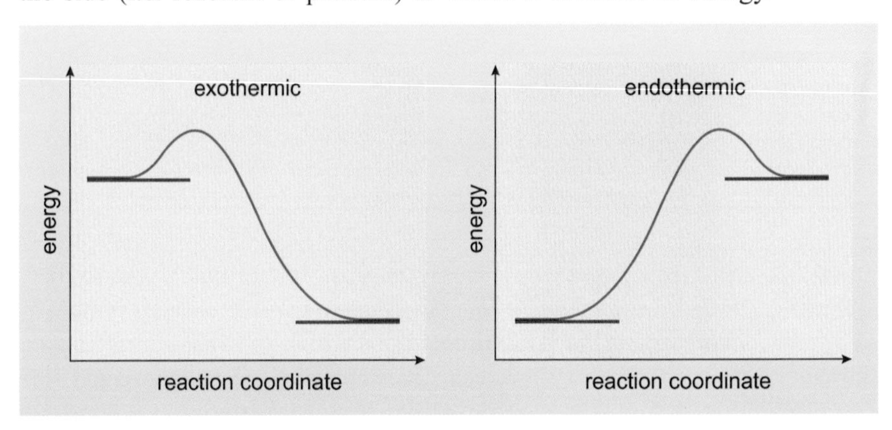

Figure 3.2 Reaction-coordinate diagram for (a) an exothermic reaction and (b) an endothermic reaction.

- ■ Figure 3.2 shows an exothermic and an endothermic reaction. For which reaction is the transition state reactant-like, and for which is it product-like?

- □ In the exothermic reaction the transition state is much closer in energy to the reactant than the product. Since it is closer energetically, we can say that it is also closer in structure, that is, it is reactant-like. In the endothermic reaction the transition state is closer in energy to the product so its structure will be product-like.

In Figure 3.1, the first transition state is closer in energy to the intermediate than to the reactant, and since they have similar energies we can propose that they will have similar structures. This being the case, their energies should respond to changes in the structure in a similar fashion. In other words, based on how different groups affect the stability of an intermediate which has a known structure, we can predict how the energy of the transition state will change.

As an example, addition of HBr to 2-methylpropene can give the so-called Markovnikov (**3.4**) or anti-Markovnikov (**3.3**) product (Equation 3.8).

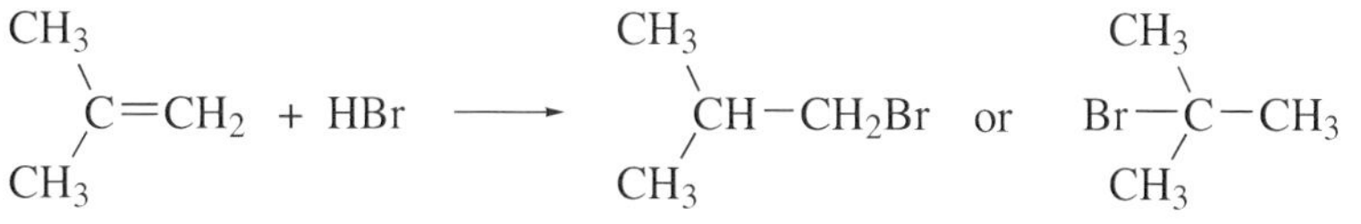

$$(CH_3)_2C{=}CH_2 + HBr \longrightarrow \underset{\mathbf{3.3}}{(CH_3)_2CH{-}CH_2Br} \text{ or } \underset{\mathbf{3.4}}{Br{-}C(CH_3)_2{-}CH_3} \quad (3.8)$$

Since the first step of the addition, as shown in Equation 3.4, is rate-limiting, the relative proportions of **3.3** and **3.4** formed in a particular period will depend upon how fast the corresponding intermediates are formed. This, in turn, depends upon the relative energies of the transition states leading to the intermediates.

We can use the Hammond postulate to get an idea of the relative energies of these transition states. Look at the two intermediates **3.5** and **3.1**.

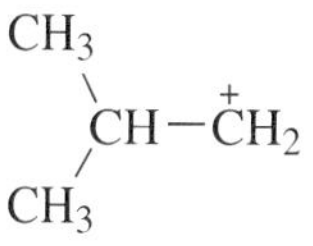

$$\underset{\mathbf{3.5}}{(CH_3)_2CH{-}\overset{+}{C}H_2} \qquad \underset{\mathbf{3.1}}{(CH_3)_2\overset{+}{C}{-}CH_3}$$

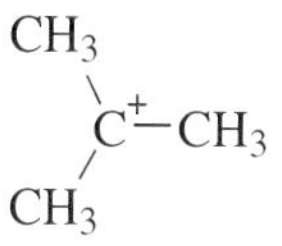

Clearly, we expect the tertiary carbocation **3.1** to be more stable than the primary carbocation **3.5**. So we can draw the reaction-coordinate diagram shown in Figure 3.3 with the transition state leading to the primary carbocation having a higher energy than that leading to the tertiary carbocation. To sum up, the Markovnikov product (**3.4**) predominates because it is formed faster, having the rate-limiting transition state with the lower energy. In such circumstances we say the products are formed under **kinetic control** and the product distribution does not necessarily reflect the thermodynamic stability of the products. As shown in Figure 3.3, quite often the thermodynamically less stable product can predominate. When the product ratio does reflect the relative thermodynamic stability, the reaction is said to occur under **thermodynamic control**.

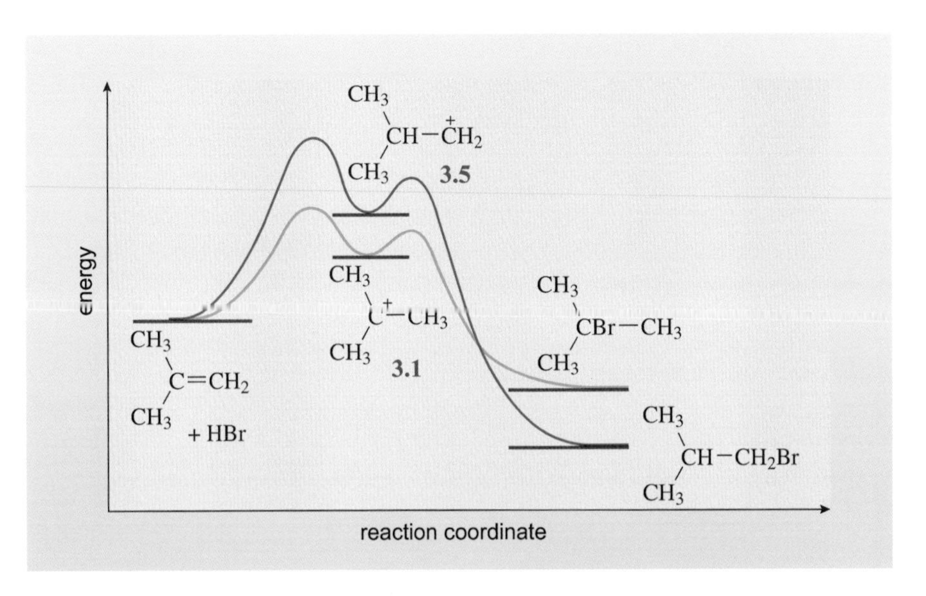

Figure 3.3 Reaction-coordinate diagram for the Markovnikov and anti-Markovnikov addition of HBr to 2-methylpropene.

3.2.2 Effect of structure on the rate of addition

Having just explained how structure controls the direction of addition, we shall now use a similar reasoning to explain the effect of structure on the rate of addition. Table 3.1 lists the relative rates of electrophilic addition to a variety of alkenes.

Table 3.1 Relative rates of electrophilic addition to various alkenes.

Alkene	Relative rate of addition
FCH_2–CH=CH_2	3.4×10^{-5}
CH_2=CH_2	1
CH_3–CH=CH_2	1.6×10^{6}
C_6H_5–CH=CH_2	1.6×10^{8}
CH_3O–CH=CH_2	5.2×10^{14}

■ Assuming the mechanism of addition discussed earlier, why is it that both FCH_2–CH=CH_2 and CH_2=CH_2 react more slowly than CH_3–CH=CH_2?

□ The order of reactivity depends on the relative energies of the transition states of the rate-limiting steps. Using the Hammond postulate, we can get an idea of these relative energies by examining the intermediates **3.6**, **3.7** and **3.8**, which arise from attack by the electrophile E^+ on the first three alkenes in Table 3.1.

FCH_2 \ $\overset{+}{C}$–CH_2E / H	H \ $\overset{+}{C}$–CH_2E / H	CH_3 \ $\overset{+}{C}$–CH_2E / H
3.6	**3.7**	**3.8**

The secondary carbocation **3.8** will be more stable than the primary carbocation **3.7** because of inductive donation by the methyl group. Similarly the inductive withdrawal of electrons by the CH_2F group will make **3.6** less stable than **3.8**. Thus **3.6** and **3.7** both have a higher energy than **3.8** and this is reflected in the energies of the transition states, in agreement with the relative rates shown in Table 3.1.

So far we have examined only the inductive effect of substituents on the rate of addition, but resonance stabilisation can also be important. For example, phenylethene undergoes addition more quickly than both ethene and propene. The intermediate formed by electrophilic attack on phenylethene has a number of resonance structures:

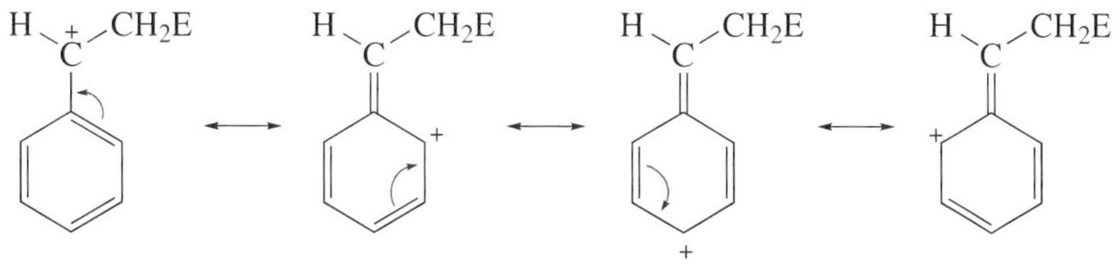

H $\overset{+}{C}$ CH_2E ⟷ H C CH_2E ⟷ H C CH_2E ⟷ H C CH_2E

It is therefore much more stable than **3.7** and **3.8**, formed from ethene and propene respectively. This is mirrored in the energies of the transition states, as shown by the relative rates in Table 3.1.

■ Why does methoxyethene react so much faster than ethene?

□ Though the inductive effect of the oxygen would make **3.9** less stable than **3.7**, oxygen has unshared pairs that can be donated to the electron-deficient centre:

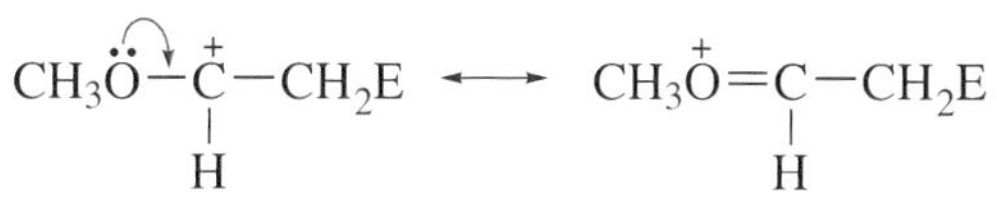

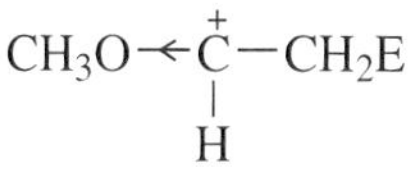

$CH_3\ddot{O}-\overset{+}{C}H-CH_2E \longleftrightarrow CH_3\overset{+}{O}=CH-CH_2E$

$CH_3O \leftarrow \overset{+}{C}H-CH_2E$

3.9

Stabilisation by resonance outweighs the destabilisation by the inductive effect such that the intermediate, and hence the transition state of the rate-limiting step for addition to methoxyethene, has a lower energy than that involved in addition to ethene. This being the case, methoxyethene will react the faster.

Now we can understand the selectivity observed in the formation of the bromohydrin **3.10**:

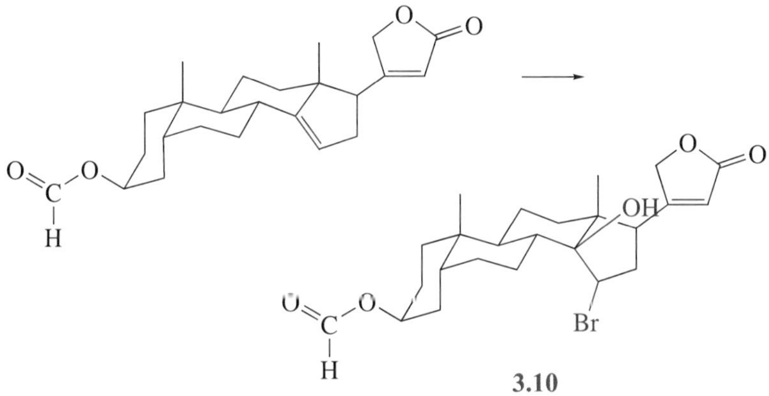

3.10

If bromonium ions rather than carbocations are involved, selectivity depends upon the relative stability of the potential carbocation intermediates.

Addition of Br and OH proceeds by initial attack of Br^+. The transition state leading to the tertiary carbocation **3.11** has a much lower energy than that leading to the secondary carbocation **3.12**. Attack by water then gives the product **3.10**.

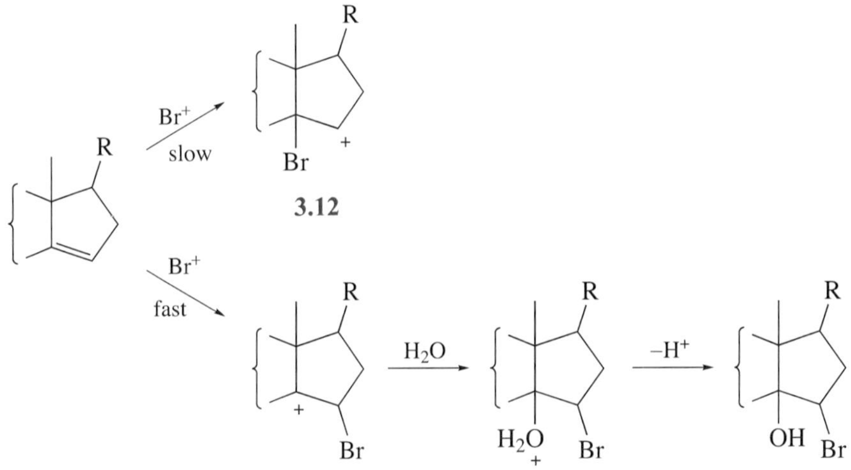

3.12

3.11

This explains the orientation of addition. But why isn't the other double bond attacked since here a tertiary carbocation (**3.13**) can also be formed?

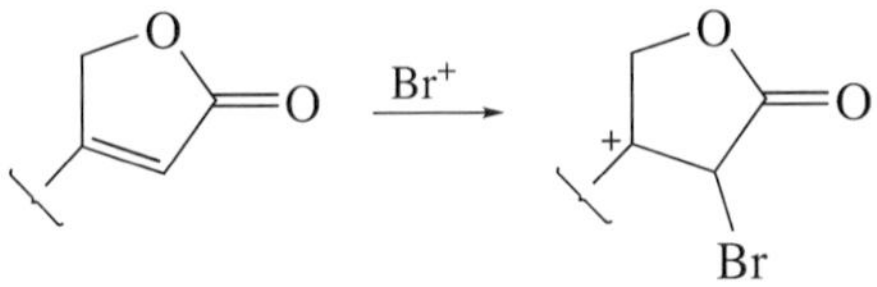

3.13

The reason is twofold. Firstly, the inductive electron-withdrawing effect of the oxygen will destabilise the carbocation **3.13**. Secondly, the energy of the alkene is lowered by conjugation with the carbonyl group. As shown in Figure 3.4, the higher energy of the intermediate is reflected in the energy of the transition state which when coupled to the lower energy of the reactant leads to a much larger activation energy. Addition to the non-conjugated alkene thus proceeds faster.

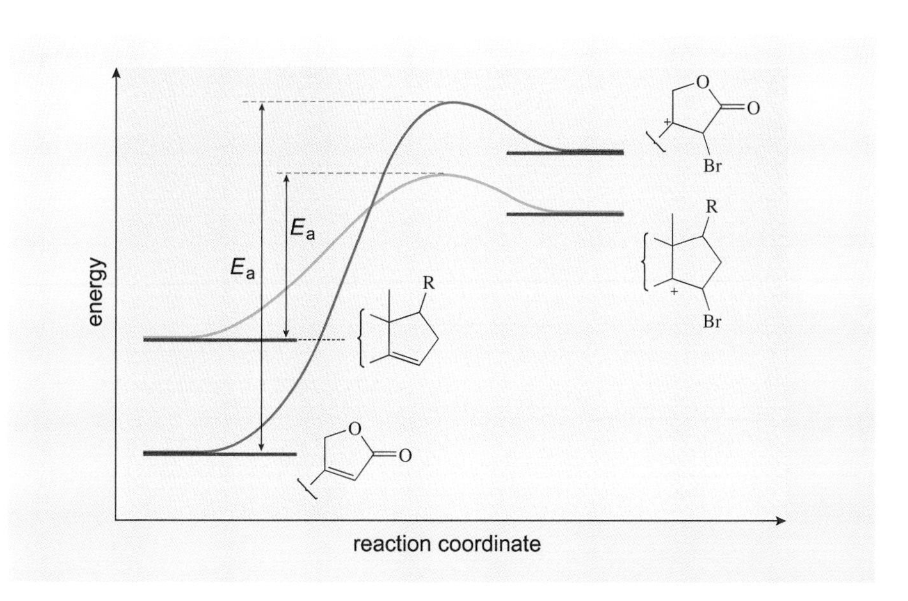

Figure 3.4 Reaction coordinate diagram for the addition of Br^+ to two alkenes.

Study note

Before moving on to Section 4, you should produce your own summary of this section and then compare it with ours. Go to Unit 3 summaries in Unit 3 resources.

4 Linear free energy relationships

Figure 4.1 shows a plot of the logarithm of the insecticidal activity of a series of diethyl phenyl phosphates, **4.1**, where X is a range of substituents in the *meta* and *para* positions, relative to the phosphate group, against the pK_a values of the corresponding substituted benzoic acids, **4.2**. We will explain what the insecticidal activity, $1/C$, means in Section 5. The important thing to notice is that there is a very good correlation of two very different properties, insecticidal activity and acidity for two different compounds, phenyl phosphates and benzoic acids. The substituents used and the data which gave the plot are shown in Table 4.1.

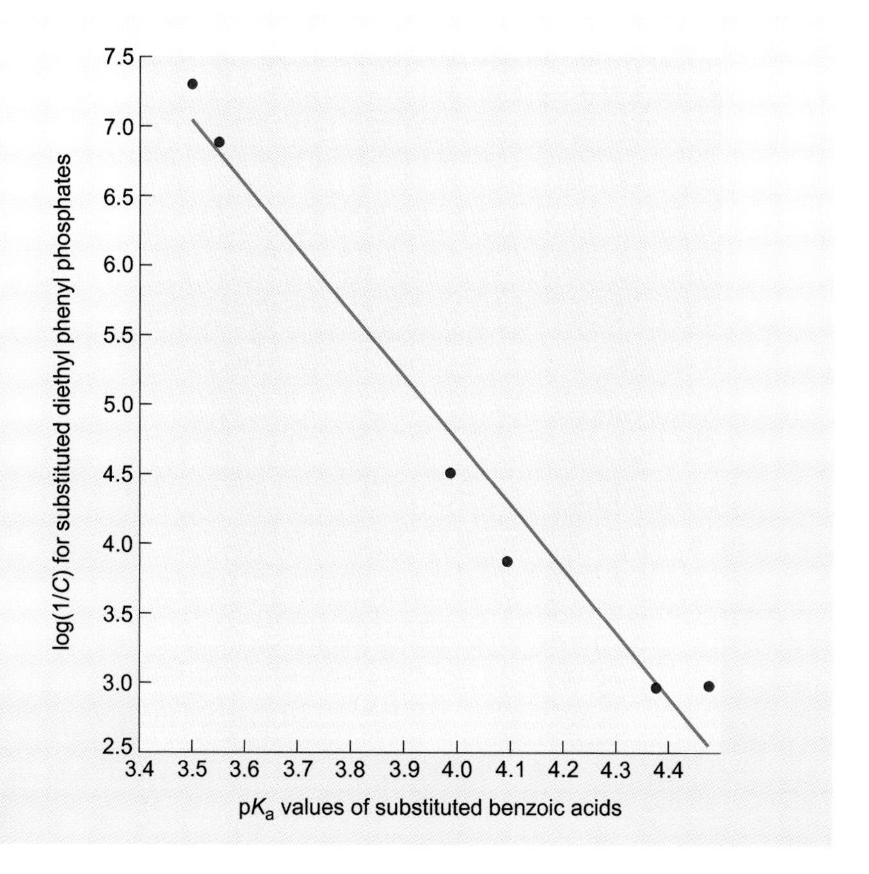

4.1 **4.2**

Figure 4.1 A plot of log($1/C$), the insecticidal activity of a series of substituted diethyl phenyl phosphates against the pK_a values of the corresponding benzoic acids.

Table 4.1 Data on the insecticidal activity of a series of substituted diethyl phenyl phosphates and the pK_a values of the corresponding benzoic acids.

Substituent X	Insecticidal activity C	$\log(1/C)$	pK_a of substituted benzoic acid*
para-nitro	2.60×10^{-8}	7.58	3.43
para-cyano	1.30×10^{-7}	6.88	3.55
para-chloro	3.00×10^{-5}	4.52	3.98
meta-nitro	5.00×10^{-8}	7.30	3.50
para-methyl	1.00×10^{-3}	3.00	4.38
meta-methoxy	1.30×10^{-4}	3.88	4.09
para-methoxy	1.00×10^{-3}	3.00	4.47

*The pK_a of benzoic acid is 4.21.

The reason why the plot is linear is because both the pK_a values of benzoic acids and the insecticidal activity behave in a predictable fashion, depending upon the electron-withdrawing or -donating effect of the substituent in the benzene ring. If you have studied the Level 2 chemistry module, you may remember the electronic effects of substituents on a benzene ring when you considered electrophilic aromatic substitution. These are summarised in Table 4.2.

Table 4.2 The activating (or deactivating) and directing effects of various substituents attached to the benzene ring.

Activating groups	*ortho*/*para*-directing:	CH_3 and other alkyl groups, OH, OR, NH_2, NHR, NR_2, NHCOR
Deactivating groups	*ortho*/*para*-directing:	Cl, Br, I
Deactivating groups	*meta*-directing:	NO_2, $^{+}NH_3$, $^{+}NR_3$, SO_3H, SO_3R, CHO, COR, CN, COOR, COOH

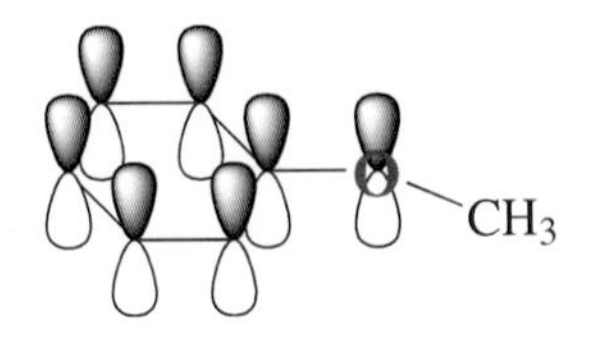

The nitro group is deactivating (electron-withdrawing) and led to *meta* substitution whereas, the methyl group is activating (electron-donating) and led to *ortho*/*para* substitution. The electronegative chloro group was electron withdrawing although it did lead to *ortho* and *para* substitution. Despite having an electronegative oxygen adjacent to the ring, the methoxy group is electron donating, leading to *ortho*/*para* substitution. This is because a non-bonded electron pair in a p orbital can overlap with the π system of the aromatic ring and donate electrons.

The electron-donating/withdrawing effect of a group is reflected in the ionisation of the corresponding benzoic acid, which involves a neutral acid forming a negatively charged benzoate anion (Equation 4.1).

The electron-withdrawing nitro group spreads the negative charge of the conjugate base, **4.3**, and this stabilises the anion leading to a greater acidity and a smaller pK_a value than the unsubstituted compound as shown in

Table 4.1. This also happens, albeit to a lesser extent, with the chloro substituent.

$$\underset{\textbf{4.2}}{X\text{-}C_6H_4\text{-}COOH} + H_2O \rightleftharpoons \underset{\textbf{4.3}}{X\text{-}C_6H_4\text{-}COO^-} + H_3O^+ \qquad (4.1)$$

The electron-donating *para*-methyl and *para*-methoxy groups concentrate the negative charge, destabilising the anion and making the corresponding benzoic acid less acidic than the unsubstituted compound, leading to a larger pK_a value, as shown in Table 4.1. In fact, the effect of a substituent across a benzene ring on a reaction centre is very consistent and this is why the change in the insecticidal activity of the diethyl phenyl phosphates mirrors that of the pK_a values of benzoic acids – we'll explain why the insecticidal behaviour is affected by electron-donating and -withdrawing groups later in this section.

Figure 4.2 shows a plot of the pK_a values of substituted benzoic acids against the pK_a values of substituted phenylacetic acids, Equation 4.2.

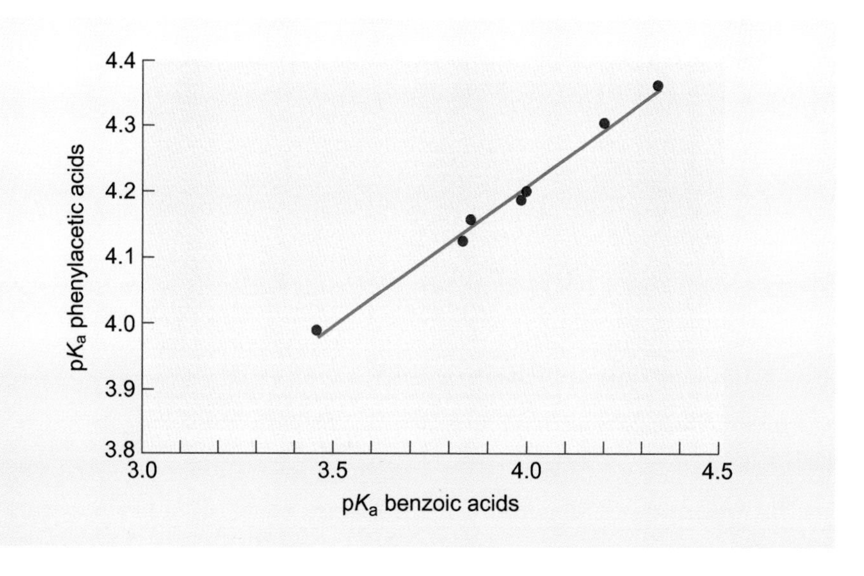

Figure 4.2 Plot of pK_a values of substituted benzoic acids against substituted phenylacetic acids.

$$X\text{-}C_6H_4\text{-}CH_2\text{-}COOH + H_2O \rightleftharpoons X\text{-}C_6H_4\text{-}CH_2\text{-}COO^- + H_3O^+ \qquad (4.2)$$

Although the substituent effect is attenuated by the $-CH_2-$ group, leading to a smaller range of pK_a values with the phenylacetic acids than with the benzoic acids, the trend in substituent effect is clear for substituents in both the *meta* and *para* positions. If substituents in the *ortho* position are included then the correlation is not so good because the *ortho* position is close to the acid group and steric effects interfere.

4.1 Hammett equation

In the 1930s, Louis P. Hammett used the acidity constants of benzoic acids to define substituent constants based on what has become known as the **Hammett equation**, Equation 4.3:

$$\log K/K_{\rm H} = \log K - \log K_{\rm H} = \rho\sigma \tag{4.3}$$

where K is the equilibrium constant for the substituted benzene compound and $K_{\rm H}$ is the equilibrium constant for the non-substituted (hydrogen) benzene compound, $\boldsymbol{\rho}$ (rho) is the reaction constant, which depends upon the type of reaction, and $\boldsymbol{\sigma}$ (sigma) is the substituent constant, which is a quantitative measure of a substituent's electron-withdrawing or -donating effect. As we said earlier, the σ values are based on the acidity of the corresponding benzoic acids and are given by:

$$\sigma = \log K_{\text{(substituted benzoic acid)}} - \log K_{\text{(benzoic acid)}}$$

Notice that here we are focusing on the log of the equilibrium constant, that is the negative of the pK_a (p$K_a = -\log K_a$).

- ■ If we plot the pK_a values of substituted benzoic acids against σ what will be the value of ρ?

- □ Since the σ values are based on the dissociation of benzoic acids the slope will have a magnitude of one. However, since the plot is against pK_a rather than $\log K_a$ the slope will be negative.

$$\begin{aligned}\sigma &= \log K_{\text{(substituted benzoic acid)}} - \log K_{\text{(benzoic acid)}}\\ &= -\mathrm{p}K_{\text{a(substituted benzoic acid)}} + \mathrm{p}K_{\text{a(benzoic acid)}}\end{aligned}$$

Table 4.3 lists some typical substituent constants, σ, for phenyl systems. A negative value implies an electron-donating group and a positive value an electron-withdrawing group. The magnitude of the electron-donating or withdrawing effect depends on the position of the group and hence the σ values are different for a substituent in the *meta* and *para* positions. The hydroxyl and alkoxy substituent are electron-donating in the *para* position but electron-withdrawing in the *meta* position. As we discussed earlier the oxygen is electronegative and thus withdraws electrons, as observed by the positive value for the *meta* position. However, a non-bonded electron pair in a p orbital on the oxygen can overlap with the π system of the aromatic ring and do.ate electrons, but only into the *ortho* and *para* positions, leading to negative values of σ.

Table 4.3 Typical substituent constants, σ, for phenyl systems.

Substituent	σ		Substituent	σ	
	meta	*para*		*meta*	*para*
CH_3	–0.069	–0.170	$NHCOCH_3$	+0.21	0.00
$CH(CH_3)_2$	–0.068	–0.151	NO_2	+0.710	+0.778
C_6H_5	+0.06	–0.01	OH	+0.121	–0.37
$COCH_3$	+0.376	+0.502	OCH_3	+0.115	–0.268
CN	+0.56	+0.660	$OCOCH_3$	+0.39	+0.31
CO_2H	+0.35	+0.406	F	+0.337	+0.062
CO_2CH_3	+0.321	+0.385	SH	+0.25	+0.15
CF_3	+0.43	+0.54	Cl	+0.373	+0.227
NH_2	–0.16	–0.66	Br	+0.391	+0.232
$N(CH_3)_2$	–0.211	–0.83	I	+0.352	+0.276

Figure 4.3 shows a plot of log K against σ for the protonation of substituted anilines, as written in Equation 4.4.

$$X\text{-}C_6H_4\text{-}NH_2 + H_2O \overset{K}{\rightleftharpoons} HO^- + X\text{-}C_6H_4\text{-}\overset{+}{N}H_3 \qquad (4.4)$$

Figure 4.3 shows a straight line with a slope of −2.7. The fact that the plot is a good straight line confirms that the electronic effect of *meta* and *para* substitutents across a benzene ring is consistent irrespective of the type of reaction. A negative slope reflects the fact that the reaction involves the formation of a positive charge. In this case the positive charge is stabilised by electron-donating substituents which spread the charge around the molecule. Electron-withdrawing substituents destabilise the products by increasing the positive charge at the reaction centre. This is the opposite trend observed with the pK_a values of benzoic acids which define the σ values and thus the slope is negative.

In fact, it is a general rule that a positive ρ value in a Hammett plot reflects a build up of negative charge during the reaction and a negative ρ value reflects a build up of a positive charge during a reaction.

The magnitude of the ρ value reflects how susceptible the reaction is to electron-donating and -withdrawing groups. For example, with dissociation of phenylacetic acids (Equation 4.2) the ρ value is 0.56 because the $–CH_2–$ group insulates the negative charge from the electronic effects of the substituents.

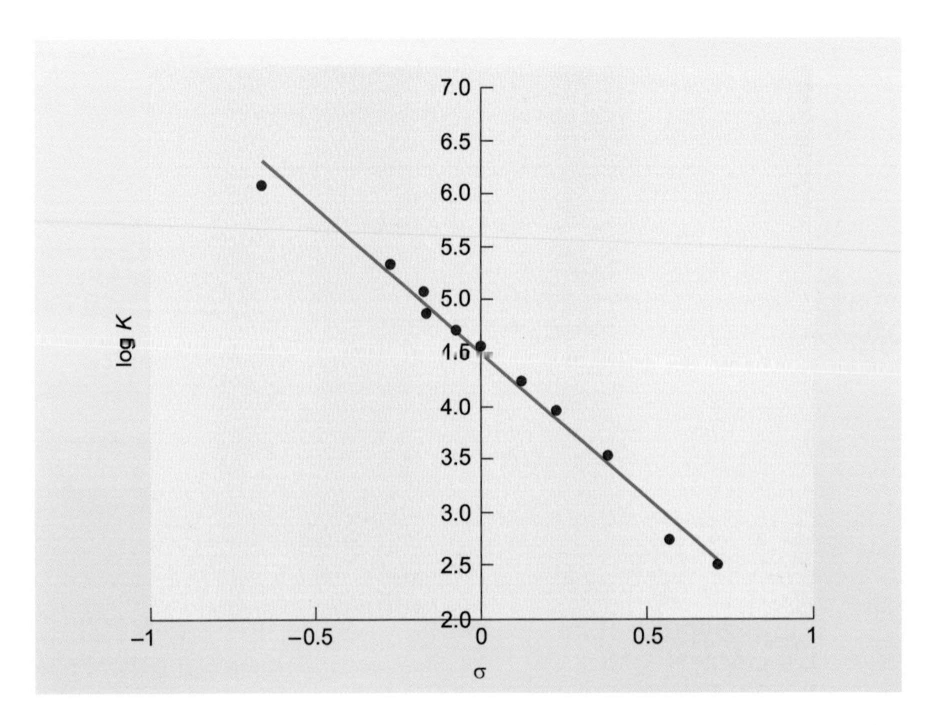

Figure 4.3 Plot of log K against σ for the protonation of substituted anilines, Equation 4.4.

The Hammett equation can be applied to rates of reaction as well as equilibrium constants:

$$\log k/k_{\text{H}} = \rho\sigma$$

where k is the rate constant for the substituted compound and k_{H} the rate for the unsubstituted (H) compound.

Figure 4.4 shows a plot of log k/k_{H} against σ for the alkaline hydrolysis of the ethyl esters of substituted benzoic acids (Equation 4.5).

$$X\text{-}C_6H_4\text{-}C(=O)\text{-}O\text{-}Et + H_2O \xrightarrow[HO^-]{k} X\text{-}C_6H_4\text{-}C(=O)\text{-}OH + EtOH \qquad (4.5)$$

Figure 4.4 suggests a value of 2.55 for ρ. The positive value for the slope, ρ, confirms the build up of negative charge during the reaction, in this case a build up of negative charge in the transition state of the rate-limiting step, as shown in Equation 4.6. The size of the slope is greater than one suggesting the rate of reaction is more susceptible to the electronic effects of *meta* and *para* substituents than are the pK_{a} values of benzoic acids. This often reflects a large charge build up adjacent to the aromatic ring.

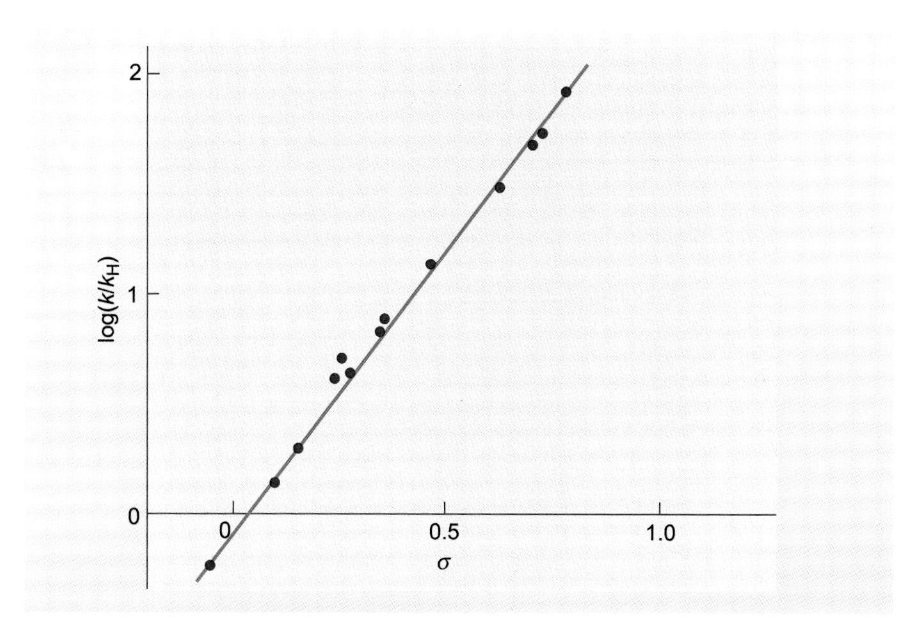

Figure 4.4 A plot of log k/k_{H} against σ for the alkaline hydrolysis of the ethyl esters of benzoic acids.

$^{-}$OH; X–C$_6$H$_4$–C(=O)OEt —(rate-limiting step)→ X–C$_6$H$_4$–C(O^{-})(OH)(OEt) —(H^{+})→ X–C$_6$H$_4$–C(=O)OH + EtOH (4.6)

In conclusion, the electronic effects of substituents on a benzene ring *meta* or *para* to a reaction centre are consistent and can be modelled using the Hammett equation log K/K_{H} or log $k/k_{\mathrm{H}} = \rho\sigma$.

Starting with neutral reactants, a positive ρ value suggests a reaction involving a build up of negative charge either in the products (equilibrium) or transition state (rates). A negative ρ value suggests the build up of positive charge during the reaction.

The magnitude of ρ reflects how susceptible the reaction is to the electronic effects of substituents and indicates the extent of charge development and how close the charge build up is to the aromatic ring.

■ A plot of the insecticidal activity (housefly) of diethyl phenyl phosphates against σ has a ρ values of +4.5. What does this tell us about the mechanism of action of these insecticides?

□ The positive ρ value suggests a build up of negative charge in the product or transition state.

In fact, the diethyl phenyl phosphate reacts with a serine residue of an enzyme called acetyl cholinesterase, as shown in Equation 4.7.

serine — OH ... EtO, EtO, P=O, O—Ph → serine — $\overset{+}{O}$—H, P(OEt)(=O)(EtO) + $^{-}$O—Ph

↓

serine — O—P(OEt)(=O)(EtO) + HO—Ph (4.7)

The first step is rate-limiting and involves a build up of negative charge on the oxygen adjacent to the benzene ring, hence the positive ρ value. Notice it is the –OPh group that is lost, not the –OEt group. This is because the –OPh is a better leaving group. As we saw in Section 2.6 a phenol is more acidic than an alkyl alcohol because the negative charge on the oxygen can be spread into the adjacent benzene ring. Acetylcholine is a neurotransmitter (chemical messenger) in the nervous system and acetylcholinesterase is an enzyme that removes the messenger once it has stimulated the nerve. The diethyl phenyl phosphate reacts with the serine and stops the enzyme working such that the acetylcholine is no longer broken down and the nerve is continually stimulated, which leads to death of the insect. Similar organophosphorus compounds are used as nerve gases and have a similar effect on mammals, for example, sarin (**4.4**), which was released in the Tokyo subway in 1996.

$(CH_3)_2CH$—O—P(=O)(CH_3)(F)

4.4

The Hammett equation is an example of a Linear Free Energy Relationship, that is substituents affect the free energy change of one reaction in a very similar way to that of another reaction. You will meet Linear Free Energy Relationship again when we examine the use of quantitative structure–activity relationships (QSAR) in drug discovery in Unit 5.

Study note

Before moving on to Section 5, you should produce your own summary of this section and then compare it with ours. Go to Unit 3 summaries in Unit 3 resources.

5 Steric effect of structure on equilibria and rates

In the earlier sections we have seen how electronic factors can affect the feasibility and selectivity of a reaction both from a thermodynamic and a kinetic viewpoint. However, there is another factor which we must consider. Take, for example, Equation 5.1 which shows the last stage of a synthesis of the aggregation pheromone (**5.1**) of the elm bark beetle.

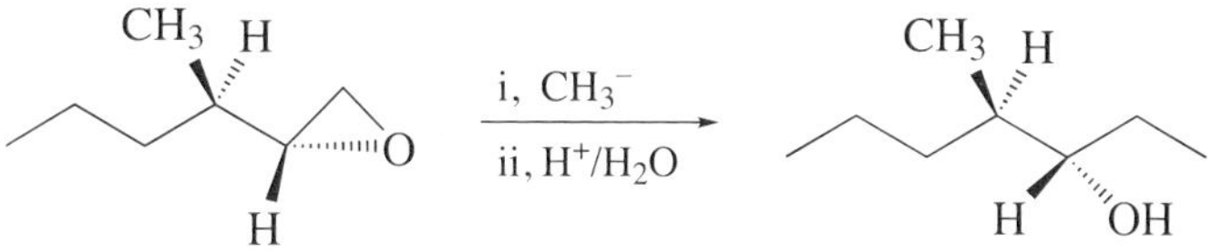

$$\text{epoxide} \xrightarrow[\text{ii, } H^+/H_2O]{\text{i, } CH_3^-} \textbf{5.1} \qquad (5.1)$$

The three-membered ring containing an oxygen is an example of a cyclic ether. Now, ethers do not normally undergo such substitution and moreover it is surprising that only one side of the ether is attacked. To explain such behaviour we must examine the stereochemistry of the molecule involved, since molecular shape can have a profound effect on chemical reactivity both in terms of equilibria and kinetics.

- ■ One of the following carboxylic acids (**5.2** or **5.3**) loses water rapidly to form a cyclic anhydride. Which one would you expect to do this and why?

- □ The formation of an anhydride involves the attack by the oxygen atom of one carboxyl group on the carbon atom of another. The rigidity of the double bond prevents this in *trans*-buten-1,4-dioic acid (**5.2**) but it allows it in *cis*-buten-1,4-dioic acid (**5.3**). Clearly, however readily electron redistribution may occur in principle, it won't occur unless the atoms concerned can physically approach each other within bonding range.

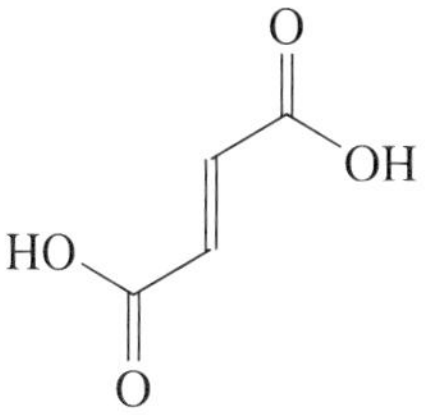

5.2 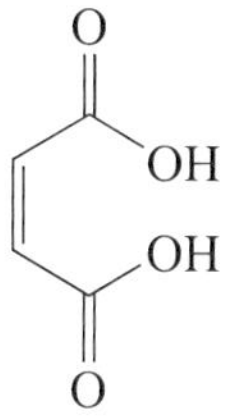 **5.3**

In this section we shall survey the basic stereochemical effects, again focusing on the energy of the reactant, product and/or transition state, and how the energy of such species increases when optimal orientation for reaction cannot be achieved. You will see that the need for optimal stereochemistry is very important when we consider transition states where the geometry is often very strict. Take, for example, a bimolecular elimination (E2) of the kind shown in Equation 5.2.

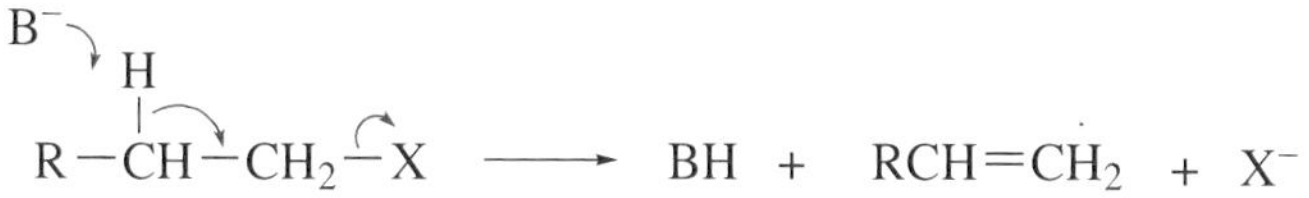

$$B^- + R{-}CH(H){-}CH_2{-}X \longrightarrow BH + RCH{=}CH_2 + X^- \qquad (5.2)$$

As you may remember, an antiperiplanar relationship between the leaving group and the hydrogen being removed is required, as shown in Figure 5.1.

In terms of orbitals, the coplanarity of the H atom, the X atom, and the two carbon atoms makes sense. As bonding develops between B and H, so a

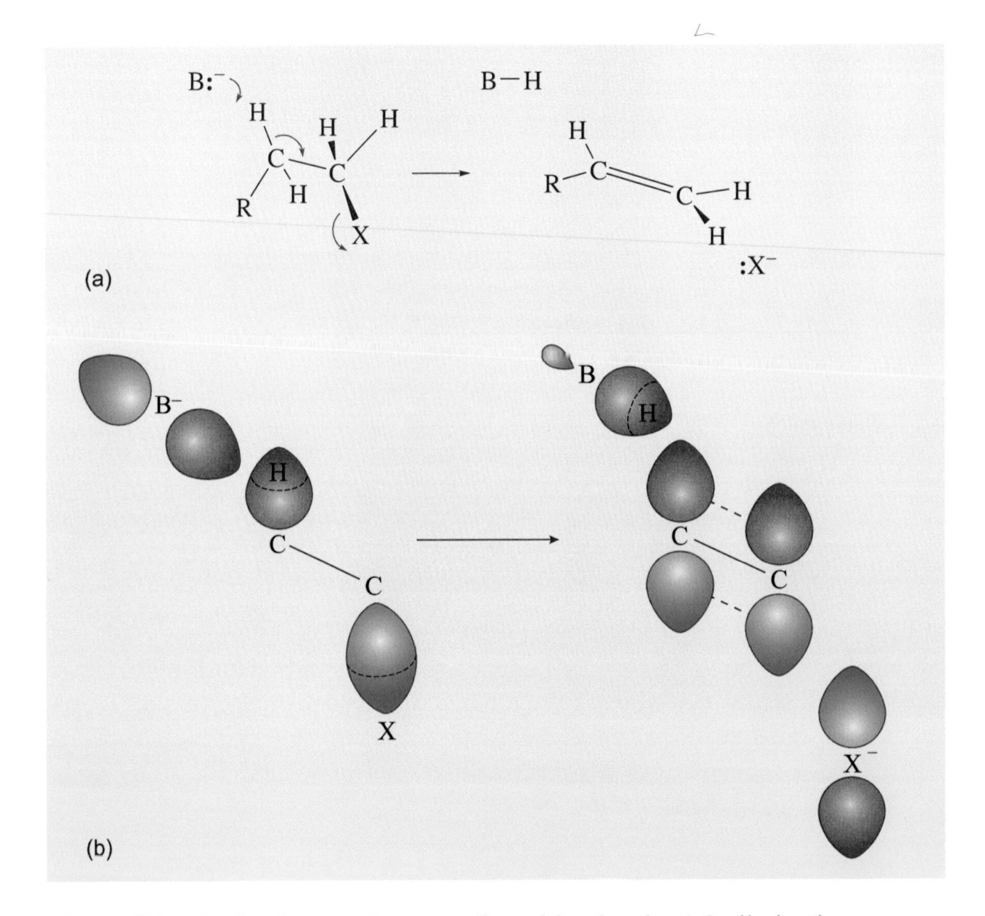

Figure 5.1 Optimal stereochemistry for a bimolecular 1,2-elimination (E2) reaction.

smooth transition occurs from the two sp^3 hybrid orbitals on the carbon atoms to a π bond and a filled p orbital on X. The stereochemistry accords with securing maximum overlap, and therefore maximum bonding, continuously throughout the reaction. It also ensures, at the same time, the best disposition of charges in the system. Thus B^- attacks remotely from the leaving group X, which develops a negative charge in the process. In a *syn* elimination the negative charge on X and B are on the same side and the need for an eclipsed conformation would make this a higher energy route:

B⁻ H X H H → H H R H R H

A further point illustrated here is that optimal stereochemistry is made up of two parts: the orientation of the reactants toward each other, and a specific internal orientation (i.e. conformation) in one or both of them. Let's now look at these stereochemical aspects in detail. This will enable us, eventually, to analyse the pattern of reactivity shown in Equation 5.1.

5.1 Steric crowding

In this section we shall examine how steric crowding in a reactant, intermediate or product affects reactivity. For example, in general, simple aliphatic aldehydes and ketones react readily with HCN to form cyanohydrins (**5.4**) and at equilibrium the percentage of cyanohydrin is usually high.

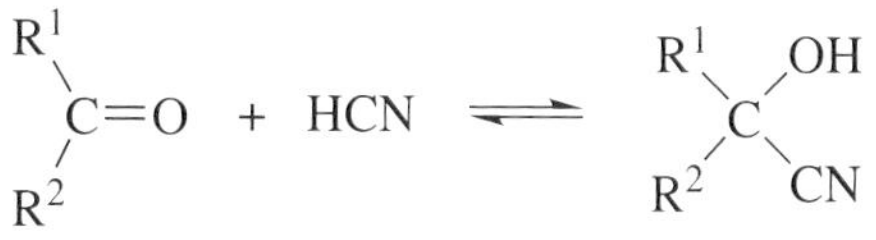

$$R^1R^2C{=}O + HCN \rightleftharpoons R^1R^2C(OH)(CN)$$

5.4

For ethanal (**5.5**) the equilibrium constant is very large, $>10^4$; for most ketones it is between 30 and 80; however, for 2,2,4,4-tetramethylpentan-3-one (di-*tert*-butyl ketone) (**5.6**) it is too small to measure.

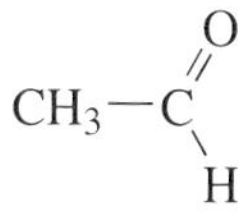

$CH_3{-}CHO$

5.5

$(CH_3)_3C{-}CO{-}C(CH_3)_3$

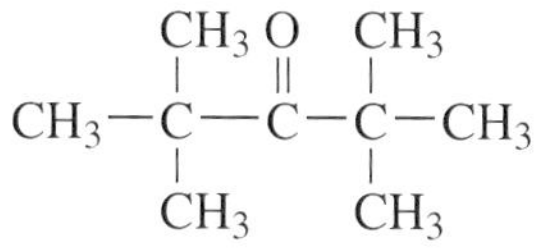

5.6

■ Why do the two bulky *tert*-butyl groups affect the addition in this way?

□ For most simple ketones where the electronic factors are fairly consistent, the equilibrium constants for cyanohydrin formation don't vary a *great* deal with different R groups.

However, the experimental results quoted above indicate that this pattern is upset when R^1 and R^2 are *both* bulky groups. The equilibrium constant becomes *very* much smaller, i.e. the value of $\Delta G^{\ominus}$ becomes less negative or even positive. In terms of molecular structure, a possible reason is that when cyanohydrin formation occurs we move from a trigonal carbon (bond angles 120°) to a tetrahedral carbon (bond angles 109° 28′), i.e. the alkyl groups are forced closer together. Steric crowding leads to an increase in energy, so we would expect the presence of bulky groups to increase the energy of the product (cyanohydrin) to a greater extent than that of the reactant (ketone). This energy change relative to that of a simple ketone, acetone, is shown in Figure 5.2. Clearly, with bulky substituents $\Delta G^{\ominus}$ will be a less negative quantity and may even be positive. We can therefore identify a **steric effect** which may influence the position of equilibrium.

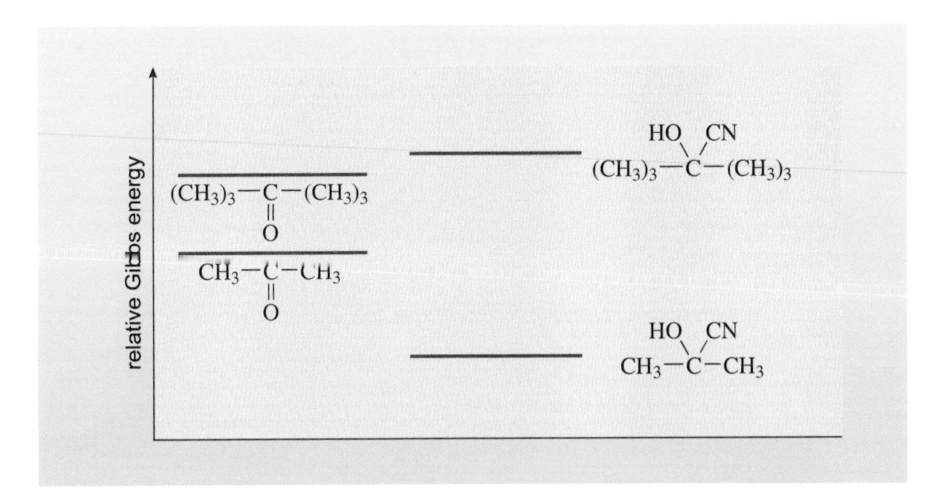

Figure 5.2 Relative variation in the energy of reactants and products in cyanohydrin formation.

Activity 5.1

Load the files dimethylcyanohydrin and dibutylcyanohydrin into Discovery Studio so that the 3D windows can be viewed next to each other. (The molecules files are available from Unit 3 resources on the module website.) Measure the C–C–C bond angle around the central carbon of the cyanohydrin. Measure the closest hydrogen–hydrogen interatomic distances between hydrogen atoms on groups on either side of the cyanohydrin central carbon.

Answer

The central C–C–C bond angle of the dibutyl cyanohydrin is expanded to about 120° whereas it is 110° in the dimethyl cyanohydrin. In the dimethyl cyanohydrin the closest hydrogen atoms are about 2.5 Å apart, whereas in the dibutyl cyanohydrin they are forced to be about 2.0 Å apart. The wider angle and the closer hydrogen atoms of the dibutyl cyanohydrin are a result of the steric crowding that increases the energy of the product relative to the reactants.

This steric effect will also influence the rate of a reaction. Table 5.1 shows the relative rates of S_N2 reactions of alkyl halides (Equation 5.3).

$$Nu^- + R^1R^2R^3C{-}X \longrightarrow Nu{-}CR^1R^2R^3 + X^- \quad (5.3)$$

Table 5.1 Relative rates of S_N2 reactions of alkyl halides.

Alkyl halide	Relative rate of reaction
$CH_3{-}X$	3000 000
$CH_3CH_2{-}X$	100 000
$CH_3CH_2CH_2{-}X$	40 000
$(CH_3)_2CHCH_2{-}X$	2 500
$(CH_3)_3CCH_2{-}X$	1
$(CH_3)_3C{-}X$	~0

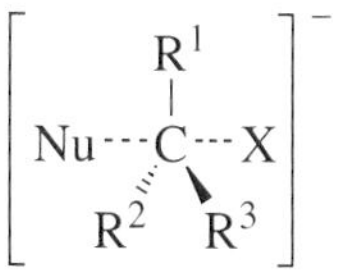

The attacking nucleophile *must* approach the substrate from the opposite side to the leaving group and therefore the ease of approach will depend upon the size of the groups R^1, R^2 and R^3. The transition state for this reaction, **5.7**, shows the central carbon to be very crowded, and as the attached groups get bulkier so the energy of the transition state increases.

$$\left[Nu \cdots C(R^1)(R^2)(R^3) \cdots X \right]^-$$

5.7

- ■ Increasing the bulk of the R groups also increases the energy of the *reactants,* so why does the rate decrease?

- □ Because the transition state is the *more* crowded, bulky groups will increase its energy to a *greater extent* than that of the reactants such that the activation energy increases.

So when R^1, R^2 and R^3 are methyl groups, the reaction goes much more slowly than when they are hydrogen atoms.

Table 5.2 shows the rates of S_N1 hydrolysis of a range of tertiary alkyl chlorides (Equation 5.4).

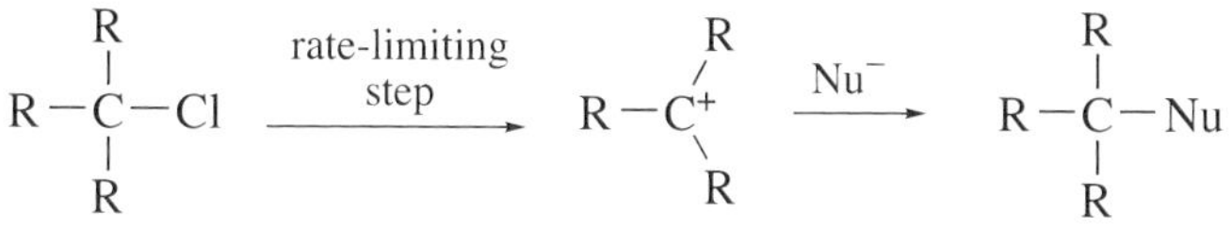

$$R_3C{-}Cl \xrightarrow[\text{step}]{\text{rate-limiting}} \underset{\textbf{5.8}}{R_3C^+} \xrightarrow{Nu^-} R_3C{-}Nu \qquad (5.4)$$

Table 5.2 Relative rates of hydrolysis of tertiary alkyl chlorides at 25 °C in 80% aqueous ethanol.

Alkyl halide	Relative rate of reaction
$Me_3C{-}Cl$	1.0
$Me_2EtC{-}Cl$	1.7
$MeEt_2C{-}Cl$	2.6
$Et_3C{-}Cl$	3.0
$Me_2(Pr^i)C{-}Cl$	0.9
$Me(Pr^i)_2C{-}Cl$	13.6

As shown in Table 5.2, replacing the methyl (Me) groups by ethyl (Et) groups increases the rate a little, and this reflects the slightly larger inductive stabilisation of the carbocation **5.8** by ethyl groups.

The introduction of one isopropyl group (Pr^i) also has little effect, but a *second* isopropyl group increases the rate considerably.

■ How would you explain this drastic change in terms of the larger steric effects of the isopropyl group?

□ The first step of the reaction is rate-limiting, and from the Hammond postulate the transition state for this step will resemble the intermediate. The central carbon atom in the alkyl chloride is sp^3 hybridised with an angle of 109° 28′ but the carbocation **5.8** is planar and sp^2 hybridised with an angle of 120°. In this case the starting material is more crowded than the transition state, so increasing the bulk of the substituent R groups will increase the energy of the alkyl chloride *more* than that of the carbocation. So, bulkier groups lead to *smaller* activation energies for S_N1 reactions, as shown in Figure 5.3. In this case the relief of steric strain in the first step leads to **steric acceleration** of the reaction rather than **steric hindrance**.

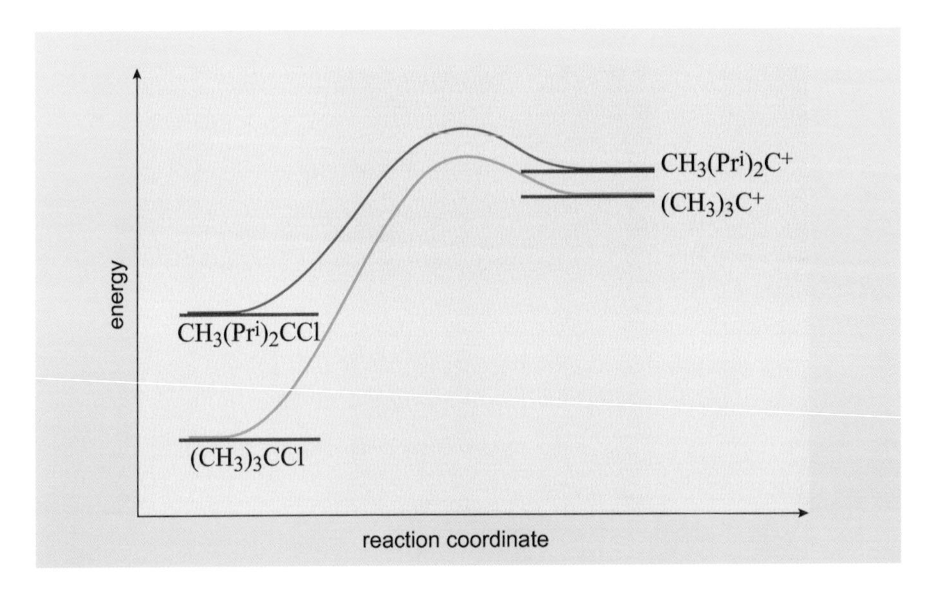

Figure 5.3 Relative variation in the energy of reactants, transition states and intermediates in S_N1 hydrolysis.

5.2 Deformation of bond lengths and bond angles

In order to achieve the correct stereochemistry for a reaction, bond angles and bond lengths are sometimes deformed. As with steric effects, a price has to be paid to accomplish this, again leading to high-energy species. Calculations and experiments show that deviations from normal bond lengths are a particularly 'expensive' way for a molecule to deform: the energy required rises steeply with bond shortening (Figure 5.4). However, deformations that occur through changes in bond angle are much easier to accommodate, as demonstrated by the existence of the (albeit very reactive) compound cyclopropane (**5.9**) and even cyclopropene (**5.10**) (explosive at room temperature!). Chemists refer to deformation of bond angle as **angle strain**.

CH_2 60° (109° preferred; angle strain 49°)
H_2C—CH_2
5.9

CH_2 60° (120° preferred; angle strain 60°)
HC=CH
5.10

Let's now examine how such deformations can affect equilibria, again using cyanohydrin formation as our example. The equilibrium constants for cyanohydrin formation for a range of cyclic ketones are given in Table 5.3.

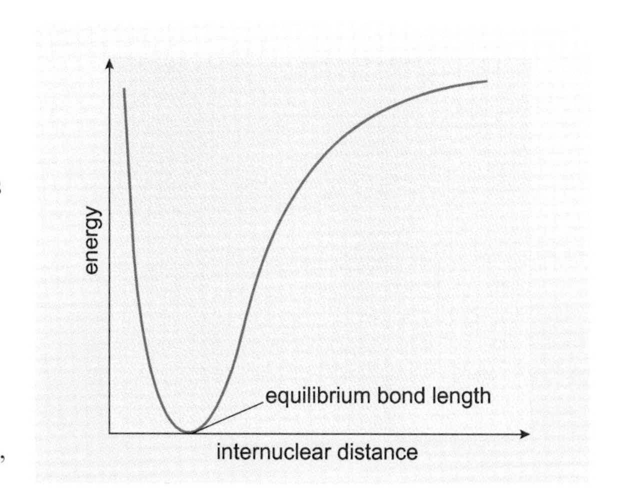

Figure 5.4 A normal energy/bond length profile.

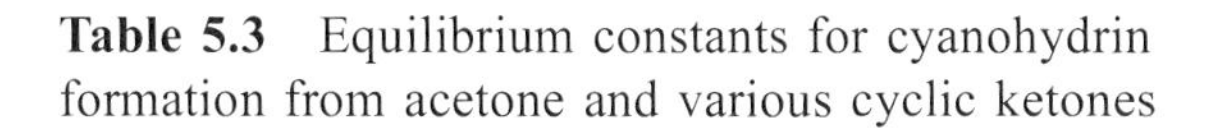

Table 5.3 Equilibrium constants for cyanohydrin formation from acetone and various cyclic ketones

Ketone	K/mol^{-1} dm^3
CH_3—C(=O)—CH_3	30
cyclopropanone: C(=O) with H_2C—CH_2	7104
cyclobutanone: H_2C—C(=O), H_2C—CH_2	100
cyclopentanone: C(=O), H_2C, CH_2, H_2C—CH_2	50

Why do you think that cyanohydrin formation is much more favoured for cyclopropanone (Equation 5.5) than for acetone?

$$(H_2C)_2C{=}O + HCN \rightleftharpoons (H_2C)_2C(OH)(CN) \qquad (5.5)$$

In cyclopropanone, the normal C–C–C bond angle (see **5.11**) is compressed from 120° to 60°, a massive strain of 60° as a result, the internal energy of the molecule is higher than expected. When the trigonal carbon becomes tetrahedral on cyanohydrin formation, the natural angle drops to 109° 28′ so the strain drops to 109° 28′ – 60°, that is 49° 28′. Obviously there is still considerable strain but equally there has been a considerable **relief of strain**. Consequently, $\Delta G^{\ominus}$ has a large negative value and the equilibrium greatly favours the cyanohydrin. Such relief of strain on cyanohydrin formation is not present with acetone so the equilibrium constant is correspondingly smaller.

5.11

With cyclobutanone, the C–C–C bond angle (**5.11**) is compressed from 120° to 90°, a strain of 30°. This strain drops on cyanohydrin formation to (109° 28′ – 90°), that is 19° 28′. Although the actual numerical value of the relief of strain in degrees is the same with cyclopropanone (60°– 49° 28′) as with cyclobutanone (30°– 19° 28′), in energetic terms the relief of strain is greater with cyclopropanone (Figure 5.5). This is because the increase in strain energy with angle deformation is much larger in very strained systems. So the relief of strain leads to a larger equilibrium constant for cyclopropanone than for cyclobutanone.

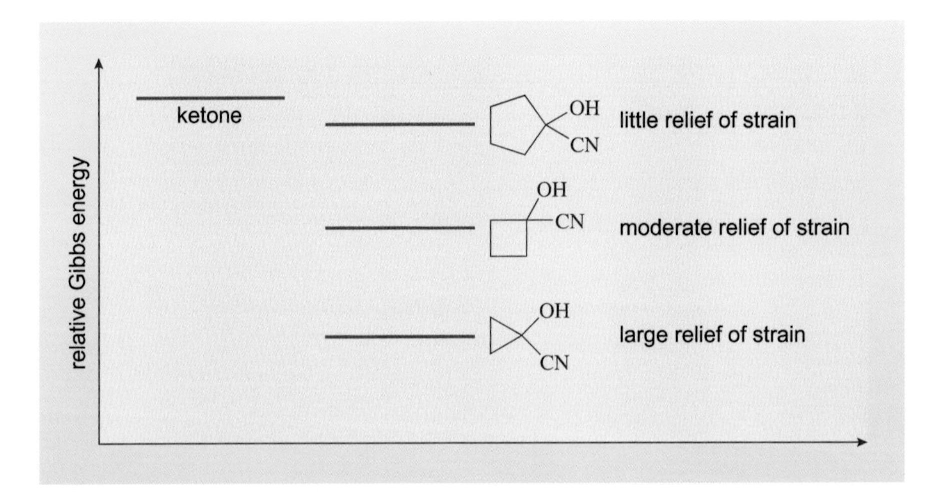

Figure 5.5 The relief of angle strain relative to the ketone on cyanohydrin formation.

■ Table 5.3 shows that *K* for cyclopentanone cyanohydrin/cyclopentanone is 50, i.e. about half the value for the cyclobutanone reaction. Is this to be expected?

□ Yes. If we assumed that the cyclopentanone ring were planar then the bond angles would be 108° and the ketone would be strained to the extent of 120° – 108° = 12°. The cyanohydrin would be strained only to the extent 109° 28′ – 108° = 1° 28′. The difference, 12° – 1° 28′ = 10° 32′, remains the same as with cyclopropanone cyanohydrin/cyclopropanone and cyclobutanone cyanohydrin/cyclobutanone but the relief of strain involved in such small variations from the normal would be considerably smaller. The equilibrium would accordingly be slightly less favourable to the cyanohydrin (Figure 5.5). In fact, the cyclopentanone ring is not planar and the bond angle is even less distorted than indicated above.

So far we have considered only reactions in which the ring remains intact, but what about ring-opening reactions? Ring strain leads to an enhancement in the ease of ring-opening reactions with small rings. For example, the C–N bond in amines, such as triethylamine is not easily cleaved, but dilute aqueous mineral acid at room temperature is sufficient to cause the hydrolysis of the strained amine, aziridine (**5.12**). Clearly, relief of ring strain leads to a smaller activation energy.

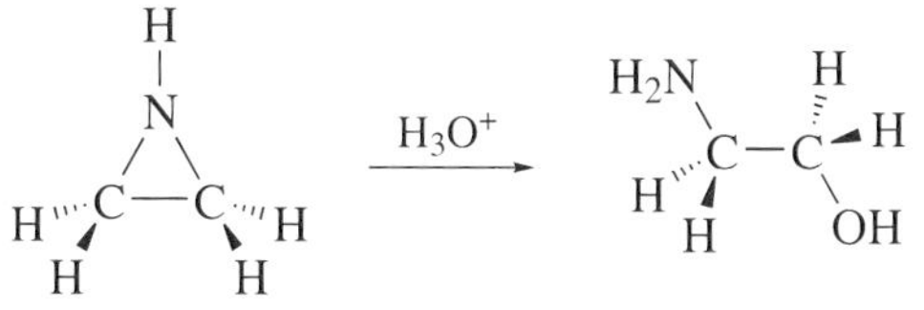

$$\xrightarrow{H_3O^+}$$

5.12 **5.13**

■ At the beginning of this section we wondered why the cyclic ether **5.14** (in Equation 5.1) underwent nucleophilic substitution, which is uncommon for ethers, and why only one side was attacked. Can you now explain these observations?

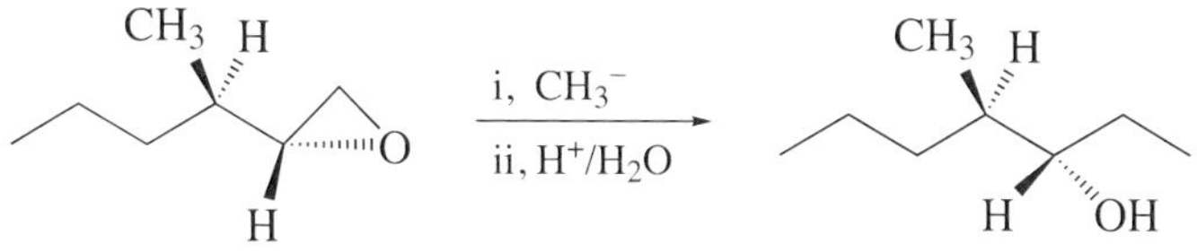

$$\xrightarrow[\text{ii}, H^+/H_2O]{\text{i}, CH_3^-} \qquad (5.1)$$

5.14 **5.1**

□ Ring strain leads to an enhancement of the rate of ring opening such that this ether readily undergoes substitution. Attack at the ether occurs at the least hindered (i.e. less substituted) side.

Aziridines and epoxides are used extensively in synthesis to form 1,2-difunctional compounds such as **5.13**. This is primarily because ring strain leads to facile ring-opening reactions. As you might expect ring strain plays an important role in ring-forming reactions, and this topic will be fully developed later in this module.

Cyclic ring systems are often used in drug backbones either because of their reactivity, if they are small rings, or because they lead to specific arrangements of functional groups that match an active site. For small rings the drug designer has to make sure that despite their reactivity they have a sufficiently long lifetime in the body to reach their target in reasonable doses. There is also a challenge for the synthetic chemist in constructing often very strained molecules.

■ Penicillins, **5.15**, and cephalosporins, **5.16**, both contain a four-membered ring made up of an amide group. What problems would the pharmaceutical chemist face in designing a drug based on these structures for oral administration?

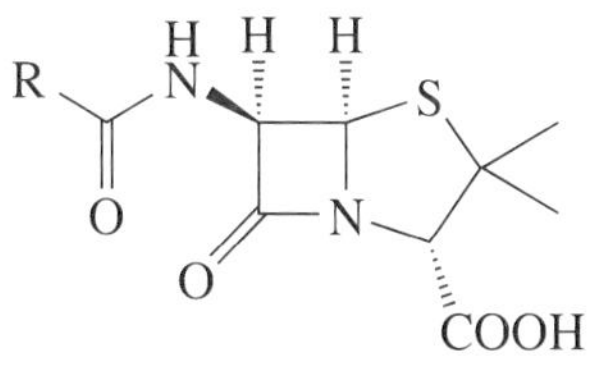

5.15 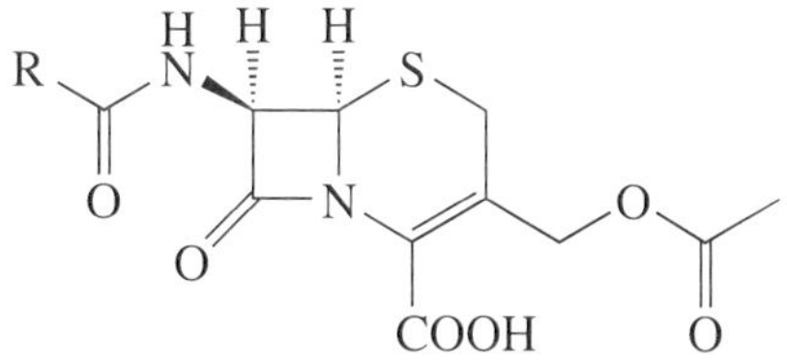 **5.16**

- The four-membered rings containing the amide are known as β-lactams. The strain in the ring means the amide bond undergoes hydrolysis readily, catalysed by acids and bases and metal ions. The ring-opened products are not active. Thus the pharmaceutical chemist needs to alter their structure by varying the substituent groups so that they are not hydrolysed in the stomach before they can be absorbed and transported round the body.

Small ring compounds, such as epoxides, are also produced in the body. A redox enzyme called cytochrome P450 can oxidise alkenes and aromatics to give epoxides. As a result of their activity, these epoxides are good alkylating agents reacting with nucleophilic groups in the body, such as proteins and DNA, and leading to toxicity. As usual, an enzyme, epoxide hydrolase, comes to the rescue converting the epoxide into a diol.

cytochrome P450

epoxide hydrolase

cytochrome P450

epoxide hydrolase

Study note

Before moving on to the next unit, you should produce your own summary of this section and then compare it with ours. Go to Unit 3 summaries in Unit 3 resources.

1 Enzyme kinetics

In the last two units we have looked at the electronic and steric effects present in small molecules. This will be important in helping us in Units 6 to 9 to understand why reactions give particular products when we synthesise specific drug targets. They explain the reactivity and selectivity observed in synthetic transformations. However, in this unit we return to the topic of drug design, where what we have learnt will help us quantify the activity of possible drug targets and thus help us in the selection of specific candidates to take forward for laboratory and large-scale synthesis.

We start by examining the rate of enzyme reactions and how drugs can affect the rate at which transformations occur in the body. We then look at the equilibrium involved in drug binding, again quantifying the influence of drug action. Finally, we examine what happens to a drug in the body once it is administered, its absorption, distribution, metabolism and elimination (ADME), a field of study known as pharmacokinetics.

The next few sections contain quite a lot of mathematics – mainly the rearrangement of equations and the interpretations of graphs. We have tried to take you through the process slowly, but some of you may find it quite challenging. If you do, don't give up, there is a summary at the end of each section that highlights the key take-home messages.

1.1 Why are enzymes important?

As we have seen earlier, the majority of drug targets are proteins and many of these are enzymes. Therefore, it follows quite naturally that, in order to understand the interactions between drugs and enzyme targets, we need to know how to characterise enzymes when they are functioning normally, but also how a drug affects the behaviour of the enzyme and consequently causes a therapeutic effect. Let us briefly consider some metabolic enzymes by looking at the information in Table 1.1.

Table 1.1 A selection of metabolic enzymes demonstrating their widely different roles.

Enzyme	Role in humans	Substrate(s)	Product(s)
arginase	part of the urea cycle for the disposal of ammonia	L-arginine	L-ornithine + urea
alkaline phosphatase	removal of phosphate groups by hydrolysis (widespread activity)	generally $ROPO_3^{2-}$	generally ROH + HPO_3^{2-}
phenylalanine hydroxylase	converts phenylalanine into tyrosine	L-phenylalanine	L-tyrosine
galactose mutarotase	changes the stereochemistry of the sugar galactose	α-galactose	β-galactose
chymotrypsin	hydrolysis of proteins and peptides	amide linkages	short peptides and amino acids

From looking at the range of enzyme activity, we can soon see that enzymes are sometimes broad and sometimes very specific in the tasks that they do. It is also easy to understand what a key role they play in maintaining the chemical steady state that is so important to good health. Just one malfunctioning enzyme can cause an imbalance that may lead to a chronic illness or even death. If we look more closely at the role of phenylalanine hydroxylase, we can appreciate one way in which this can occur.

The amino acid phenylalanine is a widespread constituent of plant and animal protein and so a protein-rich diet will provide plenty of it. In normal individuals, phenylalanine is removed by conversion into tyrosine with phenylalanine hydroxylase as the catalyst, and tetrahydrobiopterin as a coenzyme (Figure 1.1).

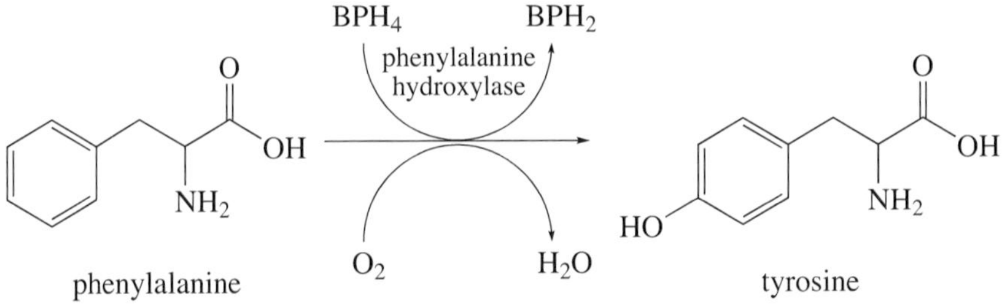

Figure 1.1 The role of phenylalanine hydroxylase in the conversion of phenylalanine into tyrosine. BPH_4 is tetrahydrobiopterin and BPH_2 is dihydrobiopterin.

The body has a large number of ways of utilising tyrosine, including its conversion into other biologically important molecules or breakdown to waste products (ultimately water, carbon dioxide and ammonia). In about 1 person in 10 000, however, a genetic condition results in greatly reduced levels of phenylalanine hydroxylase, which means that phenylalanine concentrations build to toxic levels. Some of the phenylalanine is metabolised to phenylpyruvic acid (**1.1**), and phenylacetic acid (**1.2**), the latter being responsible for a characteristic odour of the urine in affected individuals.

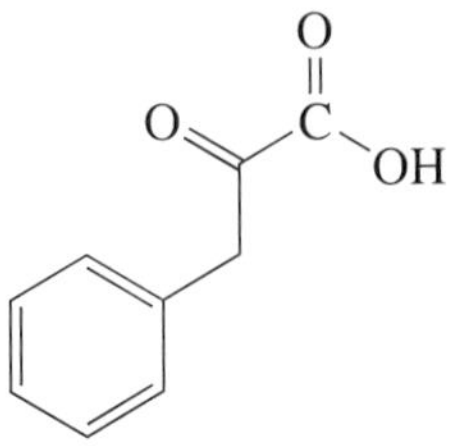

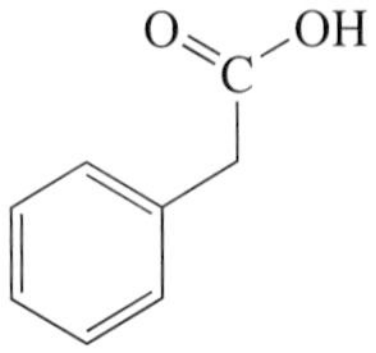

One long-term effect of these by-products can be seriously impaired mental development, so early diagnosis is essential. Detection of phenylketones in the patient's blood is one form of diagnosis (giving the disease its name of **phenylketonuria** or **PKU**), but in the study and monitoring of the disease it is also necessary to have an enzyme assay that measures the activity of phenylalanine hydroxylase. We will now look at the main ways in which enzymes, generally, have been characterised and increasingly understood as biological catalysts and how studying their reaction kinetics can give information that is important in drug development and treatment of disease.

1.2 Enzyme behaviour

As you saw in Unit 2 Section 2, conventional chemical catalysts (such as transition metal ions or added mineral acid) have been shown to work by lowering the activation energy of the rate-limiting step for the reaction(s) that they catalyse. If a strong acid such as sulfuric acid is added to an aqueous solution of an ester, then the rate of hydrolysis of that ester is dramatically increased. How does this work? The hydrolysis of most esters is extremely slow at pH 7, largely because water is a rather poor nucleophile and the rate of attack of water at the ester carbonyl group is very slow.

Scheme 1.1 shows how the addition of strong acid to the reaction medium can change this situation; here R′ is any alkyl or aryl group except a tertiary alkyl.

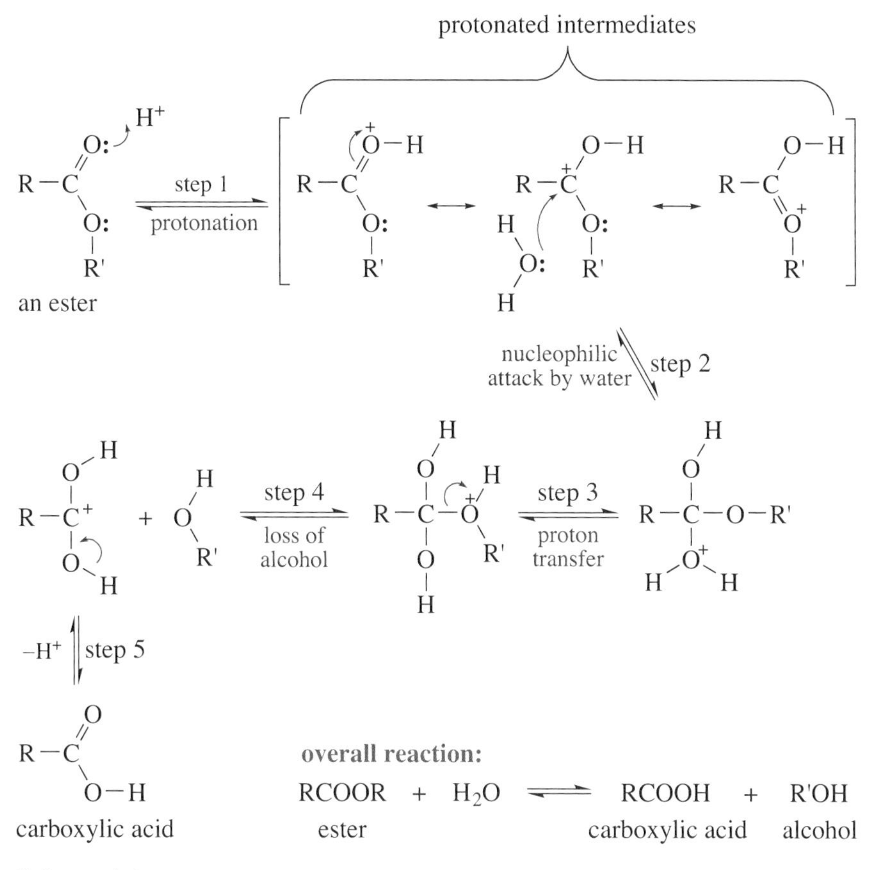

Scheme 1.1

- ■ Explain how strong acid catalyses the hydrolysis of esters based on the mechanism in Scheme 1.1.

- □ In Step 1 the ester is protonated at the carbonyl oxygen resulting in the formation of an intermediate that can be represented by a group of resonance structures, one of which shows a strongly electrophilic carbon atom. This can then react rapidly with the weakly nucleophilic water (Step 2), setting off a series of events that quickly lead to hydrolysis products (Steps 3–5). The one almost insurmountable step, namely the attack of water on the neutral ester molecule, has now been replaced by a number of intermediate steps, each of which has a relatively small activation energy. The net result is a much faster overall reaction in which equilibrium is quickly established.

Enzymes achieve a catalytic effect in much the same way, but with some important differences: they must work within a narrow pH and temperature range, which makes the challenge much greater. Despite this, enzymes are capable of an astonishing range and complexity of chemical reactions which are remarkable for their specificity, elegance and efficiency.

As we saw in Unit 2 Section 2, chymotrypsin is an enzyme that can cleave peptide bonds in proteins, by a hydrolysis reaction that is quite closely related to the hydrolysis of esters in Scheme 1.1. In fact, chymotrypsin can hydrolyse esters too, and a large part of the study of this enzyme has been conducted using relatively simple ester substrates, such as *para*-nitrophenyl esters, for example **1.3**, that have easily detectable hydrolysis products.

CH_3
C
O O
NO_2
1.3

■ You met Scheme 1.2 in Unit 2 Section 2; it shows how chymotrypsin achieves the hydrolysis of a peptide bond using the chemistry of specific amino acid side chains located at the active site. Without looking back to Unit 2, explain the action of chymotrypsin.

□ Chymotrypsin is a serine protease, which has a highly reactive serine residue as part of the catalytic triad that also includes histidine and aspartic acid residues.

Stages 1 → 2 The hydroxyl group of the active site serine attacks the carbonyl carbon of the peptide bond, forming a tetrahedral intermediate with a negatively charged, single-bonded oxygen (O^-, or oxyanion) and protonating the active site histidine.

Stages 2 → 3 The proton from the histidine is donated to the nitrogen atom of the bond to be broken, cleaving that bond and forming an intermediate with a fragment of peptide covalently bonded to the serine – the acyl-enzyme intermediate.

Stages 3 → 4 The C-terminal end of the substrate is released to be replaced by water.

Stages 4 → 5 The water molecule donates a proton to the histidine, effectively forming an OH^- group which attacks the acyl intermediate to form another tetrahedral intermediate.

Stages 5 → 6 The proton from the histidine is donated back to the serine, releasing the C-terminal end of the substrate as the second peptide product.

There are some obvious similarities with the proton-catalysed ester hydrolysis mechanism (of Scheme 1.1), but note how the enzyme generates a more potent nucleophile than water at serine 195. This avoids the need for an electrophilic carbocation, and the serine hydroxyl oxygen reacts directly with the peptide-carbonyl carbon atom.

Note also how the negative charge of the aspartate carboxylate anion is elegantly shuttled back and forth as required, in what is known as the 'charge relay' mechanism.

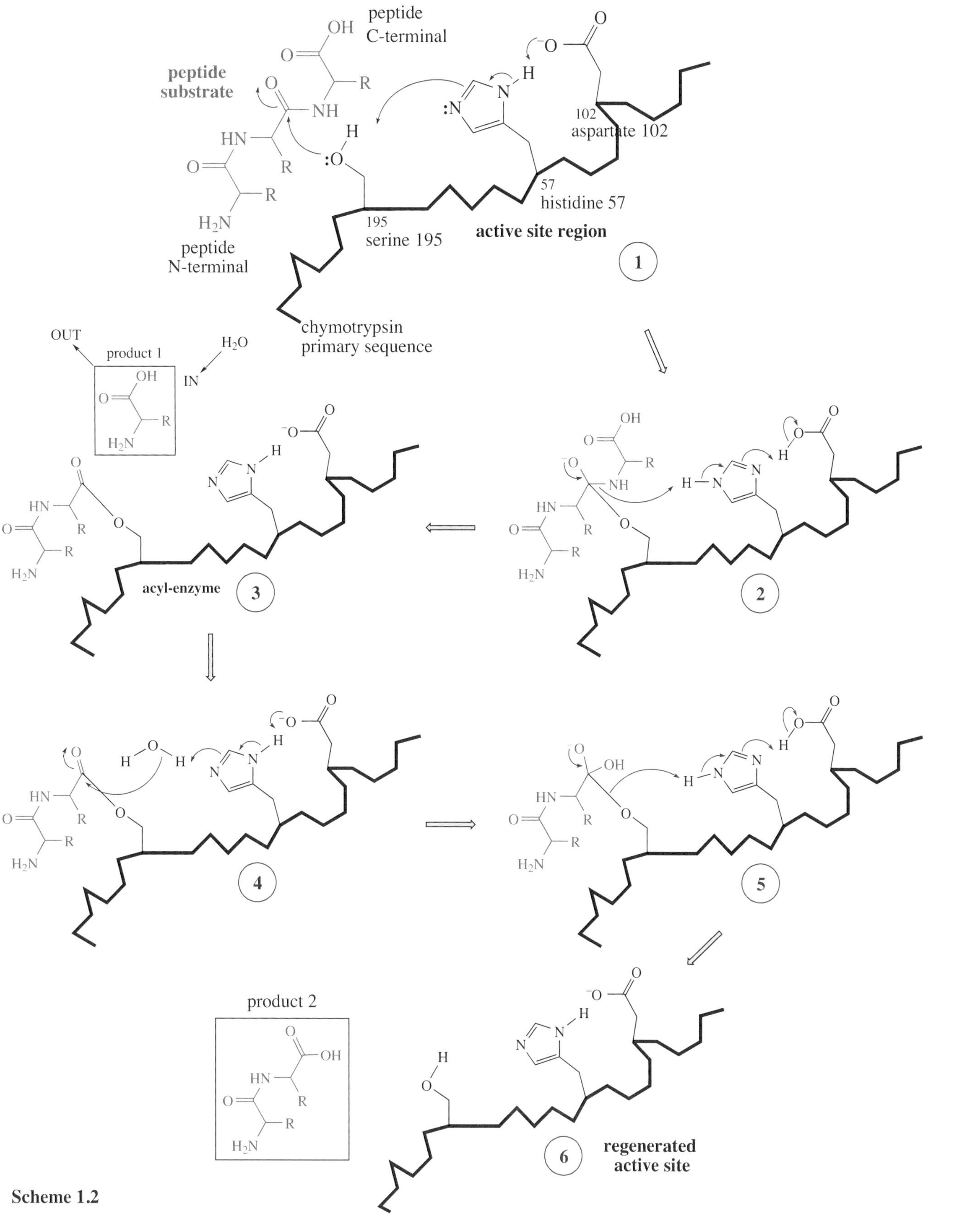

peptide C-terminal

peptide substrate

peptide N-terminal

aspartate 102

histidine 57

serine 195

active site region

chymotrypsin primary sequence

1

OUT

product 1

H_2O

IN

2

acyl-enzyme

3

4

5

product 2

regenerated active site

6

Scheme 1.2

From considering the example of chymotrypsin, it should come as no surprise that enzymes have much stricter requirements for their optimum operating conditions than traditional catalysts. These include, as we have seen in Unit 3 Section 1, the regular need for cofactors to provide atoms or fragments required in a reaction, but also an optimum range of pH, temperature and ionic strength necessary to prevent the protein from denaturing, and thereby losing its catalytic activity.

The optimum pH for chymotrypsin is pH 8 and the activity falls away quite sharply on either side of this, as we might expect from looking at the precise requirements for the protonation and deprotonation of catalytic groups during the mechanism of reaction.

1.3 Introduction to enzyme kinetics

1.3.1 The rate-limiting step

However complex the mechanism of action of a particular enzyme there will always be a slow, rate-limiting step which controls the maximum rate at which the enzyme can work. So in this sense we can simplify matters and consider the reaction rates of enzymes in relatively simple terms. For any chemical reaction, the rate J can be expressed as a **rate equation** with a particular order:

$$J = k[\mathrm{A}]^a[\mathrm{B}]^b[\mathrm{C}]^c$$

where k is the **rate constant** and [A], [B] and [C] are the concentrations of the individual reactants A, B and C. The **order of reaction** with respect to each individual reactant is given by a, b and c and the overall order for the reaction is $a + b + c$. So, for example, a reaction between reactants A and B to give products, with values of 1 for both a and b, will have an overall order of 2 (second order).

■ It is possible, by manipulating the experimental conditions, to make such a second-order reaction involving two reactants appear to be first order. How is this achieved?

□ This can be achieved by using a large excess of either A or B, so that its concentration scarcely changes while the other reactant is fully consumed. Thus, effectively the rate only changes as a result of one concentration term. Such conditions are known as **pseudo-first-order** conditions.

This can be demonstrated mathematically. For the reaction

$$\mathrm{A} + \mathrm{B} \rightarrow \text{products}$$

where the rate is given by

$$J = k[\mathrm{A}]^a[\mathrm{B}]^b \text{ (where } a = b = 1)$$

With a large excess of B for example, $[B]^1$ becomes an effective constant during the reaction such that $k[B]$ is also a constant and is termed the **pseudo-first-order rate constant** k' (where $k' = k[B]$).

So the rate equation can now be written as

$$J = k'[A]^1$$

or simply

$$J = k'[A]$$

So, by manipulation of conditions, a second-order chemical reaction will now behave as a first-order process in A, provided that those conditions are maintained. This idea is important in the study of enzyme kinetics for a number of reasons, which we will now explore.

We will start with the simplest of enzyme-catalysed reactions, involving only one substrate, S, which is converted into a product:

$$S \rightarrow \text{product}$$

This is catalysed by an enzyme E, and so we might expect an **experimental rate equation** of the form

$$J = k[E]^e[S]^s$$

Activity 1.1

In this activity you will examine the kinetics of the fumarase-catalysed conversion of malate (**1.4**) into fumarate (**1.5**), as shown in Equation 1.1.

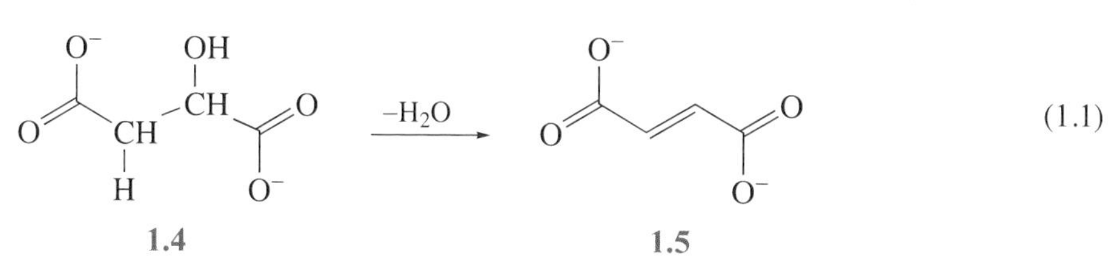

You will use the Graph plotter to analyse some initial rate data to determine the order with respect to the substrate and the enzyme. Detailed instructions are given in *Unit 5 Activities* available from Unit 5 resources on the module website.

Early experiments on enzyme-catalysed reactions agreed with the conclusions from Activity 1.1, that the rate was first order in the concentration of enzyme.

This is perhaps not surprising, since the more catalyst present the faster the reaction; so, we can simplify the rate equation:

$$J = k[\mathrm{E}][\mathrm{S}]^s$$

However, again as you saw in Activity 1.1, the variation of the rate with respect to the concentration of substrate is more complex. Figure 1.2 shows that as we increase the concentration of substrate the rate increases but eventually levels off; that is, we get to a point where the rate does not change no matter how much more substrate is added. Further analysis shows that the order with respect to the substrate s varies from one at low concentrations of substrate to zero at high concentrations of the substrate. So our rate equation can be written as

$$J = k[\mathrm{E}][\mathrm{S}]^s \quad (\text{where } s \text{ varies from } 1 \rightarrow 0)$$

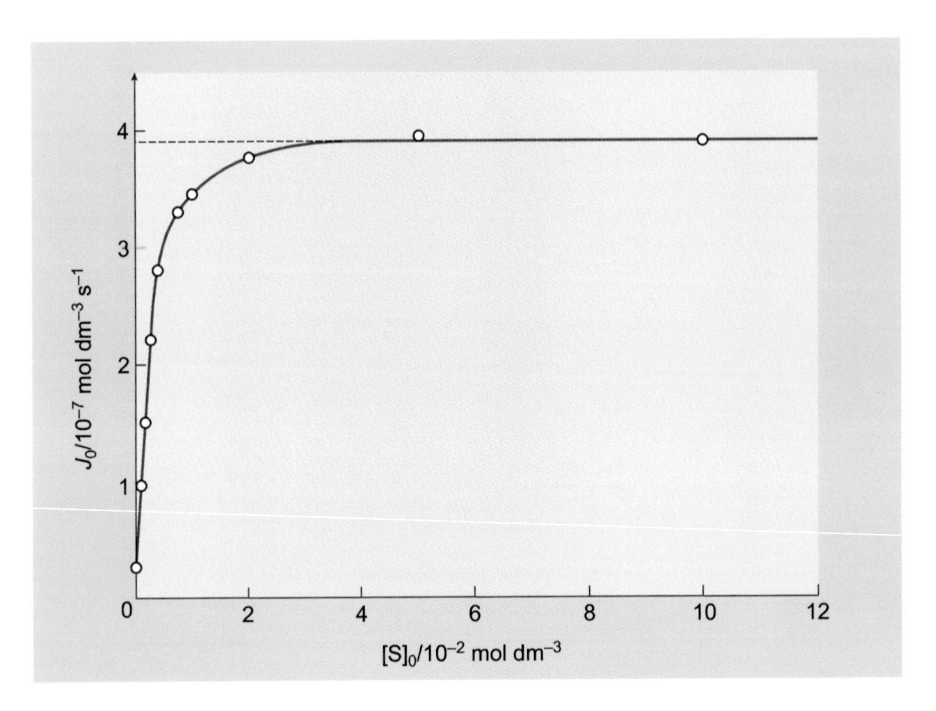

Figure 1.2 Variation in the rate of the enzyme-catalysed conversion of malate (**1.4**) into fumarate (**1.5**) (see Equation 1.1), at 293 K and pH 7; $[\mathrm{E}] = 1.6 \times 10^{-9}$ mol dm^{-3} throughout. (The dashed line indicates the J_{max} value.)

Early studies showed that for many enzyme-catalysed reactions, the change in rate on varying the substrate concentration, whilst keeping the enzyme concentration constant, could be modelled by the empirical equation

$$J = J_{\mathrm{max}} \frac{[\mathrm{S}]}{K_{\mathrm{M}} + [\mathrm{S}]} \qquad (1.2)$$

where $\boldsymbol{J_{\mathrm{max}}}$ is the maximum rate at high substrate concentration (see the dashed line in Figure 1.2) and $\boldsymbol{K_{\mathrm{M}}}$ is a constant known as the **Michaelis constant**. Notice the enzyme concentration does not appear in this equation because it is kept constant. Equation 1.2 is known as the **Michaelis–Menten equation** after its discoverers Leonor Michaelis and Maud Menten.

■ What will Equation 1.2 reduce to:

(i) at high substrate concentrations when [S] is very much bigger than K_M?

(ii) at low substrate concentrations when [S] is very much smaller than K_M?

□ (i) At high substrate concentrations, when [S] is very much bigger than K_M, [S] dominates the term (K_M + [S]), so the equation simplifies to

$$J = J_{max}\frac{[S]}{[S]} = J_{max} \quad (1.3)$$

So, not surprisingly, at high substrate concentrations the rate is a constant, the maximum value J_{max}. Since the rate does not depend upon the concentration of the substrate, the order with respect to the substrate is zero, as observed experimentally.

(ii) At low substrate concentrations, when [S] is very much smaller than K_M, K_M dominates the term (K_M + [S]), so the equation simplifies to

$$J = J_{max}\frac{[S]}{K_M} \quad (1.4)$$

As observed experimentally, under these conditions the rate is first order with respect to the substrate.

Such behaviour can be explained by a simple mechanism, as shown in Figure 1.3.

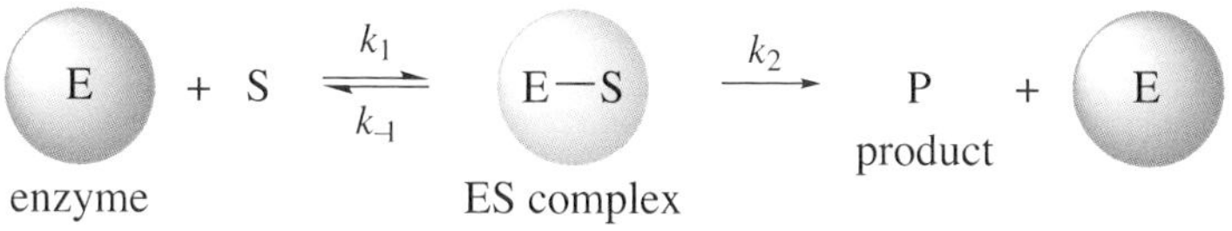

Figure 1.3 The Michaelis–Menten model for enzyme–substrate binding. (The substrate molecule(s) is specific to the enzyme.)

As you saw in Unit 2 Section 2, the substrate first binds with the enzyme in the active site to form an **enzyme–substrate complex** (ES complex). This ES complex then breaks down to give the product and the free enzyme back again. In fact, this second step almost always involves a number of reactions *in* the active site, as shown by the six stages in Scheme 1.2. However, under most conditions these separate steps don't influence the form of the experimental rate equation and the pathway can be simplified to that shown in Figure 1.3.

In most cases the second step is rate limiting and, thus, we can write the theoretical rate equation

$$J = k_2[\text{ES}] \tag{1.5}$$

So how do we explain the observed change in order with respect to the substrate on increasing the substrate concentration? The key is that since the enzyme is a catalyst it is always present in very small quantities. Let's examine what happens to the enzyme at high and low substrate concentrations.

1.3.2 Effect of substrate concentration on the concentration of ES

High substrate concentration

When the substrate concentration is large, the first equilibrium, between E, S and ES in Figure 1.3, is completely on the right-hand side and, thus, virtually all of the added enzyme exists as the ES complex and there is very little free enzyme. Thus, increasing the concentration of the substrate has no effect on the concentration of ES, which is effectively at its maximum, and the order with respect to the substrate is zero. Thus, if we replace the term for [ES] by the concentration of enzyme we added to the reaction $[\text{E}]_0$ (which is subsequently completely converted into [ES]) we obtain a rate equation that is first order in the initial concentration of enzyme, as expected, and **zeroth order** in substrate:

$$J = k_2[\text{E}]_0 \tag{1.6}$$

Effectively, as soon as we add the enzyme to the substrate virtually all of the enzyme is consumed in forming the ES complex. As soon as it reacts to give the product, the free enzyme formed is consumed by reacting with more substrate and so the concentration of ES remains constant at its maximum, $[\text{ES}] = [\text{E}]_0$.

Combining Equations 1.3 and 1.6 at high concentration of substrate we get

$$J = J_{\text{max}} = k_2[\text{E}]_0$$

Low substrate concentrations

When the concentration of the substrate is low, the first equilibrium in Figure 1.3 lies almost completely to the left-hand side and so the concentration of ES is small with respect to the concentration of added enzyme and the concentration of free enzyme [E] approximately equals that added at the beginning $[\text{E}]_0$.

In this case the first step is effectively at equilibrium – a **pre-equilibrium** exists between E, S and ES (made possible by the relatively slow transformation of ES into products);

$$E + S \rightleftharpoons ES$$

■ Write out an expression for the equilibrium constant for this reaction.

□ $K = \frac{[ES]}{[E][S]}$

■ Based on this pre-equilibrium equation for K, express [ES] in terms of K, [E] and [S].

□ $[ES] = K[E][S]$

So, substituting this expression for [ES] in Equation 1.5 gives us the theoretical rate equation when the concentration of substrate is relatively small:

$$J = k_2\, K[E]_0[S]$$

Under these conditions the reaction is first order in the enzyme concentration, as expected, and first order in the substrate concentration, as observed at low concentrations of substrate.

Notice that since $K = k_1/k_{-1}$ we can write

$$J = \frac{k_1 k_2}{k_{-1}}[E]_0[S] \tag{1.7}$$

Thus, we can explain the kinetic behaviour of the two extreme cases of low and high substrate concentrations and the curvature in Figure 1.2 can be explained by the change in position of the first equilibrium in Figure 1.3 from being completely on the left-hand side to completely on the right-hand side.

■ How would you expect the position of the equilibrium to change on increasing the substrate concentration?

□ From **Le Chatelier's principle**, increasing the concentration of one of the reactants in an equilibrium has the effect of shifting the equilibrium from the left-hand side to the right-hand side.

Despite this being a simple model, this turns out to be a very good one that holds true for the vast majority of enzymes and only breaks down when the substrate is almost exhausted. For this reason it is important to measure rates early on, before too much substrate has been consumed and the approximation starts to break down. This is why the data we analysed in Activity 1.1 involved *initial rates*.

Comparison of Equation 1.7 and Equation 1.4, which both apply at low substrate concentrations, shows that

$$J_{\max}\frac{[S]}{K_{\mathrm{M}}} = \frac{k_1k_2}{k_{-1}}[\mathrm{E}]_0[\mathrm{S}]$$

Rearranging this equation and substituting $k_2[\mathrm{E}]_0$ for $J_{\max}$ (don't worry, you don't need to do this) shows that

$$K_{\mathrm{M}} = \frac{k_{-1}}{k_1}$$

These equations tell us that $J_{\max}$ provides information on the rate of the second (rate-determining) step k_2 and K_{M} gives information on how well the substrate binds with the enzyme.

■ Will a large value of K_{M} correspond to a large affinity of the substrate for the enzyme or a small affinity?

□ K, the equilibrium constant for the binding of E and S in the first step, is given by k_1/k_{-1} and so K_{M} is the inverse of this; hence, large values of K_{M} correspond to a low affinity of the substrate for the enzyme.

You should note that K_{M} is equal to k_{-1}/k_1 only when the second step in Figure 1.3 is rate limiting; this is not always the case, and in such circumstances (i.e. when the second step is not rate limiting) K_{M} is given by $(k_{-1} + k_2)/k_1$. However, unless you are told otherwise, you should assume that the second step is rate limiting.

1.3.3 Calculating the $J_{\max}$ and K_{M}

Activity 1.2

In this activity you will start to look at ways in which $J_{\max}$ and K_{M} can be calculated. Detailed instructions are given in *Unit 5 Activities*.

As you saw in Activity 1.2, once standard conditions for temperature, pH and other factors have been established, you can measure the initial rate J for ever-increasing concentrations of substrate (at constant enzyme concentration), and what you observe is a 'topping out' of the observed rate. You can then measure $J_{\max}$ from the graph and K_{M} from the substrate concentration when $J = \frac{1}{2}J_{\max}$.

In practice there are real problems in trying to estimate $J_{\max}$ from experimental data. It is hard to extrapolate the data to get an accurate $J_{\max}$. Often, other factors, such as substrate inhibition of the rate, occur at large substrate concentrations, so an underestimate usually is made. A solution to this problem can be found by rearranging Equation 1.2 so that it gives the equation of a straight line. This leads to

$$\frac{1}{J} = \frac{K_{\mathrm{M}} + [\mathrm{S}]}{J_{\max}[\mathrm{S}]} = \frac{1}{J_{\max}} + \frac{K_{\mathrm{M}}}{J_{\max}[\mathrm{S}]} \qquad (1.8)$$

where a plot of $1/J$ against $1/[\mathrm{S}]$ gives a straight line with a y-axis intercept of $1/J_{max}$ and a gradient of K_M/J_{max}. Such a plot is called a **Lineweaver–Burk plot**, from which J_{max} and K_M can be determined with more confidence.

Activity 1.3

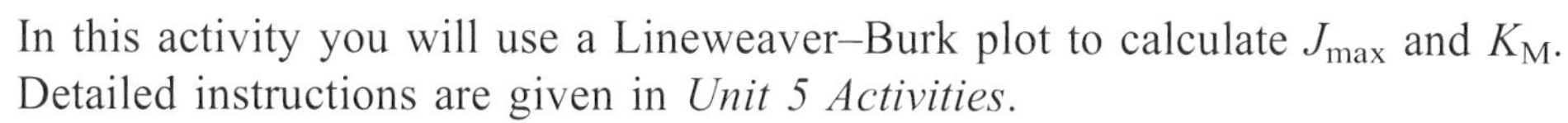

In this activity you will use a Lineweaver–Burk plot to calculate J_{max} and K_M. Detailed instructions are given in *Unit 5 Activities*.

All this reassures us that the Lineweaver–Burk plot is a robust tool for obtaining accurate estimates of the enzyme parameters of interest. It does, however, have one drawback, in that the gradient of the line of best fit in Figure 1.4 relies most heavily on the data points of lowest [S] and J, where we know our approximations are the least valid and where our accuracy of measurement is poorest.

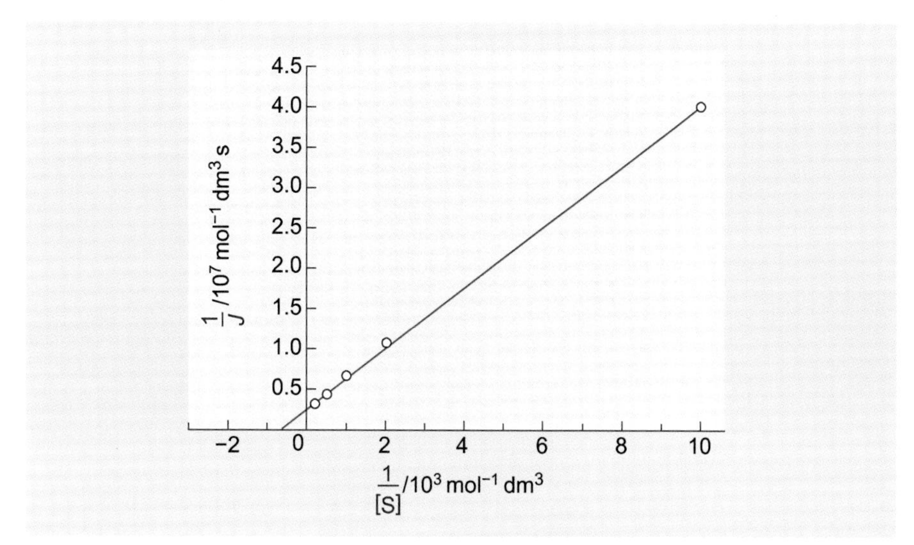

Figure 1.4 A Lineweaver–Burk plot of the data used in Activities 1.1–1.3.

There have been a number of ways suggested for overcoming this, but we won't consider them all here. Perhaps the most popular solution is the **Eadie–Hofstee plot** (Figure 1.5). Here, Equation 1.2 is rearranged to a different linear form:

$$J = J_{max} - K_M \frac{J}{[\mathrm{S}]} \tag{1.9}$$

This plot of J against $J/[\mathrm{S}]$ spreads the experimental error more evenly over all of the data range, making the line of best fit more reliable in gradient and intercept. Another advantage is that the y-intercept gives J_{max} directly as 3.85×10^{-7} mol dm^{-3} s^{-1}. The gradient represents the negative value of K_M, -1.51×10^{-3} mol dm^{-3} in this case. The Eadie–Hofstee plot is therefore recommended when interpreting experimental data that has rather more scatter than would be acceptable for a Lineweaver–Burk plot.

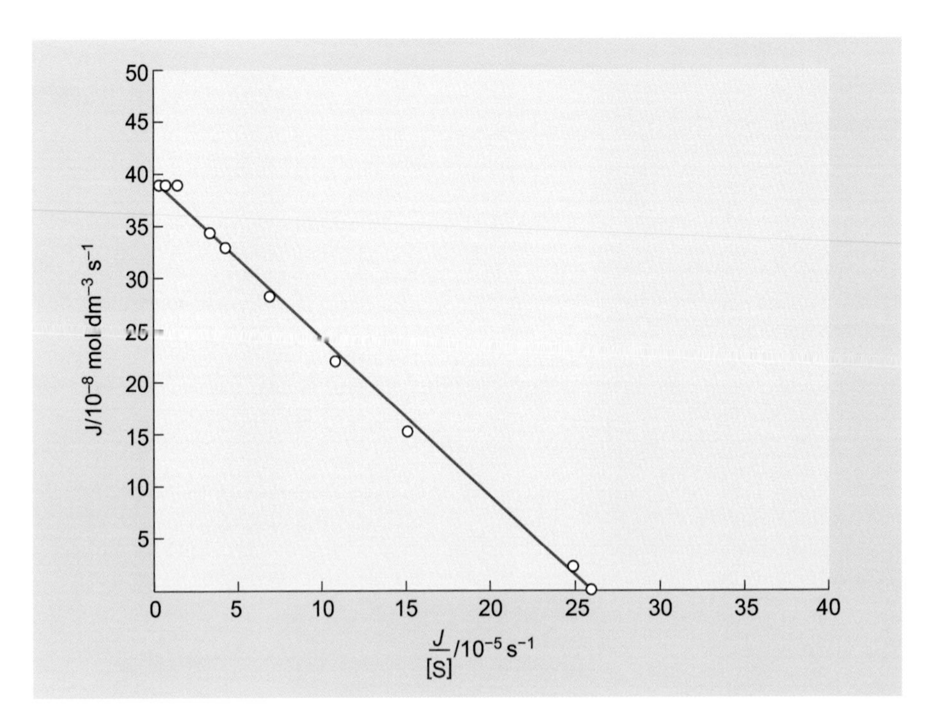

Figure 1.5 An Eadie–Hofstee plot of the data used in Activities 1.1–1.3.

1.4 Enzyme inhibition

We have seen how enzymes control vital biochemical processes and it is not unusual for drugs to act as enzyme inhibitors. Such inhibitors slow, or sometimes stop altogether, the reaction of an enzyme with its natural substrate. As we saw in Unit 3 Section 1, aspirin, for example, is an inhibitor of the enzyme cyclooxygenase, which is involved in a crucial step in the synthesis of prostaglandins. Some of the beneficial effects of aspirin, therefore, come from reduction in the quantities of synthesised prostaglandins with an associated reduction in inflammation in the patient. Evidence for drug action can be found in observed changes to the enzyme parameters J_{max} and K_M. Sometimes the changes observed in the enzyme inhibition are reversible. This can be demonstrated by either removing the inhibitor or adding more of the substrate. Sometimes these changes are permanent, meaning that new enzyme must be expressed before activity can be restored. Heavy metal ions, such as divalent mercury or lead, which are poisonous, can complex to amino groups on the side chains of amino acids causing significant conformational changes and subsequent loss of activity. This kind of inhibition is non-specific, whereas molecules designed to target active sites can be very specific indeed. Finding such inhibitors is a key feature of drug design.

When inhibitors are added to enzymes, it is important to understand which of three recognised types of inhibition are in operation: competitive, uncompetitive or mixed/non-competitive inhibition. We will look at each type of inhibition in turn.

1.4.1 Competitive inhibition

Figure 1.6 shows the effect of adding an inhibitor to a typical enzyme. As expected, the rate J is lower in the presence of an inhibitor for a given substrate concentration. However, if enough substrate is added it increases to the maximum value, which is the same as that observed in the absence of inhibitor (J_{max} is unchanged). In contrast, K_M has changed, and we can see this from the higher value of substrate concentration needed to reach $\frac{1}{2}J_{max}$. These are the hallmarks of **competitive inhibition**.

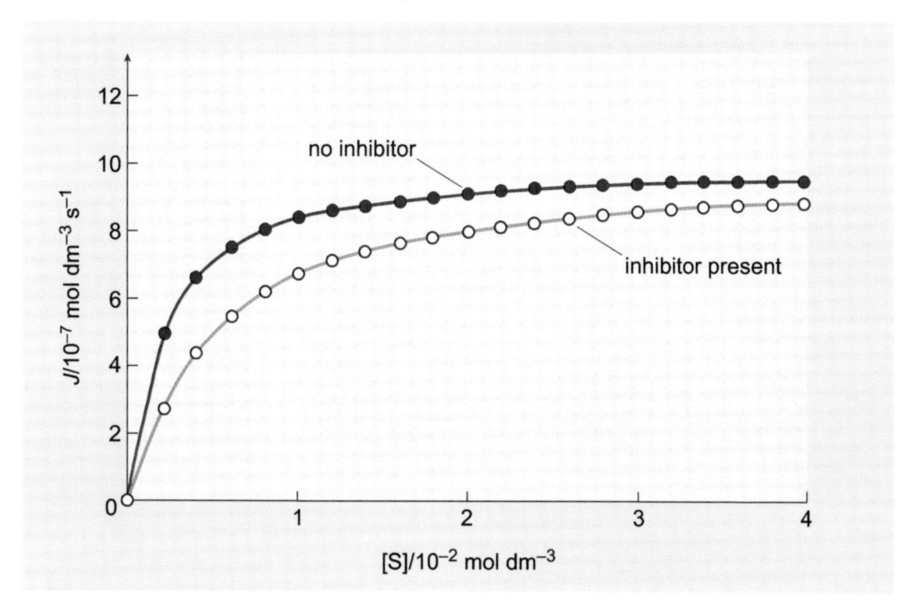

Figure 1.6 The effect of adding a competitive inhibitor to a typical enzyme reaction.

In order to put accurate values on these changes we can use a Lineweaver–Burk plot like the one shown in Figure 1.7.

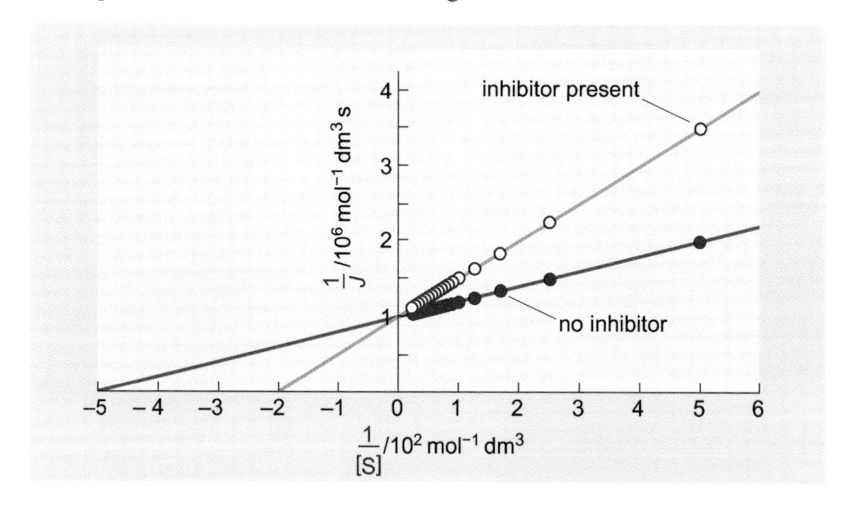

Figure 1.7 A Lineweaver–Burk plot for the data shown in Figure 1.6.

The y-intercepts clearly show us that J_{max} is the same in each experiment, but the gradient has increased with inhibitor present. Since this value represents K_M/J_{max}, we can calculate the new value of K_M, which will be larger. This value of K_M with inhibitor present is called the *apparent* K_M ($K_{M\ app}$). How do we interpret this new K_M? We need to refer to the accepted mechanism for competitive inhibition shown in Figure 1.8.

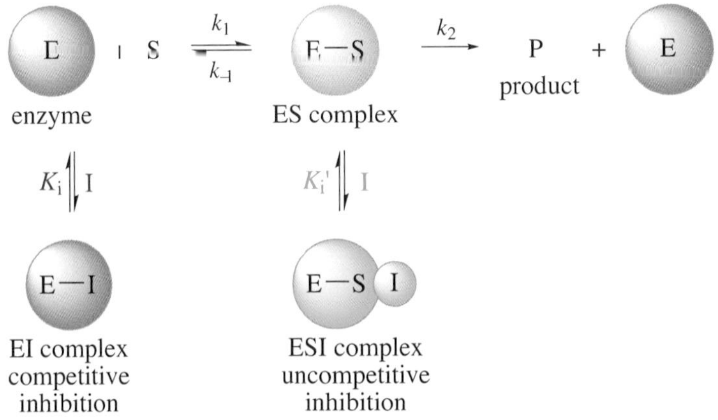

E + S $\underset{k_{-1}}{\overset{k_1}{\rightleftharpoons}}$ E—S $\xrightarrow{k_2}$ P + E

enzyme
ES complex
product

K_i I
K_i' I

E—I
E—S I

EI complex
competitive
inhibition

ESI complex
uncompetitive
inhibition

Figure 1.8 A model for the possible ways that an inhibitor can bind to an enzyme.

For the moment, ignore the green part of the scheme. Competitive inhibition is represented by the formation of an **enzyme–inhibitor** (EI) complex (red) in competition with the formation of an ES complex (grey). In other words, the inhibitor competes with the substrate for occupation of the active site, and the inhibitor removes active sites from circulation.

■ What effect will the presence of a competitive inhibitor have on the concentration of the ES complex and, thus, the rate of reaction compared with its concentration and rate in the absence of the inhibitor?

□ The presence of an inhibitor will mean that some of the enzyme will be tied up as the EI complex and so there is less enzyme to form the ES complex; so, the concentration of ES will be less and the rate of the reaction catalysed by the enzyme will be lower.

This will be true at lower substrate concentrations. However, if we add a large amount of substrate it will swamp the effect of the inhibitor so that virtually all of the added enzyme is in the form of the ES complex. Consequently, the derived J_{max} is the same in experiments with or without a competitive inhibitor present. However, because it took more substrate to counteract the effect of the inhibitor and reach J_{max}, K_M increases.

What we need to interpret $K_{M\ app}$ is a modified version of the Michaelis–Menten equation (Equation 1.2).

We will write this as

$$J = J_{max} \frac{[S]}{K_{M\ app} + [S]} \qquad (1.10)$$

where J_{max} and $K_{M\ app}$ can be calculated from the inverse plots as before.

- ■ We can define a variable α which is the ratio of $K_{M\ app}$ to K_M, i.e. $\alpha = K_{M\ app}/K_M$. Will α be greater or less than one?
- □ Because $K_{M\ app}$ is bigger than K_M, α is always greater than one.

It is helpful to think of α as a correction term for the enzyme molecules which are lost to the formation of the EI complex. In fact, the term α is given by

$$\alpha = \frac{K_{M\ app}}{K_M} = 1 + \frac{[I]}{K_i} \qquad (1.11)$$

where K_i is the dissociation constant for the EI complex in Figure 1.8:

$$EI \rightleftharpoons E + I$$

$$K_i = \frac{[E][I]}{[EI]}$$

As with K_M, the smaller the value of K_i, the better the binding.

- ■ How will α vary when the concentration of inhibitor is increased?
- □ As more inhibitor is added, [I] increases and so α increases. Looking at this another way, as more inhibitor is added so more substrate is needed to swamp the effect of the inhibitor and so $K_{M\ app}$ increases. This means that α, which equals $K_{M\ app}/K_M$, increases.

Although we don't have space to go through this, if we measure $K_{M\ app}$ at a particular inhibitor concentration we can calculate α from the ratio of $K_{M\ app}$ to K_M and thus determine K_i, since it will equal $[I]/(\alpha - 1)$ (from rearranging Equation 1.11).

Extremely potent competitive inhibitors are known where K_i has values that are expressed in *nanomolar* (10^{-9} mol dm^{-3}) concentrations. To indicate that the inhibitor is a competitive inhibitor, we can use the symbol K_{ic} which is generally reserved for the inhibition constants of competitive inhibitors.

Competitive inhibitors are very often structurally related to the substrate of the enzyme that they inhibit. Determination of K_i values for inhibitors informs drug developers about the potency of structural variants. For example, in pathogenic bacteria, enzymes utilise *p*-aminobenzoic acid (PABA, **1.6**) in the synthesis of folic acid. Bacteria need folic acid as a cofactor in order to grow and reproduce. Inhibition of the biosynthesis of folic acid will, therefore, arrest the bacterial development. Comparison of the natural substrate (PABA) with a competitive inhibitor (sulfanilamide, **1.7**) for the relevant enzyme (dihydropteroate synthase) helps us to appreciate this substrate–inhibitor relationship. A more modern variant (sulfamethoxazole, **1.8**) is also shown, which is commonly used to treat urinary tract infections.

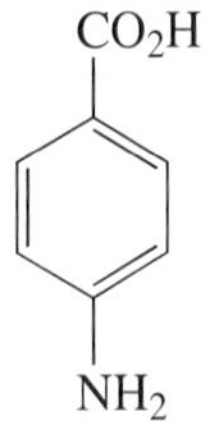

1.6 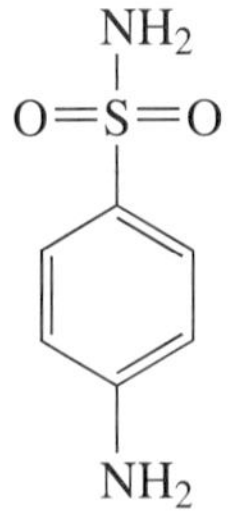 **1.7** 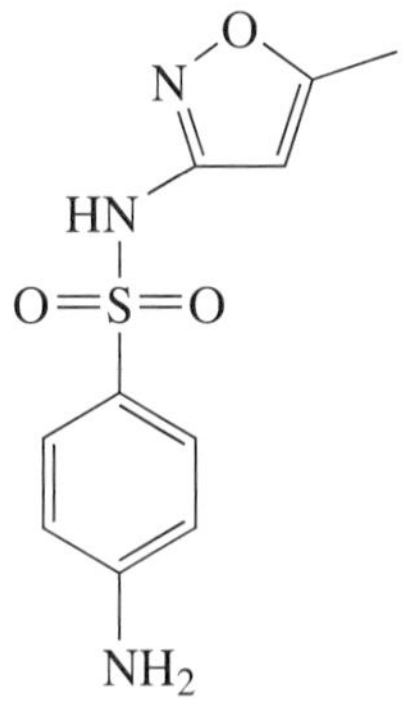 **1.8**

1.4.2 Uncompetitive inhibition

The possibility that an inhibitor may not bind directly to an enzyme's active site must also be considered. Instead, the inhibitor binds to a place remote from the active site, which has been exposed during the substrate binding – the inhibitor only binds to the ES complex, not to the free enzyme. This gives rise to the **enzyme–substrate–inhibitor (ESI) complex** in Figure 1.8, in green, which does not represent a pathway to product and, therefore, removes the ES complex from the system. (For this part of the discussion you need to ignore the red EI complex part of Figure 1.8.) The formation of the ESI complex is described as **uncompetitive inhibition** and is effectively the opposing scenario to competitive inhibition. In this case the derived values of K_M and J_{max} are both *different* in experiments with or without an uncompetitive inhibitor present. This can be explained in terms of the inhibitor, I, removing some ES from the equilibrium system (as ESI) and thereby decreasing the maximum possible concentration of ES. This in turn results in a reduction of J_{max} (remember that $J_{max} = k_2[ES]_{max}$ in Figure 1.8). There will also be a corresponding *decrease* in the value of K_M. This is because the formation of both ESI and ES appears to move the equilibrium further to the right, giving an apparently stronger binding of substrate. Again, we need a modified version of Equation 1.2, and this time the equation becomes

$$J = J_{max\ app} \frac{[S]}{K_{M\ app} + [S]} \tag{1.12}$$

In this case both $J_{max\ app}$ and $K_{M\ app}$ are less than J_{max} and K_M, respectively, determined in the absence of the inhibitor.

Thus, we define a variable β, where

$$\beta = \frac{J_{max}}{J_{max\ app}} \quad \text{and} \quad \beta = \frac{K_M}{K_{M\ app}}$$

- ■ Will β be greater or less than one?
- □ Because $J_{max\ app}$ and $K_{M\ app}$ are less than J_{max} and K_M, β is always greater than one.

As before, the term β is given by

$$\beta = 1 + \frac{[\mathrm{I}]}{K'_\mathrm{i}}$$

where K'_i is the uncompetitive dissociation constant of the ESI complex given in Figure 1.8:

$$\mathrm{ESI} \rightleftharpoons \mathrm{ES} + \mathrm{I}$$

$$K'_\mathrm{i} = \frac{[\mathrm{ES}][\mathrm{I}]}{[\mathrm{ESI}]}$$

Suppose we were to examine the kinetics of an enzyme-catalysed reaction in the absence and presence of an uncompetitive inhibitor, how would that affect the appearance of the results? This can be seen in Figure 1.9. The most striking difference is the large reduction in the apparent J_{max} in the presence of the enzyme inhibitor. We can use the Lineweaver–Burk plot (Figure 1.9b) to find both $K_{M\ app}$ and $J_{max\ app}$. The graph shows that the y-intercept ($1/J_{max}$) is greater in the presence of the inhibitor, leading to a smaller J_{max} (because it is the inverse). Since the slopes of the two lines are similar they have an equal value of K_M/J_{max}, and so any decrease in J_{max} must be matched by a similar decrease in K_M.

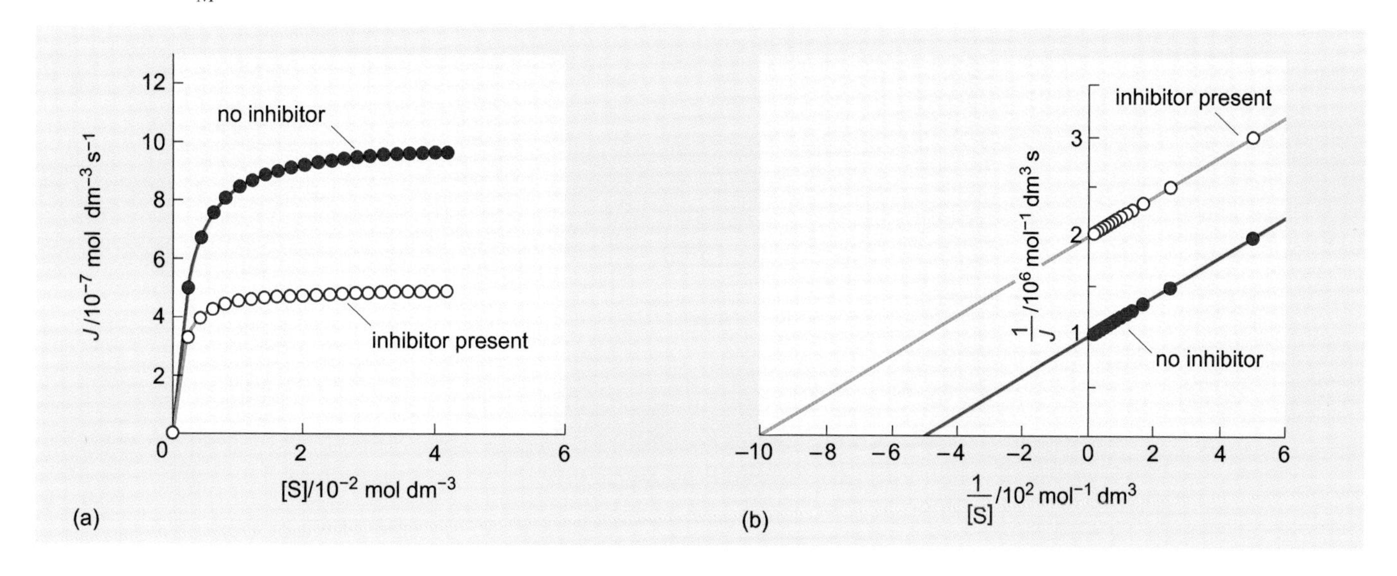

Figure 1.9 (a) The effects of adding an uncompetitive inhibitor. (b) A Lineweaver–Burk plot of the data in (a).

Based on the values for $K_{M\ app}$ and $J_{max\ app}$ we can again calculate the dissociation constant for uncompetitive binding (K'_i). $\boldsymbol{K_{iu}}$ is the symbol used for the inhibition constants of uncompetitive inhibitors. The dissociation constant K'_i has *low* values when it refers to a potent inhibitor, just as in the cases of K_M and K_{ic}. True cases of 'pure' uncompetitive inhibition are quite rare, though it is sometimes observed that substrate itself can cause inhibition by binding to another site as well as the active site. This usually occurs at high substrate concentrations and is attributed to the formation of ESS (instead of ESI) in Figure 1.8. Substrate inhibition is usually detected by a decrease in J (after a maximum) as [S] is increased.

1.4.3 Mixed and non-competitive inhibition

Frequently, inhibitors are able to compete effectively with the normal substrate for occupation of the active site, and also bind to the alternative site mentioned in Section 1.4.2. In such cases the inhibition observed is intermediate between competitive and uncompetitive, and is termed **mixed inhibition**. In order to understand mixed inhibition fully we must combine our two equations for competitive and uncompetitive inhibition, Equations 1.10 and 1.12, respectively. This gives

$$J = J_{max} \frac{[S]}{\alpha K_M + \beta [S]} \tag{1.13}$$

where

$$\alpha = 1 + \frac{[I]}{K_i} \quad \text{and} \quad \beta = 1 + \frac{[I]}{K'_i}$$

Notice there are two different inhibitor dissociation constants used here (look back at Figure 1.8):

- K_i, which refers to the equilibrium between EI and E, I:

  $$EI \rightleftharpoons E + I$$

- K'_i, which refers to the equilibrium between ESI and ES, I:

  $$ESI \rightleftharpoons ES + I$$

Figure 1.10 shows the data for an experiment where mixed inhibition is operating. The data is expressed as a Lineweaver–Burk plot, for experiments with and without the mixed inhibitor. We can see that the lines of best fit are neither parallel (as in uncompetitive inhibition) nor do they both cross at the y-axis at the same point (as in competitive inhibition). We clearly have a different kind of inhibition here, and one of the distinctive features of mixed inhibition is that the lines cross at a negative reciprocal substrate concentration value.

Although we will not go through the derivation, it is possible to determine values for α and β in Equation 1.13 from the slopes and intercepts of such graphs and thus determine values for K_i and K'_i.

In addition to the mixed inhibition described, a special case sometimes arises when the inhibitor is coincidentally able to bind equally well to both the active site and the neighbouring binding site (i.e. $K_i = K'_i$). This means that, now, $\alpha = \beta$ and the kinetic equation simplifies to just

$$J = J_{max\ app} \frac{[S]}{K_M + [S]} \tag{1.14}$$

where $J_{max\ app} = J_{max}/\beta$. This special case is termed **non-competitive inhibition**, since there is no discrimination between the bindings to two sites.

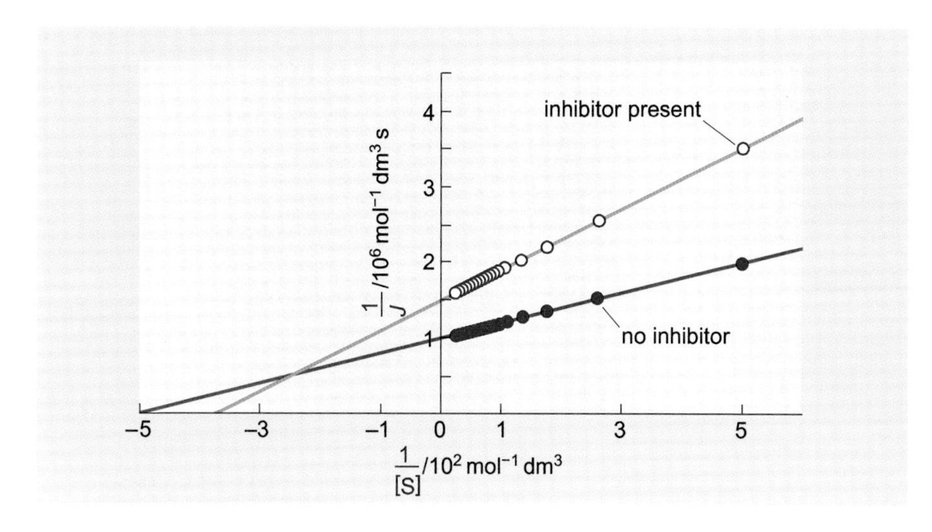

Figure 1.10 The effects of mixed inhibition.

Non-competitive inhibition is characterised by the inhibitor reducing J_{max} while leaving the apparent K_M unchanged, in contrast to mixed inhibition, where both J_{max} and K_M are affected by inhibitor.

1.5 Recognising different types of inhibition

Although we have now seen how the appropriate use of Lineweaver–Burk (and occasionally other types) of data plots can yield values of K_M, K_i, K'_i and J_{max}, we have confined ourselves to a comparison of behaviour with and without inhibitor, by using a single experiment for each. Real experimental data is usually less reliable than that used in our discussion, so it is good practice to repeat the rate measurements over a range of inhibitor concentrations and then repeat the experiment several times (typically three to six times) at different substrate concentrations. The data can then be presented as a **Dixon plot** (Figure 1.11), which is similar to a Lineweaver–Burk plot but displays reciprocal rate ($1/J$) against inhibitor concentration ([I] as distinct from 1/[S]).

The substrate concentration is then varied over a wide range, but it must never be allowed to fall low enough to compromise the initial rate measurements. The real benefit of a Dixon plot is that multiple lines of best fit will converge around points on the graph that allow the determination of important enzyme parameters, which in turn give clues to help determine the mechanisms by which the enzymes work and provide quantitative data on binding. The problem with just two lines is that they will cross at a point whether that point is correct or not. The Dixon plot is much more reliable, as it highlights any suspicious data sets and allows interpreters to use their own judgement about the exact location of intercepts and intersections.

An alternative plot is a plot of [S]/J against [I], again at several different substrate concentrations. We will call this a **Cornish-Bowden plot**, after the enzyme kineticist who introduced it (Figure 1.12).

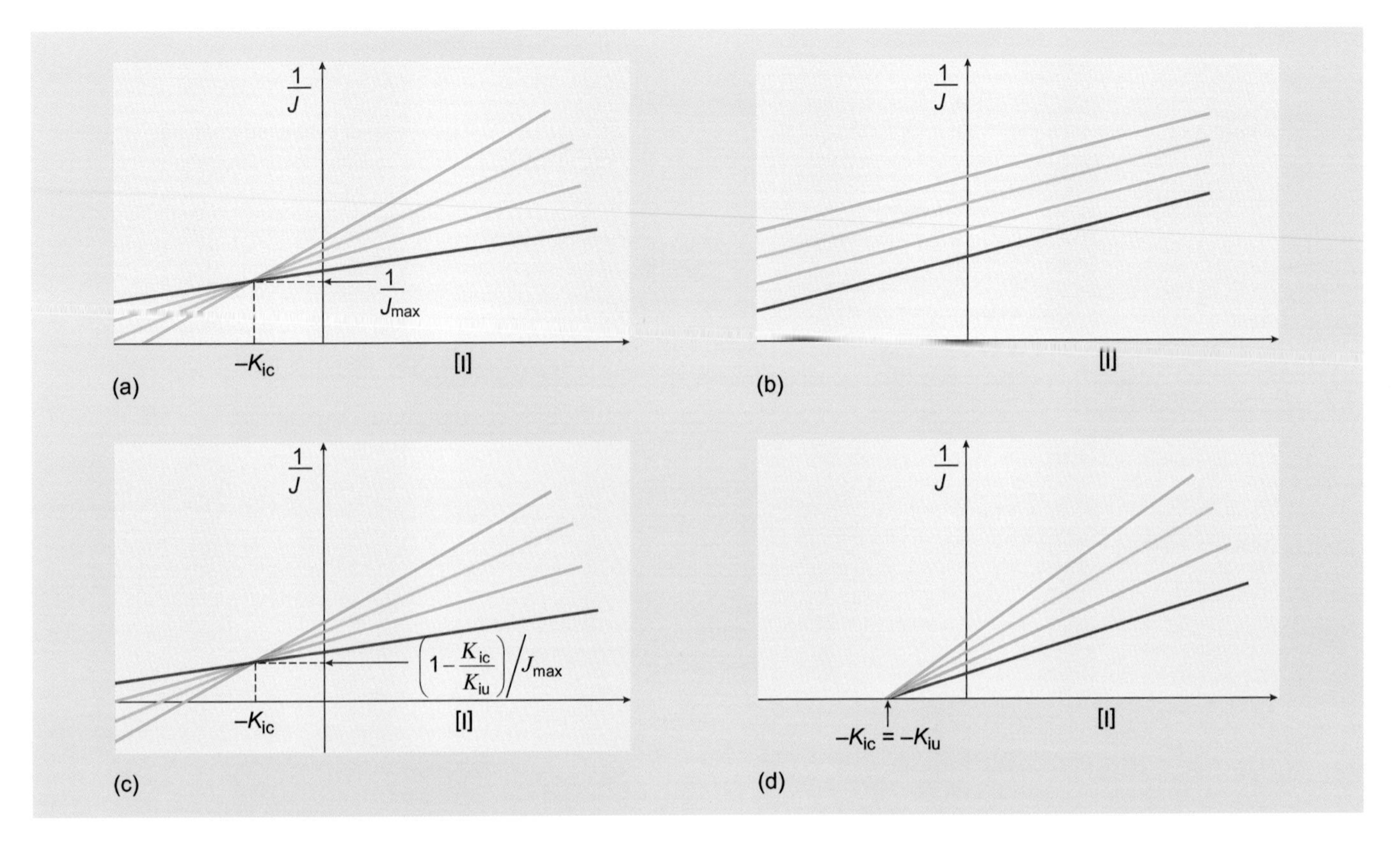

Figure 1.11 Dixon plots for the (a) competitive inhibition, (b) uncompetitive inhibition, (c) mixed and (d) non-competitive inhibition. (Remember, $K_i = K_{ic}$ and $K'_i = K_{iu}$.)

We will not analyse the mathematical relationships necessary to explain the reasoning behind Dixon and Cornish-Bowden plots, but they are a logical extension of our discussion in previous sections. Note how each line represents an experiment in varying the inhibitor concentration [I] at a given substrate concentration [S], and several different values of [S] must be chosen to obtain a convincing intersection or convergence on an axis. Together the two plot types are a powerful tool for evaluating the important enzyme parameters.

1.6 Summary of Section 1

- Just like all catalysts, the behaviour of enzymes can be analysed using kinetics.
- The rate equations for enzyme-catalysed reactions are usually first order with respect to the enzyme.
- The rate equations for enzyme-catalysed reactions are usually first order with respect to the substrate at low substrate concentrations but zeroth order with respect to the substrate at high substrate concentrations.
- Empirical analysis of enzyme kinetics leads to the Michaelis–Menten equation (at constant enzyme concentration, $J = J_{max}\,[S]/(K_M + [S])$, where

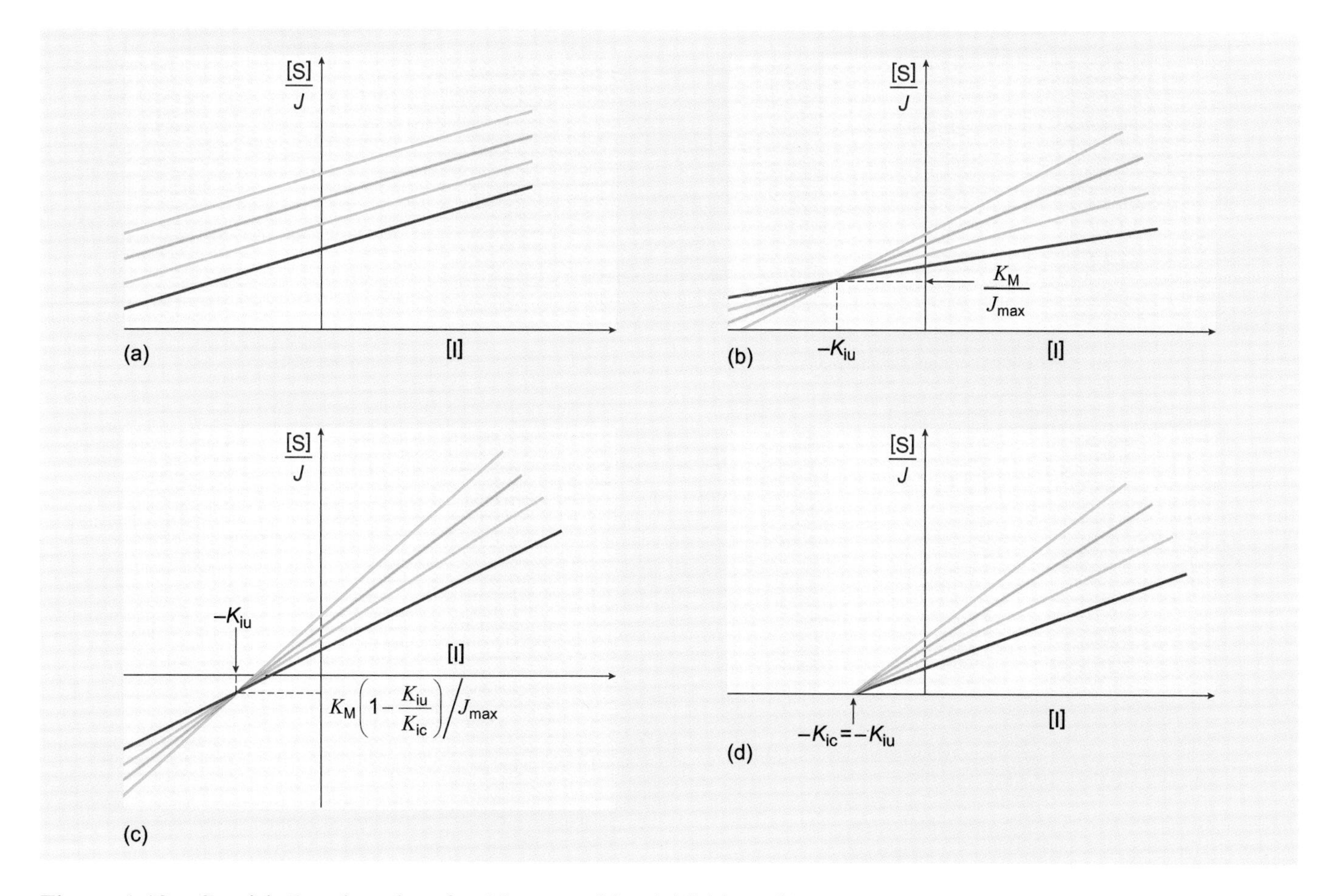

Figure 1.12 Cornish-Bowden plots for (a) competitive inhibition, (b) uncompetitive inhibition, (c) mixed and (d) non-competitive inhibition.

J_{max} is the maximum rate, obtained at high substrate concentration, and K_M is the Michaelis constant.

$J = k[E][S]^s$ (where s varies from 1 to 0 on increasing concentration of substrate).

- The kinetic behaviour corresponds to the simple mechanism shown in Figure 1.3, where $J_{max} = k_2[E]_0$ and $K_M = k_{-1}/k_1$.
- K_M can be calculated from the substrate concentration when $J = \frac{1}{2}J_{max}$. However, a more accurate method of determining J_{max} and K_M is to use the Lineweaver–Burk plot, $1/J$ against $1/[S]$, which gives a straight line of gradient K_M/J_{max} and a y-intercept of $1/J_{max}$.
- There are different types of inhibition: competitive, uncompetitive or mixed/non-competitive inhibition.
- Competitive inhibition involves the inhibitor competing with the substrate for occupation of the active site. This leads to an increase in K_M whilst J_{max} remains the same. Knowledge of the $K_{M\ app}$ values enables K_i, the dissociation constant for the EI complex, to be calculated

  $EI \rightleftharpoons E + I$

$$K_i = \frac{[E][I]}{[EI]}$$

- Uncompetitive inhibition involves the inhibitor binding to a place remote from the active site, which has been exposed during the substrate binding – the inhibitor only binds to the ES complex and the resulting ESI complex does not lead to the product. This leads to a decrease in both K_M and J_{max}. Knowledge of the $K_{M\ app}$ and/or $J_{max\ app}$ values enables calculation of the dissociation constant of the ESI complex.

  $$ESI \rightleftharpoons ES + I$$

  $$K'_i = \frac{[ES][I]}{[ESI]}$$

- Mixed inhibition involves the inhibitor binding at the active site and at the alternative site. This leads to a change in both K_M and J_{max}. Kinetic analysis enables the calculation of the dissociation constant for the EI complex and the dissociation constant of the ESI complex.
- Dixon and Cornish-Bowden plots can be used to identify the mode of inhibition. Each line represents an experiment in varying [I] at a given [S] and several different values of [S] must be chosen to obtain a convincing intersection or convergence on an axis.

Study note

Now move on to Section 2 where we consider the binding of drugs.

2 Drug binding

2.1 Drug administration

For a drug to be effective it must be introduced into the body of the patient in a way that eventually allows the drug to reach its target. This can be achieved in a variety of ways, including by injection (**intravenously**), by mouth (**orally**), through the skin (**trans-dermally**), via the lungs (**pulmonary delivery**) and even through the large intestine. Whilst it is easy to appreciate that most if not all of these approaches make some use of the blood supply to convey the drug to the target, each delivery route presents its own set of challenges. The range of factors, such as solubility of the drug, the local pH, length of time for absorption to occur, exposure to enzymes, exposure to blood vessels, the amount of local fatty tissue, varies widely for each type of delivery. Consequently, drug molecules are under attack almost from the moment of first contact with the patient, and it is essential to know how much can survive to reach the target. Table 2.1 gives some examples of the ways in which drugs can be administered to patients.

Table 2.1 Selected routes for drug administration.

Administration route	Example of drug	Therapeutic use	Specific advantage
oral	paracetamol	painkiller	quick and easy
trans-dermal	nicotine patch	smoking cessation	small dose, long acting
subcutaneous injection	lignocaine	local anaesthetic	local and direct
intravenous injection	penicillin G	antibiotic	avoids digestive tract
inhaler (pulmonary)	salbutamol	anti-asthmatic	direct to target tissue

The issues related to method of administration and a drug molecule's survival in reaching the target will be discussed further in Section 3, when we look at ways in which drugs distribute themselves in a patient. For now, though, we will concentrate on the important phenomenon of drugs binding to proteins.

2.2 Drug binding to proteins

We are already familiar with the idea that proteins are distributed widely throughout the body. We also know that drugs are very often designed to bind to proteins in order to have a therapeutic effect.

- Identify some of the ways in which molecules of aspirin (**2.1**), acetylcholine (**2.2**) and ibuprofen (**2.3**) could bind to the peptide (**2.4**).

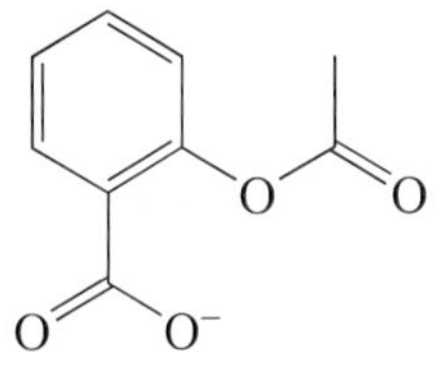

2.1 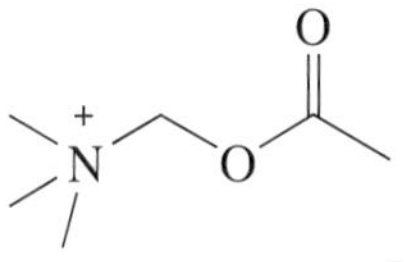 **2.2** 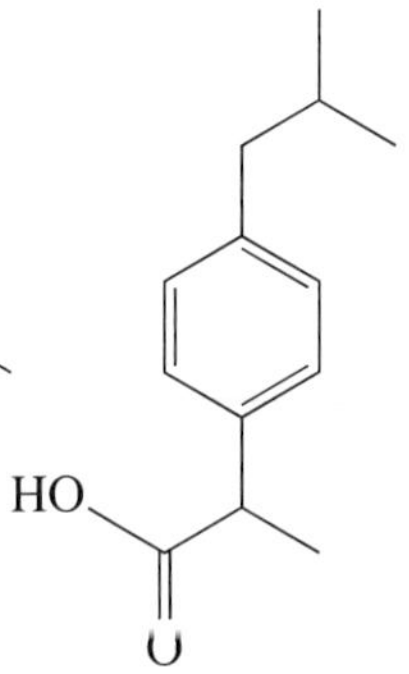 **2.3**

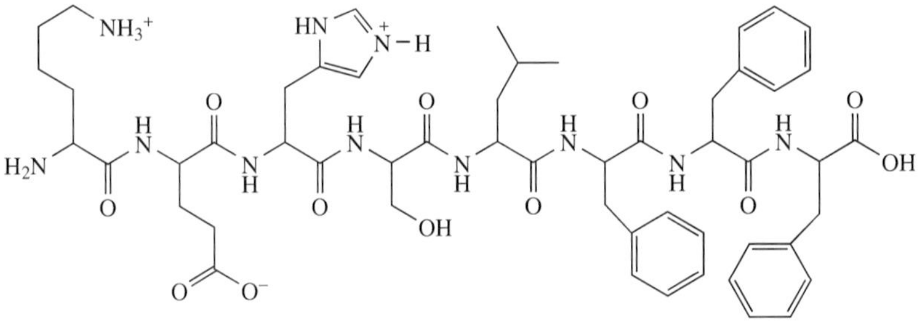

2.4

□ Figure 2.1 suggests hypothetical ways in which molecules of aspirin, acetylcholine and ibuprofen could bind to a peptide, using hydrogen bonding, ionic interactions (salt bridge) and van der Waals forces.

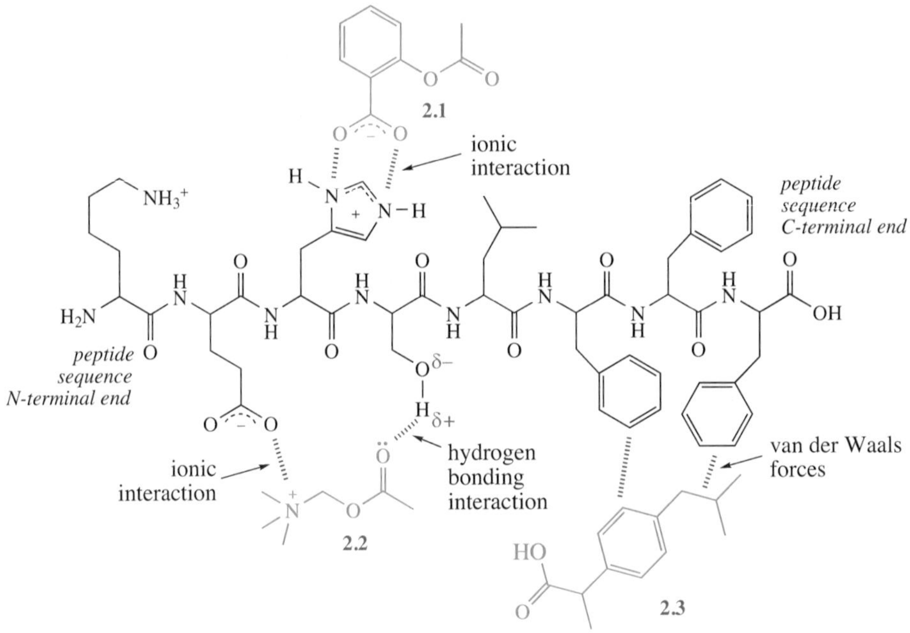

Figure 2.1 Hypothetical interactions between various drugs and a peptide.

The peptide sequence **2.4** could be part of a protein found in a wide variety of environments. It could be a receptor, soluble protein or enzyme. So it is important to appreciate that drug–protein binding is widespread and occurs throughout the drug's lifetime in the patient. The 'tightness' of binding and the quality of 'fit' are dependent on the structure of the drug and the region of the protein to which it is binding.

This helps us to understand how drugs can bind strongly with certain proteins and not with others and explains how drugs can be designed to bind specifically to their targets. If the structure of the active site or receptor target is known, which is increasingly the case, then molecular modelling can be used to explore possible drug candidates before synthesis and testing begin.

It is important to quantify the binding of drugs to proteins in solution, so that we can compare the affinities of drugs for different proteins. To do this we need to recognise this binding as a dynamic equilibrium. The standard protein adopted for this kind of measurement is **serum albumin protein**. There are many proteins found in blood plasma, but albumin represents approximately 60% of the total protein present and is responsible for the majority of drug binding. At the normal blood pH of about 7.4, serum albumin is negatively charged overall. It has a molecular mass of 66 300 and occurs in concentrations of between 30 and 50 g dm^{-3} (4.5–7.5 × 10^{-4} mol dm^{-3}).

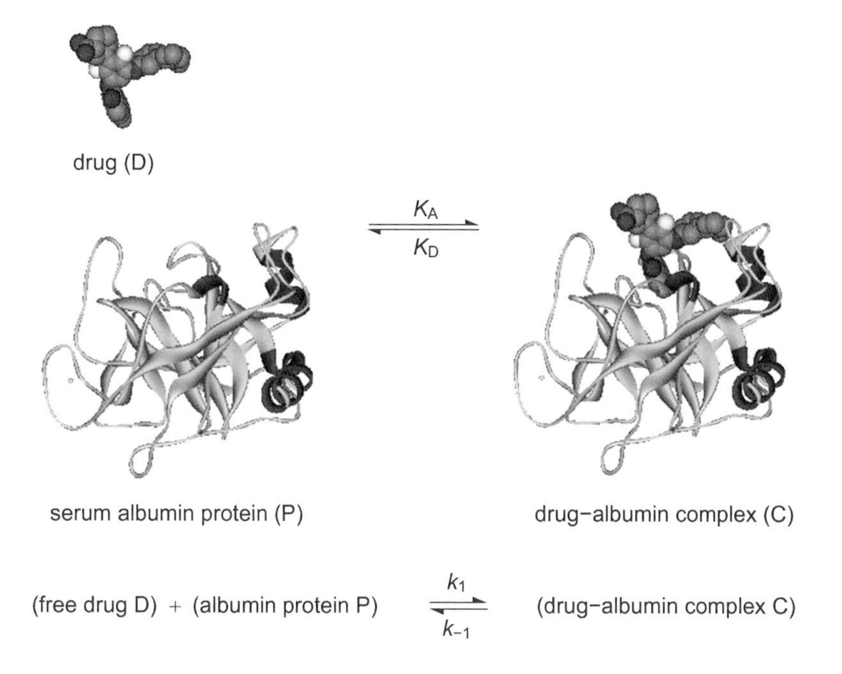

Figure 2.2 The binding of drugs to proteins is a dynamic equilibrium.

Figure 2.2 shows the binding of a hypothetical drug and draws a distinction between association and dissociation of the drug–protein complex. The 'tightness' of the binding can be expressed either as a dissociation constant K_D or as an association or affinity constant K_A (not to be confused with the acid dissociation constant for an acid in aqueous solution).

- With reference to Figure 2.2, define the **dissociation constant K_D** and the **affinity constant K_A**.

□ With reference to Figure 2.2, we can define the dissociation constant K_D as

$$K_D = \frac{[P][D]}{[C]} \quad (2.1)$$

The inverse of this is K_A, the affinity constant.

$$K_A = \frac{[C]}{[P][D]} = \frac{1}{K_D} \quad (2.2)$$

2.2.1 Using real data

NH$_2$–SO$_2$–C$_6$H$_4$–NH$_2$

2.5

We will now look at some real data (Table 2.2) from an experiment to determine the protein binding constants for the drug sulfanilamide (**2.5**) to serum albumin. (You met sulfanilamide in Section 1 as structure **1.7**.) In this experiment a 70 g dm^{-3} (1.06×10^{-3} mol dm^{-3}) solution of albumin, buffered at pH 8, is used as the aqueous protein solution. A 2.5×10^{-3} mol dm^{-3} solution of sulfanilamide is used as the source of the drug. The experimental work involves mixing the solutions as directed in Table 2.2, the first tube containing the drug and buffered water and the second tube containing the drug and serum albumin in buffered water. The tubes were left to equilibrate at room temperature for about 5 min, then ammonium sulfate (NH_4SO_4) was added to each tube. This will have no effect in tube 1, but in tube 2 all of the protein is precipitated with the bound drug still attached.

Table 2.2 Results from an experiment to determine the protein binding constants for the drug sulfanilamide (**2.5**) to serum albumin. In tube 1 there is no serum albumin, whereas it is present in tube 2.

Tube	Sulfanilamide/10^{-6} dm^3	Albumin (pH 8)/10^{-6} dm^3	Buffer (pH 8)/10^{-6} dm^3	NH_4SO_4/g
1	300	0	900	0.7
2	300	600	300	0.7

Precipitation of the protein with the bound drug will inevitably reduce the drug concentration in the remaining solution after the protein has been removed by centrifugation. In tube 1 (the control) this will have no effect on the drug concentration. Now it is necessary to determine the drug concentrations remaining in solution for each tube. This is done by converting sulfanilamide into a highly coloured azo dye and then reading the absorbance (A_{545}) of the resulting solution at 545 nm. The details of this process need not concern us here. A calibration plot for this assay tells us that

$$[\text{sulfanilamide}] = \frac{A_{545}}{1.231 \times 10^3\ \text{mol}^{-1}\ \text{dm}^3} \quad (2.3)$$

■ The absorbance at 545 nm for each solution is given in Table 2.3. Calculate the concentration of sulfanilamide in each tube and add the data to Table 2.3.

Table 2.3 The absorbance at 545 nm for the solutions in tube 1 and tube 2.

Tube	A_{545}	[sulfanilamide]/10^{-3} mol dm^{-3}	% unbound	% bound
1	0.757		100	0
2	0.424			

□ Using Equation 2.3 we can write:

For tube 1

$$[\text{sulfanilamide}] = \frac{0.757}{1.231\times10^{3}\ \text{mol}^{-1}\ \text{dm}^{3}} = 6.15\times10^{-4}\ \text{mol dm}^{-3}$$

For tube 2

$$[\text{sulfanilamide}] = \frac{0.424}{1.231\times10^{3}\ \text{mol}^{-1}\ \text{dm}^{3}} = 3.44\times10^{-4}\ \text{mol dm}^{-3}$$

Note that from Table 2.2 we can see that the stock sulfanilamide (300×10^{-6} dm^{3}) solution is diluted and ends up in a volume of 300 + 900 = 1200×10^{-6} dm^{3}. It has therefore been diluted by a factor of 300/1200 or 0.25. We would therefore expect our concentration in tube 1 (where no binding has occurred) to be $0.25 \times 2.5 \times 10^{-3}$ mol dm^{-3} (0.625×10^{-3} mol dm^{-3}). The value obtained from the assay is therefore acceptably close at 0.615×10^{-3} mol dm^{-3}.

We can now also see from Table 2.3 that after the bound drug has been removed (tube 2) the drug concentration has fallen to 3.44×10^{-4} mol dm^{-3}. It is now a relatively simple matter to calculate the percentage of drug that has bound to the protein.

■ Based on the assay figure for the tube 1 drug concentration, 6.15×10^{-4} mol dm^{-3}, calculate the percentage of the drug in tube 2 that remained unbound. Enter this figure in Table 2.3 together with the percentage of drug bound in tube 2.

□ The percentage unbound will equal the concentration in tube 2 divided by the concentration in tube 1 multiplied by 100:

$$\%\ \text{unbound} = \frac{3.44\times10^{-4}}{6.15\times10^{-4}}\times100 = 56\%$$

Thus the percentage bound is 44%.

We are now in a position to estimate K_D and K_A for sulfanilamide. Table 2.4 displays some of the data that we need.

Table 2.4 Data for the calculation of K_D and K_A.

	Drug concentration [D]/mol dm^{-3}	**Serum albumin concentration [P]/mol dm^{-3}**	**Protein–drug complex concentration [C]/mol dm^{-3}**
before equilibrium	6.15×10^{-4}	5.30×10^{-4}	0
after equilibrium	3.44×10^{-4}		

■ What will be the concentration of the protein–drug complex after equilibration? Add this to Table 2.4.

□ The concentration of the protein–drug complex after equilibration is the same as the concentration of the bound drug, which will equal the concentration of the drug before equilibration minus the concentration of unbound drug after equilibration

$$[C] = 6.15\times10^{-4}\ \text{mol dm}^{-3} - 3.44\times10^{-4}\ \text{mol dm}^{-3}$$
$$= 2.71\times10^{-4}\ \text{mol dm}^{-3}$$

■ What will be the concentration of the uncomplexed serum albumin? Add this to Table 2.4.

□ The concentration of the uncomplexed serum albumin will equal the concentration of the serum albumin before equilibration minus the concentration of complexed serum albumin after equilibration:

$$[C] = 5.30\times10^{-4}\ \text{mol dm}^{-3} - 2.71\times10^{-4}\ \text{mol dm}^{-3}$$
$$= 2.59\times10^{-4}\ \text{mol dm}^{-3}$$

From this data and Equation 2.1 we can now say that

$$K_D = \frac{2.59\times10^{-4}\ \text{mol dm}^{-3}\times3.44\times10^{-4}\ \text{mol dm}^{-3}}{2.71\times10^{-4}\ \text{mol dm}^{-3}}$$
$$= 3.29\times10^{-4}\ \text{mol dm}^{-3}$$

and from Equation 2.2:

$$K_A = \frac{2.71\times10^{-4}\ \text{mol dm}^{-3}}{2.59\times10^{-4}\ \text{mol dm}^{-3}\times3.44\times10^{-4}\ \text{mol dm}^{-3}}$$
$$= 3.04\times10^{3}\ \text{mol}^{-1}\ \text{dm}^{3}$$

Finally, there are two points that need to be added to our discussion so far. First, it is important to note that our calculations of K_D and K_A above *assume* that each molecule of the protein is binding to only one molecule of drug. We can never rely on this though, without first demonstrating it using experimental evidence. Whenever this is not the case, then modified versions of Equations 2.1 and 2.2 would be needed for a 'true' K_D or K_A. This is discussed further in Section 2.3.

Second, relatively speaking, sulfanilamide is a fairly weakly bound drug and its close relative sulfadimidine (**2.6**) can be shown to be about 70% bound to albumin under the same conditions as our earlier experiment with sulfanilamide. Other drugs, which bind even more strongly, are capable of displacing weakly bound ones from their albumin binding sites. It should therefore be remembered that experimental values of K_D and K_A are altered by the presence of strongly binding molecules, and the terms $K_{D\ app}$ and $K_{A\ app}$ are used in an analogous way to the term $K_{M\ app}$ encountered in Section 1.4 when considering the inhibition of enzymes. In such cases, the more strongly binding drugs are effectively behaving as binding inhibitors.

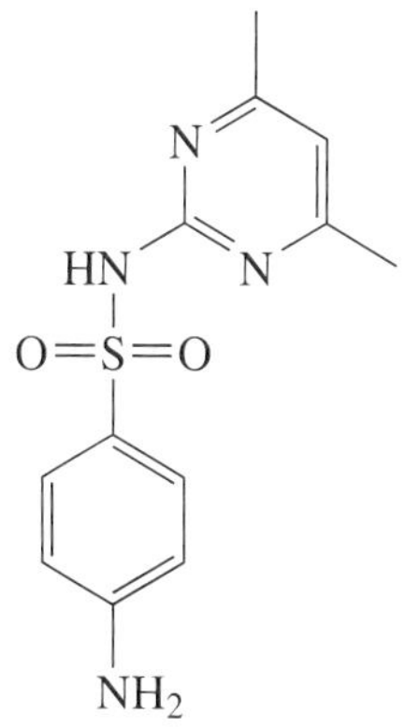

N N HN O=S=O NH_2

2.6

2.3 The Scatchard equation

This equation is named after George Scatchard (1892–1973), although the contribution made by H.E. Rosenthal to this area should not be overlooked.

As we have already seen in Section 2.2, consideration of drug binding to proteins confronts us with some theoretical concerns about how to calculate and interpret values of binding constants. The **Scatchard equation** helps us to deal with some of these concerns by recognising that there may well be multiple binding sites for the drug on a single molecule of protein. An assumption is made that the drug binds to multiple sites, but always with the same value of K_A. The Scatchard equation, therefore, defines K_A as

$$K_A = \frac{r}{[D](n-r)} \qquad (2.4)$$

where $r = [C]/[P]$, [D] is the concentration of unbound drug, [C] is the concentration of bound drug, [P] is the concentration of the total protein present and n is the number of drug binding sites on the protein.

This equation is easily rearranged to give a linear equation:

$$\frac{r}{[D]} = K_A n - K_A r \qquad (2.5)$$

Plotting r/[D] versus r gives a straight line of gradient $-K_A$. The y-axis intercept will be $K_A n$, so it is possible to deduce both the affinity constant and the number of binding sites from this exercise.

We have seen earlier how it is possible to estimate the equilibrium unbound drug concentration and thereby deduce the concentration of drug that is bound to protein. If we carry out a range of experiments similar to those summarised in Tables 2.3 and 2.4, then by varying the initial drug concentration $[D]_0$ over a suitable range we can determine r (the ratio of bound drug concentration to total protein present) for each $[D]_0$ value. Table 2.5 gives data for a typical experiment of this type.

Table 2.5 Data from an experiment in which non-albumin protein ([P] = 0.9×10^{-6} mol dm^{-3}) is equilibrated with a range of drug concentrations [D]. The actual drug and protein are not important here.

Initial [D]	Equilibrium [D]	Equilibrium [C]	r	r/[D]
$[D]_0/10^{-6}$ mol dm^{-3}	$[D]_{unbound}/10^{-6}$ mol dm^{-3}	$[D]_{bound}/10^{-6}$ mol dm^{-3}	[C]/[P]	$r/[D]_{unbound}/10^{6}$ mol^{-1} dm^{3}
0.1	0.028	0.072	0.080	2.857
0.2	0.058	0.142	0.158	2.720
0.4	0.121	0.279	0.310	2.562
0.8	0.287	0.513	0.570	1.986
1.6	0.695	0.905	1.006	1.447
3.2	1.92	1.28	1.422	0.741

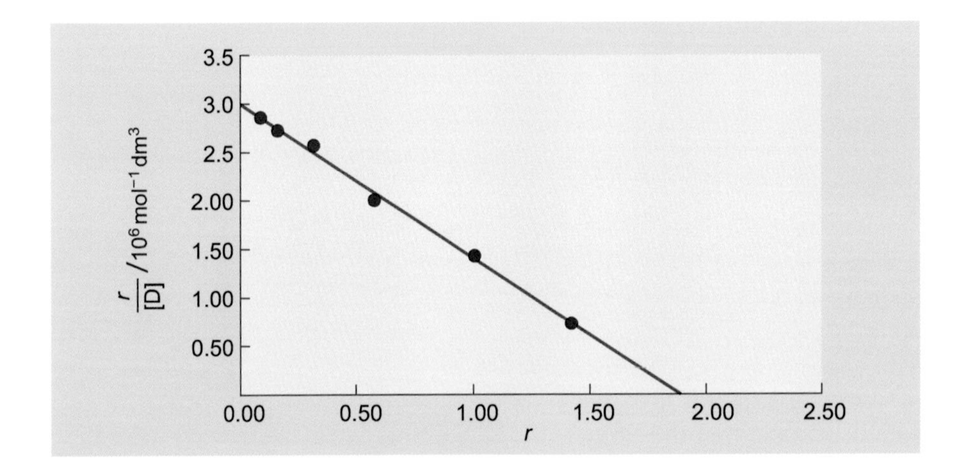

Figure 2.3 A Scatchard plot of the data in Table 2.5.

Figure 2.3 shows a Scatchard plot of r/[D] versus r using the data in Table 2.5. This shows a straight line with the equation

$$y = -1.569 \times 10^{6}x + 2.979 \times 10^{6}$$

The gradient of the line therefore gives a value of $-K_A$, so K_A = 1.6×10^{6} mol^{-1} dm^{3}.

More interestingly, the point at which the line cuts the y-axis gives the value of $K_A n$.

As the line intercepts the y-axis at 3.0×10^{6} mol^{-1} dm^{3} and as we know K_A = 1.6×10^{6} mol^{-1} dm^{3}, we can calculate n:

$$n = \frac{3.0\times10^{6}\ \text{mol}^{-1}\ \text{dm}^{3}}{1.6\times10^{6}\ \text{mol}^{-1}\ \text{dm}^{3}} = 1.9$$

To the nearest integer, this has a value of 2. You may also have noticed that the x-intercept (where the extrapolated line hits the x-axis) also gives the value of n *directly.*

2.4 Dose–response curves

In assessing the efficacy of drugs there are many parameters that can be determined, and these will vary according to the specific drug target. To overcome this complication, the idea of a dose–response relationship has developed. This is an attempt to represent the effectiveness of the drug through measuring a specific biological response. The actual response could be almost anything as long as it is appropriate to the action of the drug. Let's say we are measuring the activity of an enzyme that is known to be expressed in a particular disease. Increasing the concentration of drug could either increase or suppress the activity depending on the way the drug is intended to work. Let's say the drug should cause more enzyme to be expressed and increase the activity found in the enzyme assays for a patient. Raised levels of the enzyme in the patient will therefore be the desired response from taking the drug. The **dose–response curve** will look something like the plot shown in Figure 2.4.

Note that there is a maximum effect that can be achieved at high dose levels. This is in effect a measure of drug **potency**, and the term **EC_{50}** is used to express the concentration of drug required to induce 50% of the maximum response. The quantity of drug administered is often loosely referred to as the 'dose', but is probably best expressed as the maximum plasma concentration of the drug after administration.

Figure 2.4 A typical dose–response curve for a drug whose action causes an increase in activity or response.

- ■ Would an effective drug have a high or a low EC_{50}?
- □ An effective drug would have a low EC_{50}. This is because as small a dose as possible to achieve half of the maximum effect is desirable because it is cheaper to manufacture and less likely to have undesirable side effects.

2.5 Inhibition curves

If a drug is acting as an inhibitor, then a chosen response in the patient may be decreased in order to provide a beneficial effect. Suppose, for example, the drug is acting as an enzyme inhibitor and the desired response is a lowering of the enzyme activity. It might be appropriate to conduct experiments with a fixed concentration of a natural substrate and add increasing amounts of an inhibitor drug. The curve (known as an **inhibition curve**) will then start with a high response and decrease as the drug is added (Figure 2.5). Just as in the dose–response curve in Figure 2.4, there will be a point where adding further drug has no more effect. We can relate this point to a 'saturation' level in a real sense if we think in terms of the drug binding to a protein (or perhaps some other macromolecule) to achieve the inhibitory effect. As before, we can identify a concentration of drug where the response is half of that observed at 'saturation'; this is known as the **IC_{50}**.

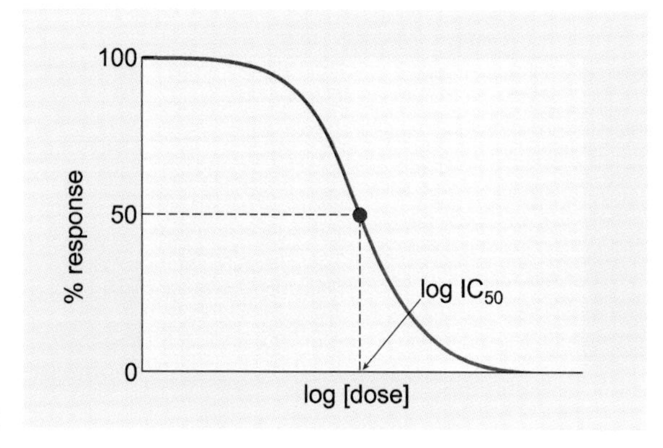

Figure 2.5 A typical inhibition curve for a drug whose action causes a reduction in activity of some parameter as its response.

Very high doses of a drug can produce a desirable level of response (e.g. lowering of cholesterol levels), but can also be toxic as a result of side-effects. Consequently, the idea of **therapeutic index** (TI) has been introduced and is usually defined as TI = LD_{50}/ED_{50}, where LD_{50} is the ingested quantity of drug that kills 50% of a population (not usually patients!) and ED_{50} is the ingested dose needed to give the same response as the EC_{50} or IC_{50}. High values of TI indicate a wide margin of safety with respect to overdose.

2.6 Summary of Section 2

To summarise, at this point, if a drug's mode of action is explicable in terms of some kind of equilibrium binding to a protein, Figure 2.2, then we can evaluate parameters such as the affinity constant K_A and the dissociation constant K_D from a knowledge of the concentration of free drug and protein in solution and the concentration of protein–drug complex. We can use the Scatchard plot, r/[D] versus r, to determine n, the number of equivalent binding sites on a protein. However, if we want to know the drug's dose–response relationship then we have to measure some property of a patient (or experimental animal) in order to test that response and assign an EC_{50}, the concentration of drug required to induce 50% of the maximum response. If the drug is an inhibitor, we can give it an IC_{50} value which represents its effectiveness as an inhibitor.

Study note

You should now move on to Section 3.

3 Transport mechanisms

We have seen in Section 2 that there are several ways in which drugs can enter the body and that when considering transport mechanisms it is important to distinguish between these. The 'drug' itself is dependent upon its pharmaceutically active ingredient, and for a new drug this is called the **new chemical entity** (NCE). For an NCE there has to be a development phase, during which the exact procedure for introducing the drug into the body is worked out. The science related to this, whether it be preparation of a tablet or developing a stable suspension with the right properties for delivering the drug, is called **pharmaceutics**.

Under the umbrella of transport mechanisms we are really concerned with the possible events that can occur after administration, when the pharmaceutists have done their work. As the drug molecules are released into the circulatory systems of the body, they will travel through them and eventually arrive at the target. We are also concerned with what happens to the drug after it has reached its target and how it is eliminated from the body. Naturally, this is another large topic and varies greatly from one drug and one target to another. If we are to understand how a drug can survive and function during its passage through the body, we need a thorough understanding of its chemical and physical properties. Some drugs, known as pro-drugs, such as Prontosil™ or the proton pump inhibitors, are administered in an inactive form and it is essential that an early decomposition reaction or functional group interconversion occurs to release the active molecule. However, it is vital that other drugs, such as penicillins, stay intact for as long as possible.

3.1 Pharmacokinetics

Pharmacodynamics is essentially the study of the effect of the drug on the body, and this is discussed in detail in Unit 3 Section 1. **Pharmacokinetics**, on the other hand, is the study of what the body does to the drug, and is crucially important to an understanding of transport mechanisms. Effective drug delivery requires a detailed understanding of how the drug distributes itself after administration and in turn how this changes the 'effective concentration' of a drug and, therefore, its availability at the target.

Several processes can be involved in the modification of the drug; some of these can change its structure irreversibly and others reversibly. We will now look at the major processes in turn.

3.1.1 Chemical stability

Chemical stability is, of course, a major factor, as the body contains a wide array of reagents that can be reactive towards functional groups in the drug. The environment in the stomach is acidic, so acid-catalysed reactions can occur easily with some drugs.

Penicillin G (**3.1**), for example, is not usually taken orally as its β-lactam ring is too prone to acid-catalysed hydrolysis, as shown in Scheme 3.1. Since it is relatively stable at pH 7 it can be administered by intravenous injection.

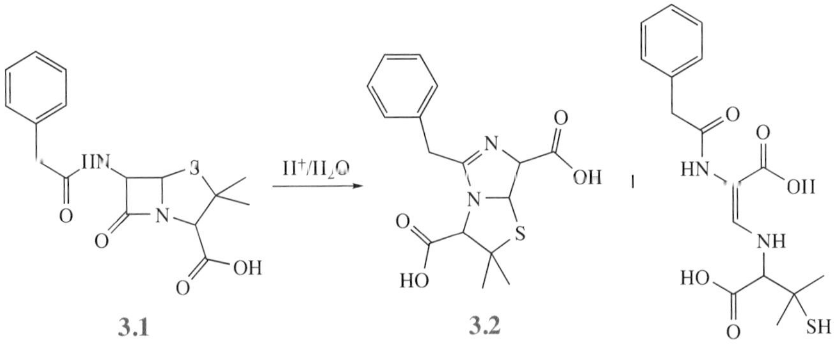

H^+/H_2O

3.1 → 3.2 + other products, 3.3

Scheme 3.1

Scheme 3.1 shows that the hydrolysis is not straightforward and that protonation of the molecule initiates a cascade of reactions that leads to a number of possible products. Penicillic acid (**3.2**) is in fact a very reactive isomer of penicillin, whereas penamaldic acid (**3.3**) requires the addition of one molecule of water. These compounds are broken down into smaller fragments by further hydrolysis.

Sometimes this chemical instability is advantageous and intentional. For example, omeprazole (**3.4**, a proton-pump inhibitor) undergoes an acid-catalysed ring closure reaction to give the active sulfenamide **3.5**.

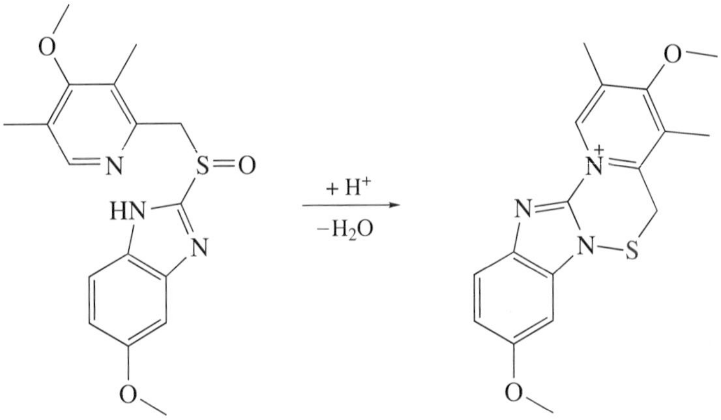

3.4 → ($+H^+$, $-H_2O$) → 3.5

Omeprazole is itself inactive, but the divalent sulfur (in red) of the sulfenamide, formed from acid-catalysed elimination of water, attacks its target H^+/K^+ ATPase protein to form an irreversible S–S link that deactivates the enzyme.

Reactive esters can undergo similar acid-catalysed hydrolysis in the stomach, but hydrolysis reactions are also catalysed by enzymes and will, therefore, be mentioned under metabolic stability.

3.1.2 Metabolic stability

Metabolic stability refers to how resistant or vulnerable a drug is to a wide range of enzymatic degradation processes. If a drug enters the body through the alimentary canal (digestive system, usually from the small intestine) then it will encounter the hepatic portal vein, which is the recipient of blood coming from the network of vessels associated with the small intestine. This blood is then carried straight to the liver where it will encounter the full force of the liver's detoxification systems. An impressive array of enzymes is housed in the liver, and these can perform a wide range of chemical operations, some of which we will consider later under the topic of elimination at the end of this section. Removal of drug in this manner is often called the **first pass effect**, and drugs need to be sufficiently resistant in order to leave the liver whilst still functional and join the general circulation. Equally crucially, any breakdown products that are formed must be relatively non-toxic.

Other metabolic enzymes are distributed all over the body, and degradation or modification continues before and after interaction with the target. Generally, after a variable period of equilibration, the decay of drug concentrations in the blood plasma follows pseudo-first-order kinetics, so it is acceptable to assign half-lives to individual drugs. Aspirin, for example, has a half-life in aqueous acid at pH 2 (stomach pH) of approximately 10 h at body temperature. In the blood plasma though, this can be as little as 15–20 min. Esterase enzymes are responsible for most of this increase in reaction rate, and the drug is quickly degraded to salicylic and ethanoic acids. Salicylic acid has a much longer half-life, but is still an effective analgesic. The acetic acid by-product is an abundant natural metabolite and causes no problem to the patient.

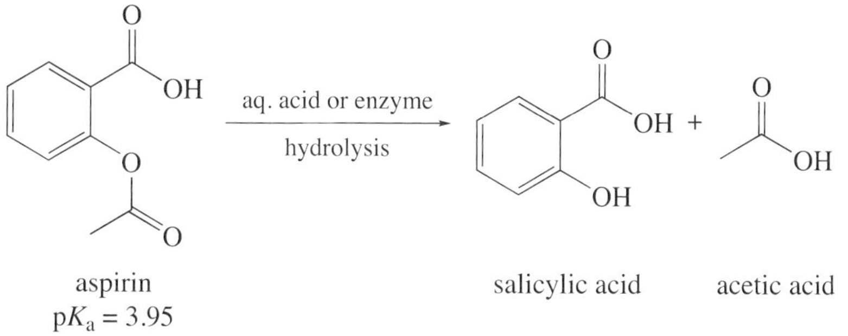

aspirin $\xrightarrow[\text{hydrolysis}]{\text{aq. acid or enzyme}}$ salicylic acid + acetic acid (3.1)

aspirin
$pK_a = 3.95$

salicylic acid acetic acid

Just as in chemically induced degradation, sometimes the metabolic, enzymatic degradation is a necessary step in the conversion of a pro-drug into its active form. The compound 3,4-**D**ihydr**O**xy-L-**P**henyl**A**lanine (L-DOPA, **3.6**) is given to sufferers of Parkinson's disease, as it is readily decarboxylated by the enzyme DOPA decarboxylase to give dopamine, **3.7**.

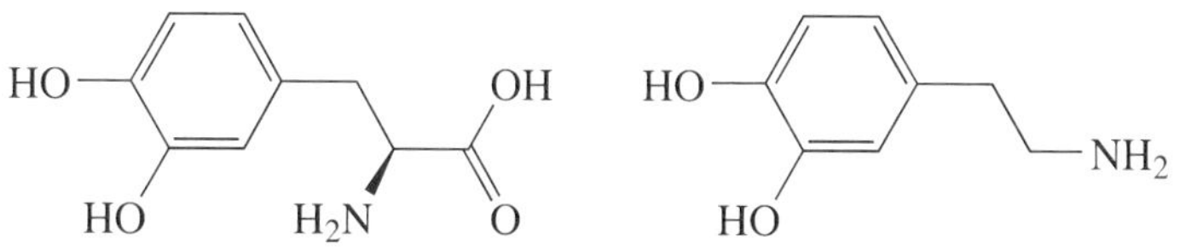

3.6 **3.7**

Dopamine is a neurotransmitter that is used by motor neurons in the brain to control voluntary movement. In Parkinson's disease sufferers, dopamine is in short supply, but simply giving dopamine as a drug has little effect. It is unable to cross the blood–brain barrier to reach its target receptors. L-DOPA, on the other hand, is able to cross the blood–brain barrier, and once into the brain tissue can be released as dopamine by the DOPA decarboxylase activity present there.

3.1.3 Hydrophilic/hydrophobic balance

Hydrophilic/hydrophobic balance is an issue that can greatly affect drug transport. The relative proportions of non-polar (usually hydrocarbon) structure and polar functional groups (such as alcohol or carboxylic acid) can impose dramatic differences upon the physical properties of a molecule. For instance, we know from our experience of vinegar that ethanoic acid is completely soluble in water, as is ethanol. We explain this through hydrogen bonding to water involving the polar functional group (–COOH or –OH). Increasing the relative quantity of hydrocarbon structure in a molecule, for example by adding two propyl groups to ethanoic acid to give valproic acid, **3.8**, dramatically reduces the water solubility. Valproic acid is only sparingly soluble in water (1.3 g dm^{-3}), suggesting that the hydrophilic/hydrophobic balance is dominated by the non-polar parts of the molecule.

O OH | $pK_a = 4.8$ | O O^- | + H^+ (3.2)

3.8 **3.9**

Table 3.1 shows how this pattern can be used to rationalise the water solubility (one measure of hydrophilicity) of organic molecules. As expected, replacing the methyl group of ethanoic acid with a benzene ring dramatically reduces solubility from infinity (miscible in all proportions) to only 29 g dm^{-3}. Similarly, extending the chain length of ethanol reduces the solubility until at heptanol (seven-carbon chain) it is only 1 g dm^{-3}. Curiously, adding a further polar group to benzoic acid to give salicylic acid or its isomer 4-hydroxybenzoic acid decreases, rather than increases, the solubility. Here, we must argue that the intermolecular forces in crystals of hydroxybenzoic acid are so strong that hydrogen bonding to water is insufficient to dislodge molecules. The whole phenomenon of solubility is indeed a complex balance between counteracting forces, and the solubility of the hydroxybenzoic acids in ethanol is much greater than in water, owing to the presence of hydrogen-bonding capacity and non-polar regions in the ethanol molecule.

Table 3.1 The solubilities, in water, of a range of organic molecules.

Molecule	Structure	Solubility at 25 °C/g dm^{-3}
methylbenzene	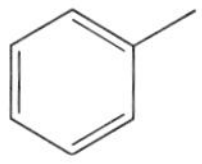	0.53
phenol	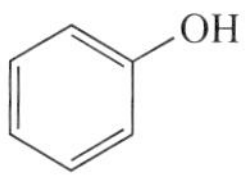 OH	83
ethanol	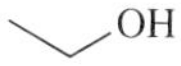 OH	∞
propanol	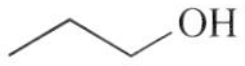 OH	∞
butanol	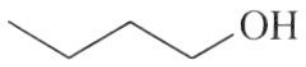 OH	~ 90
heptanol	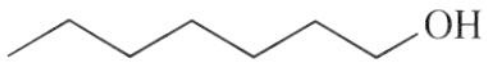 OH	1.0
benzoic acid	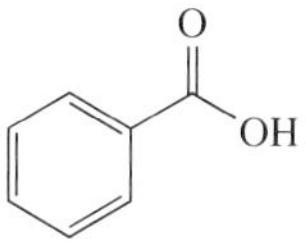 O, OH	29
salicylic acid	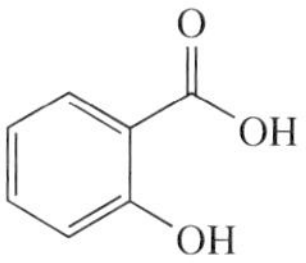 O, OH, OH	2
aspirin	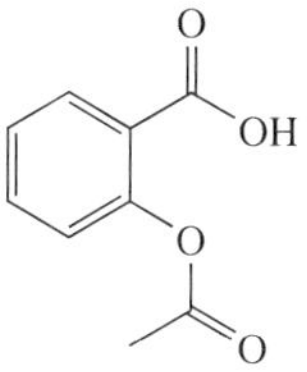 O, OH, O, O	~ 6–8
4-hydroxybenzoic acid	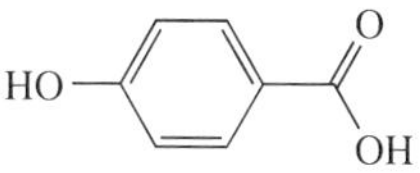 HO, O, OH	6

At pH values greater than about 5, valproic acid (**3.8**) exists as its anionic form, the valproate anion (**3.9**), as shown in Equation 3.2. The sodium salt of this anion is very water soluble and is used as a drug to treat epilepsy and bipolar disorder. The main advantage of the anion is that it can be administered as an aqueous solution either by mouth or by intravenous injection. Once in the stomach (pH ~2) the molecule mainly reverts to its free acid form (RCOOH), but in the blood (pH 7.4) it will exist as the anion.

Although the free acid forms of some drugs like aspirin can be absorbed, to some extent, by the stomach wall, uptake of most drugs in the stomach is slow. The majority occurs in the small intestine, where the pH (pH ~8) is much higher than in the stomach (pH ~2). For drugs like valproate and aspirin, their uptake relies on sufficient hydrophobic character to overcome their hydrophilic negative charge, while crossing the hydrophobic regions of the cell membranes of the small intestine.

In Unit 3 you learnt that for the following equilibrium:

$$HA \rightleftharpoons H^+ + A^- \qquad (3.3)$$

$$pK_a = -\log K_a = -\log\left(\frac{[H^+][A^-]}{[HA]}\right) = -\log[H^+] - \log\left(\frac{[A^-]}{[HA]}\right)$$

Thus

$$pK_a = pH - \log\left(\frac{[A^-]}{[HA]}\right)$$

This can be rearranged to give

$$\frac{[A^-]}{[HA]} = 10^{(pH - pK_a)}$$

■ What will be the preferred form of the compound when the pH is greater than the pK_a or less than the pK_a?

□ When the pH is greater than the pK_a, $pH - pK_a$ will be positive and thus $10^{(pH - pK_a)}$ will be larger than 1; thus the conjugate base, A^-, is the preferred form and the equilibrium in Equation 3.3 lies to the right.

When the pH is less than the pK_a, $pH - pK_a$ will be negative and thus $10^{(pH - pK_a)}$ will be smaller than 1; thus the acid (protonated) form, HA, is the preferred form and the equilibrium in Equation 3.3 lies to the left.

In the case of dopamine ($pK_a = 10.6$, see Scheme 3.2), at physiological pH in the body (pH ~7) the protonated form of the amine, which corresponds to the conjugate acid, HA, will be favoured. In addition to the phenolic groups present, this makes dopamine an extremely hydrophilic (water-loving) molecule, which helps to explain why it is unable to cross the blood–brain barrier. We can argue that L-DOPA, on the other hand, carries both a negative charge on the carboxylate ion and a positive charge at the protonated amine group at pH 7. The amino group in L-DOPA has a pK_a value of 8.72, and at pH 7 the amine will be predominantly protonated – only about 2% of the amine groups are as the 'free' unprotonated form.

$$R{-}NH_2 + H^+ \xrightleftharpoons{pK_a = 8.72} R{-}NH_3^+$$

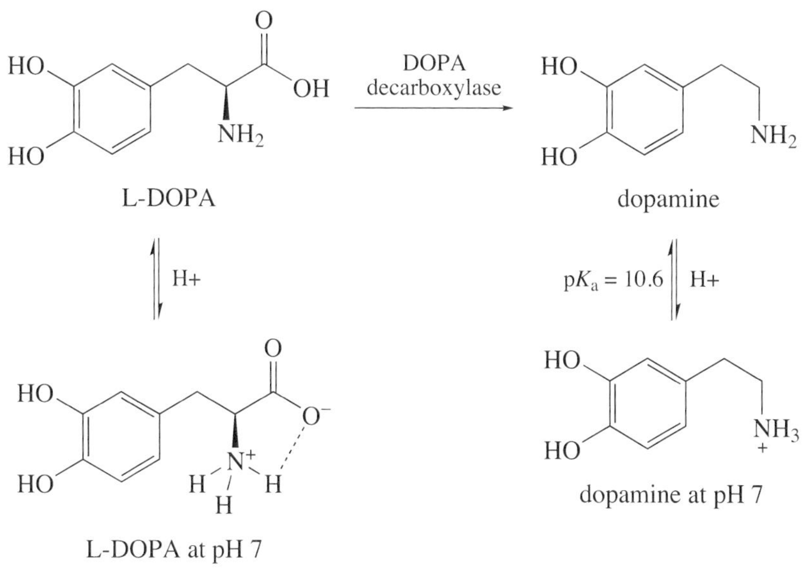

L-DOPA —DOPA decarboxylase→ dopamine

L-DOPA ⇌ (H+) L-DOPA at pH 7

dopamine ⇌ (pK_a = 10.6, H+) dopamine at pH 7

Scheme 3.2

This means that, at physiological pH, L-DOPA is a zwitterion and has an overall charge of zero. These properties give L-DOPA a similarity to many L-amino acids, for which there is an active transport system across the blood–brain barrier, and so it finds its way into the brain.

If a drug does not have the right level of hydrophobicity ('water hating') it will not develop sufficiently high concentrations in the tissues where it is designed to act. A drug that is too hydrophobic will lodge in fat deposits and fail to circulate or be effective. If it is too hydrophilic the drug does not penetrate lipids, and is usually rapidly excreted. As we can see, levels of ionisation are crucial to hydrophilic/hydrophobic balance, and many drugs are acids or bases or sometimes both (amphoteric). It is therefore very important to know how pH will affect the ionisation levels of molecules of a drug. As we saw earlier, for any acidic or basic drug it is a relatively simple matter to calculate the fraction of the protonated (or deprotonated) form of the drug, providing we know the pK_a value – see Figure 3.1.

An important conclusion is that the hydrophobicity of most drugs varies with pH. This will be examined in more detail when we consider partition (or distribution) coefficients and hydrophobicity constants.

3.1.4 Molecular size and hydrogen bonding

Molecular size can influence the rate at which molecules are absorbed and transported around the body. Most drugs are small (M_r < 1000) and so relatively easily absorbed. Smaller drug molecules can pass between cells rather than through them on their way to the target site. Molecular size can also influence the rate at which a drug is excreted, as the kidneys are size selective about which molecules are allowed to pass into the urine.

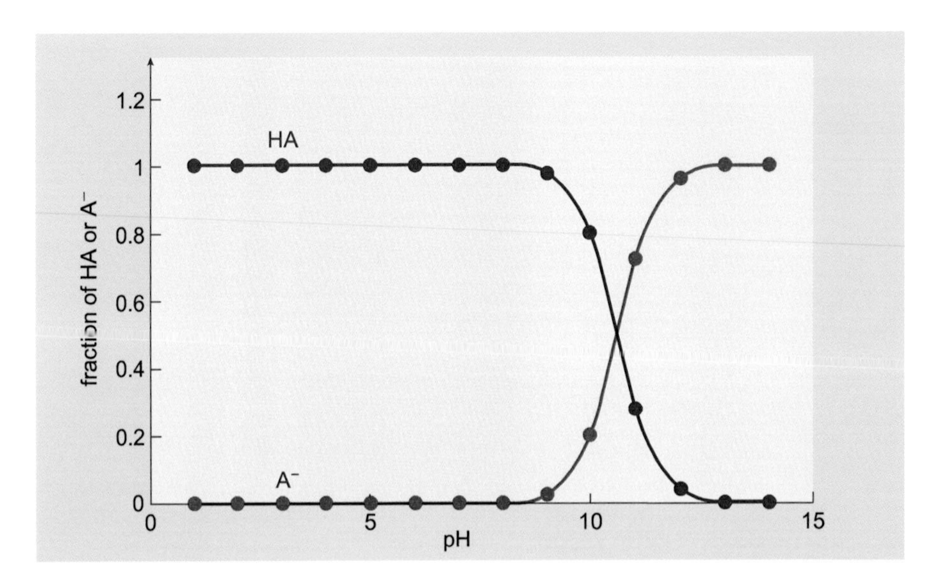

Figure 3.1 The fraction (relative to the amount of material added) of HA or A^- at a given pH for an acid of pK_a 10.6. Note that when pH = pK_a, [HA] = [A^-].

The number of hydrogen-bonding interactions can also strongly influence the absorption of a drug. Very polar, strongly hydrogen-bonding molecules are mostly poorly absorbed, for reasons that we have already mentioned. **Lipinski's 'rule of five'** successfully attempts to draw together the factors which conspire to make an effective oral drug. The rule states that a drug molecule has a good probability of being absorbed if three or more of the criteria are met.

It's called the 'rule of five' as all these values have multiples of five in their name.

The dalton is defined as 1/12th of the mass of a ^{12}C atom.

- Molecular mass M_r is under 500 daltons
- $\log P < 5$ (P is the partition coefficient which will be discussed in Section 3.2)
- no more than 5 hydrogen-bond donors (NH or OH)
- no more than 10 hydrogen-bond acceptors (N: or O:)

For L-DOPA (M_r = 197, $\log P = -2.39$, five hydrogen-bond donors, five hydrogen-bond acceptors) all of these criteria are met.

3.2 Quantitative structure–activity relationships

Quantitative structure–activity relationships (QSARs) is a branch of medicinal chemistry that attempts to quantify the activity of drug molecules in terms of key chemical and physical parameters. From Section 2 we are familiar with the terms EC_{50} or IC_{50}, representing the drug concentration required for half of the maximum response (for a receptor) and inhibition (for an enzyme). In a QSAR we use the idea that drug **activity** ($1/C$) can be defined in terms of a number of measurable parameters (V, W, X, …) for each drug:

$$\frac{1}{C} = vV^v + wW^w + xX^x \ldots + \text{constant}$$

The term C is taken to mean the concentration of drug required to produce an appropriate response and may be taken as EC_{50} and IC_{50} or some other measurement of a drug concentration such as an oral dose that produces a therapeutic response in 50% of the patients taking it (ED_{50}). The terms v, w and x are empirically derived coefficients and the powers v, w and x have small integer values usually 1 or 2. The parameters V, W and X … are physical parameters that can be measured for each drug molecule (or part of a drug molecule) and can be values for partition or distribution coefficients, substituent constants, or other factors which will be defined in the following discussion. The resulting equations from this approach are known as **Hansch equations** and will be returned to in Section 3.2.4.

3.2.1 Partition and distribution coefficients

A **partition coefficient** is a measure of how much solute (drug) will reside in each of two immiscible solvents, once equilibrium has been established under standard conditions. Partition coefficients can be determined for any organic compound and any pair of immiscible solvents (e.g. water and hexane), so the pharmaceutical industry has adopted the standard pairing of octanol and water for sound practical reasons. The standard definition of the partition coefficient P is therefore:

$$P = \frac{[\text{drug}]_{\text{octanol}}}{[\text{drug}]_{\text{water}}}$$

- ■ Will P be large or small for non-polar drugs?
- □ Clearly, drugs that have non-polar structures and carry no formal charges will reside mainly in the octanol (upper) layer in a partitioning experiment and P will be large.

Conversely, P will be small when drugs are charged or polar, as they will be predominantly solvated by water.

As we have already seen, some molecules change their hydrophilic/hydrophobic balance with pH. This must be allowed for in our calculation of P. A molecule with no ionisable groups will only have a single P value under standard conditions. However, drugs with ionisable groups (such as $-NH_2$ and $-COOH$) have a variable P value that must be recalculated for each pH of interest. To allow for this, pharmacists have introduced D, the distribution coefficient of a drug.

$$D = P \times f_{\text{u}} = \frac{\text{total }[\text{drug}]_{\text{octanol}}}{\text{total }[\text{drug}]_{\text{water}}}$$

The term total $[\text{drug}]_{\text{octanol}}$ refers to the sum of all concentrations of the various species of drug (free acid, free base, anionic form, etc.) that are found in the octanol layer. Likewise, the term total $[\text{drug}]_{\text{water}}$ refers to the equivalent species found in the water layer, and these will sum to the total concentration of drug used in the experiment.

Note that f_u (the fraction of un-ionised drug) is pH dependent for acidic or basic drugs since, depending upon the pK_a, as the pH changes the amounts of ionised and un-ionised forms will vary and thus the distribution of the drug between the octanol and water layers will change. As f_u is a fraction, values of f_u must fall between 1 and 0; in fact, the red line in Figure 3.1 shows how the fraction of un-ionised drug f_u, in this case free amine, varies with pH for dopamine with a pK_a of 10.6.

- ■ How will f_u vary with pH for a drug with no acidic or basic groups?
- □ For a drug with no acidic or basic groups f_u will not vary and will have a value of 1.0 (all of it is un-ionised) at any pH and, therefore, $P = D$.

3.2.2 Substituent hydrophobicity constants

It is possible to study how P varies with the addition of common substituents (e.g. –Cl,–CH_3, –NO_2) and determine parameters known as **substituent hydrophobicity constants** π. These allow drug developers to predict the effect of adding a substituent and avoid the laborious process of preparing the compound and determining P. We can define π for a given substituent (X) as

$$\pi_X = \log\left(\frac{P_X}{P_H}\right)$$

where P_X is the observed partition coefficient, P, with the substituent X present, and P_H is the observed P in the absence of substituent (i.e. with H present instead).

A worked example will illustrate how π values can be used. First we need a table of common π values. Note that different values are needed for substituents placed in aliphatic and aromatic environments.

Table 3.2 Hydrophobicity constants for a range of substituents on aliphatic or aromatic systems.

Group	–CH_3	–Bu^t	–OH	–OCH_3	–CF_3	–Cl	–Br	–F
$\pi_{aliphatic}$	0.50	1.68	−1.16	0.47	1.07	0.39	0.60	−0.17
$\pi_{aromatic}$	0.52	1.68	−0.67	−0.02	1.16	0.71	0.86	0.14

Provided we have the correct π values we can predict log P from the simple relationship

$$\log P_{pred} = \log P_{std} + \pi_{subst\ 1} + \pi_{subst\ 2} + \pi_{subst\ 3} \cdots$$

For example, to calculate the predicted log P (log P_{pred}) for phenol we need the log P value for our standard, the structure of which we deduce by replacing the –OH in phenol with an –H. This gives us benzene as our standard. Since $\log P_{benzene} = 2.13$, we can calculate $\log P_{phenol} = 2.13 - 0.67 = 1.46$ very close to the experimentally determined value of 1.49. This means that $P_{phenol} = 10^{1.46} = 29$.

So phenol (**3.10**) is 29 times more soluble in octanol than water. Benzene by comparison is $10^{2.13} = 135$ times more soluble. Positive values for π indicate that the substituent is more hydrophobic than hydrogen, whereas negative values indicate a lower hydrophobicity (greater water solubility) than H.

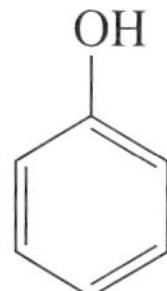

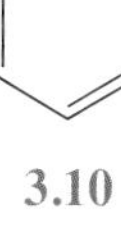

3.10

- ■ Calculate log P for trichlorophenol. The positions of the substituents are ignored in our estimation and we use phenol, rather than benzene, as our new standard.

- □ Since we use phenol as our new standard, we simply say:

  $\log P_{\text{pred}} = 1.46 + 0.71 + 0.71 + 0.71 = 3.59$

  so $P_{\text{trichlorophenol}} = 10^{3.59} = 3890$

A large increase in octanol solubility has, therefore, resulted from the substitution. The practically determined log P for 2,4,5-trichlorophenol at pH 7 is about 3.7, so our estimate seems reliable.

How does the value of log P of a drug impact upon its activity? Over a relatively narrow range from a low starting point, the activity generally increases as log P increases. However, over a wide range, the activity reaches a maximum and then falls away as log P continues to increase (Figure 3.2).

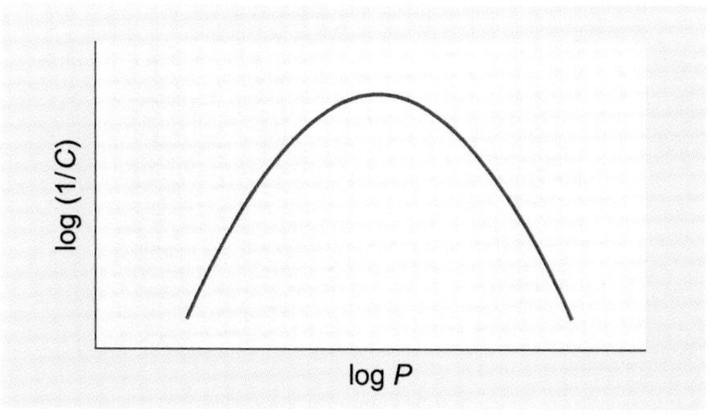

Figure 3.2 Variation in the activity of a drug ($1/C$) with hydrophobicity (log P).

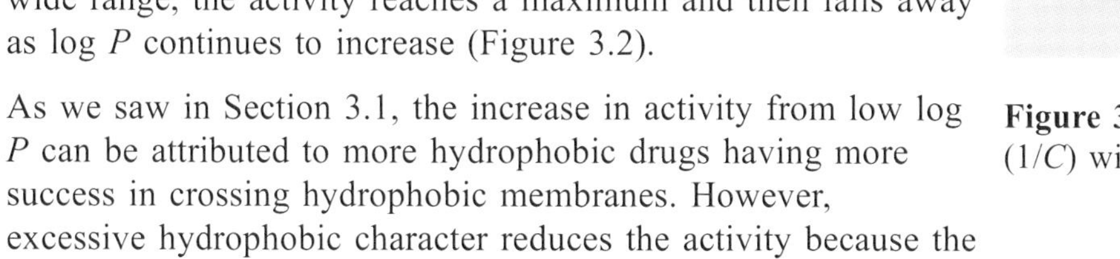

As we saw in Section 3.1, the increase in activity from low log P can be attributed to more hydrophobic drugs having more success in crossing hydrophobic membranes. However, excessive hydrophobic character reduces the activity because the drug lodges in the fatty tissues and fails to circulate around the body.

Activity 3.1

In this activity we use Accelrys Draw to calculate the partition coefficient of a drug. Detailed instructions are given in the *Study Guide for Unit 5* on the website.

3.2.3 Electronic factors (substituent constants or sigma, σ, constants)

Substituent constants σ are similar in concept to hydrophobicity constants π, but they essentially indicate how electron withdrawing or donating a substituent is. They are less versatile than π values in that they are only really successful in molecules with an aromatic core.

As we saw in Unit 3 Section 4, σ values are defined based on the acidity of substituted benzoic acids:

$$\sigma = \log K_{(\text{substituted benzoic acid})} - \log K_{(\text{benzoic acid})}$$

Table 3.3 shows some typical σ values.

Table 3.3 Typical σ values for *meta* and *para* substituents on a benzene ring.

Group	$-CH_3$	$-Bu^t$	$-OH$	$-OCH_3$	$-NH_2$	$-CF_3$	$-Cl$	$-Br$	$-F$	$-NO_2$
σ_{meta}	−0.069	−0.09	0.121	0.115	−0.16	0.43	0.373	0.391	0.337	0.710
σ_{para}	−0.170	−0.15	−0.37	−0.268	−0.66	0.54	0.227	0.232	0.062	0.778

The Hammett equation can be used to correlate the effect of substituents on an equilibrium constant or rate constant of any reaction adjacent to a benzene ring:

$$\log(K/K_H) = \log K - \log K_H = \rho\sigma$$

$$\log(k/k_H) = \log k - \log k_H = \rho\sigma$$

As with π, the effect of a substituent Y (Y = $-Cl$, $-CH_3$, $-NO_2$, etc.) is compared with a standard substituent (H).

The linear free energy relationships, and the Hammett equation in particular, can be used to predict or account for changes in the proportions of ionised forms of acids or bases on changing a substituent on a benzene ring. They can also account for changes in rates, such as the hydrolysis of esters or amides adjacent to an aromatic ring.

In practice, though, σ values are only reliable when the substituent Y is situated *meta* or *para* to the functional group attached to the ring whose properties are being studied. Substituents positioned *ortho* to the functional group of interest are often close enough to interact with each other directly, rather than through the ring electrons; this can cause our definition of σ to break down and the relationship becomes unreliable.

■ Will electron-withdrawing substituents have positive or negative σ values?

□ Broadly speaking, the more electron-withdrawing a substituent is, the higher the value of σ. A positive value means a substituent is more electron-withdrawing than hydrogen and a negative value that it is more electron-donating. For H itself, $\sigma = 0$, which is expected from the definition of σ used above.

It is interesting to note that some substituents appear to be significantly more electron withdrawing in the *meta* positions (e.g. $-OH$, $-OCH_3$ and $-NH_2$) compared with the *para*. This can be explained by arguing that σ values are a composite of two factors. The **inductive effect** decides how much electron density is withdrawn via the σ bond frameworks and the **mesomeric effect** is responsible for how much electron density is fed back through the π-system. The balance between these two opposing effects gives us the observed value for σ. Like π values, σ values can be used with some success in an additive way to give a 'net σ' for a molecule with more than one substituent.

3.2.4 Hansch equations

At the beginning of Section 3.2 we saw how drug activity can be equated to the combined effects of a number of parameters such as hydrophobicity (represented by substituent π values), electronic factors (represented by substituent σ values) and more unusually by steric or other factors which will not be involved in our discussion here. An equation which does this successfully is known as a Hansch equation (after Corwin Hansch, born 1918), and although this has to be derived by experimental investigation of a number of representative examples, it allows the accurate estimation of activity for a wide range of new examples, conforming to the class of drug being developed, without the need for preparing each one. Hansch equations are therefore a powerful drug development tool. For example in the case of early beta-blocker drugs, the lead compounds of the time, suggested that their structure should be of the form as shown by **3.11**.

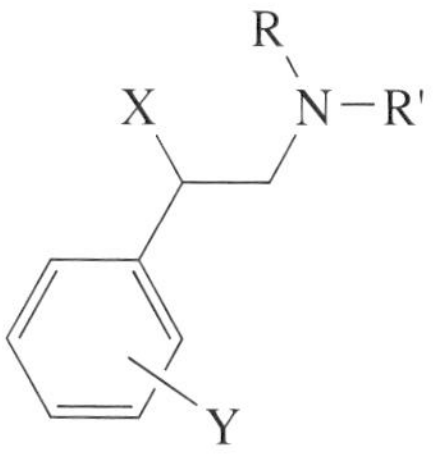

3.11 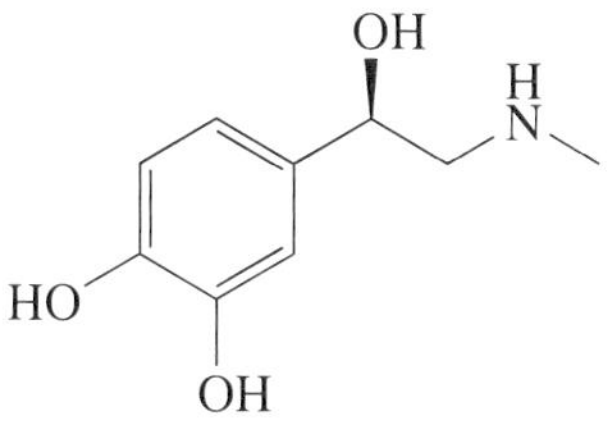 **3.12**

where X is a halogen and R and R′ are typically methyl groups. Note the similarity to adrenaline (**3.12**), the natural agonist for the β-receptors in question.

The Hansch equation appropriate to this class of compounds is

$$\log(1/C) = 1.22\pi_Y - 1.59\sigma_Y + 7.89$$

The equation is written in terms of σ and π for the ring substituent Y in the *meta* or *para* positions relative to the side chain. We can see that the activity of the drug will be increased by increasing π, and by decreasing σ of the ring substituent Y. In other words, the ring substituent should be hydrophobic and electron donating for optimum activity.

■ Can you suggest some suitable substituents for Y?

□ We can look at our earlier tables and suggest that, rather than preparing substituted examples at random, the drug development team should consider preparing structures with tertiary butyl ($-Bu^t$) groups attached to the ring. The likely candidates would be the *para*-substituted and the di-substituted meta compound.

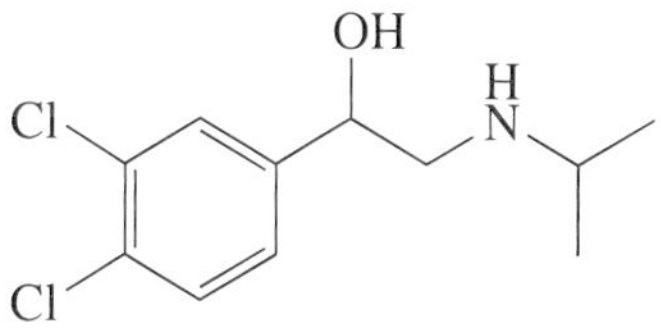

There is a danger, though, that the drug may be very active, but too hydrophobic to be easily transported to the target, or perhaps too toxic for clinical use. The first beta-blocker on general release was dichloroisoprenaline (**3.13**), which we would expect to be more hydrophilic than our suggestions

3.13

above, but the reason why this was chosen is clear from the structure–activity relationship even though some compromises had to be made in its development.

3.2.5 Craig plots

As we have seen, Hansch equations allow us to predict the activity for a drug variant, provided we have values for the necessary substituent parameters. In recognition of this fact, the **Craig plot** (named after Paul N. Craig) has been created to assist drug developers in the search for suitable substituents. For two parameters (usually σ and π, although others are used) there will be four possible ways of pairing values in a Hansch equation, namely (positive π : positive σ), (positive π : negative σ), (negative π : positive σ) and (negative π : negative σ). The Craig plot, Figure 3.3, conveniently orders a host of substituents into four quadrants, allowing easy selection of those with favourable characteristics for optimisation of activity as predicted by the Hansch equation.

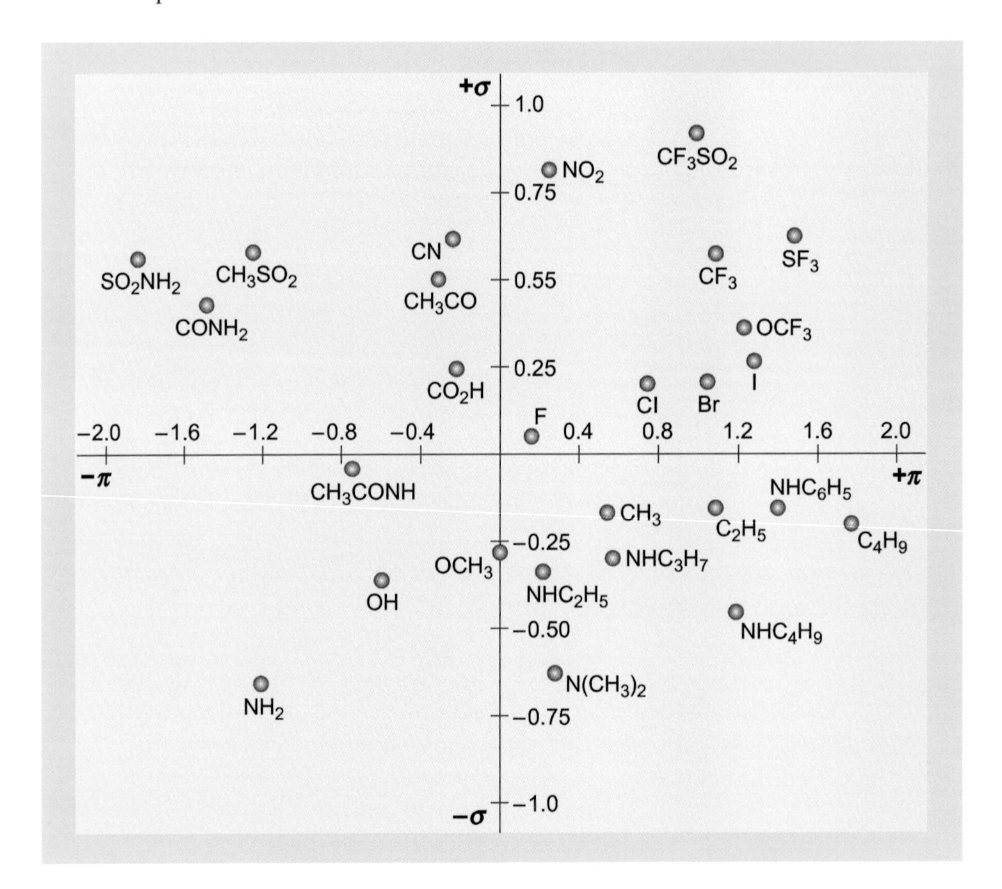

Figure 3.3 A Craig plot for π and σ.

The desirable properties of substituent Y in our earlier example include positive π and negative σ. The Craig plot in Figure 3.3 leads us immediately to consider alkylamine or arylamine and alkyl substituents as strong contenders. Craig plots also tell us a number of important things about QSAR generally. There is clearly no overall relationship between σ and π, and sometimes superficially different functional groups can offer very similar influences when introduced to a drug structure (–I and –CF_3 for example). This can be valuable during the development stages where toxicity is monitored. Craig plots offer us alternatives if an unexpectedly toxic candidate has to be modified, as well as suggesting suitable substituents for study during the evaluation of the relevant Hansch equation for a family of drug structures. The full range of activity can be obtained by synthesising examples from each quadrant of the plot.

3.2.6 A summary of ADME processes

We have looked in some detail at the range of factors that must be considered in order to prepare a drug that is fit for purpose, but before a drug can be declared ready for clinical use, other aspects of drug transport need to be carefully investigated as part of the characterisation of the drug. These are the so-called **ADME processes**. While some of the aspects of ADME have been mentioned already, we will conclude by considering the whole transit of a drug from administration to complete elimination from the body.

3.2.7 Absorption

■ Identify at least three ways in which drugs could be administered.

□ Drugs can be administered in a number of ways for example:

- by mouth (orally)
- given by injection (e.g. intravenously)
- applied to the skin (cutaneously)
- sprayed into the nose and absorbed through the nasal membranes (nasally).

The standard approach to monitoring absorption of a drug in the body is to track the blood plasma concentration C_p over time. Let's consider the key differences between a drug that is injected directly into a vein and one that is taken by mouth. After administration, blood samples may be removed and analysed to give the current value of C_p. Figure 3.4a shows how administration by mouth differs from intravenous injection. The curves show the administration of the same dose in each case, but note how the intravenous injection (lilac curve) has its maximum concentration from the moment of injection and then the concentration falls with time.

The remaining three curves illustrate how absorption rates can differ from one drug to another, and this will affect the value and the timing of the peak concentration in the plasma. The delay is clearly due to the time taken for the drug to be absorbed into the bloodstream through an indirect route such as the gastro-intestinal tract. It is important to note here that all of the drugs shown in Figure 3.4a have a **bioavailability** of 100%, that is all of the drug makes it into the bloodstream once it has been administered. Many drugs have bioavailabilities of less than 100% because not all of the drug makes it into the bloodstream, as a result of degradation or removal from the body by other processes before it makes the bloodstream.

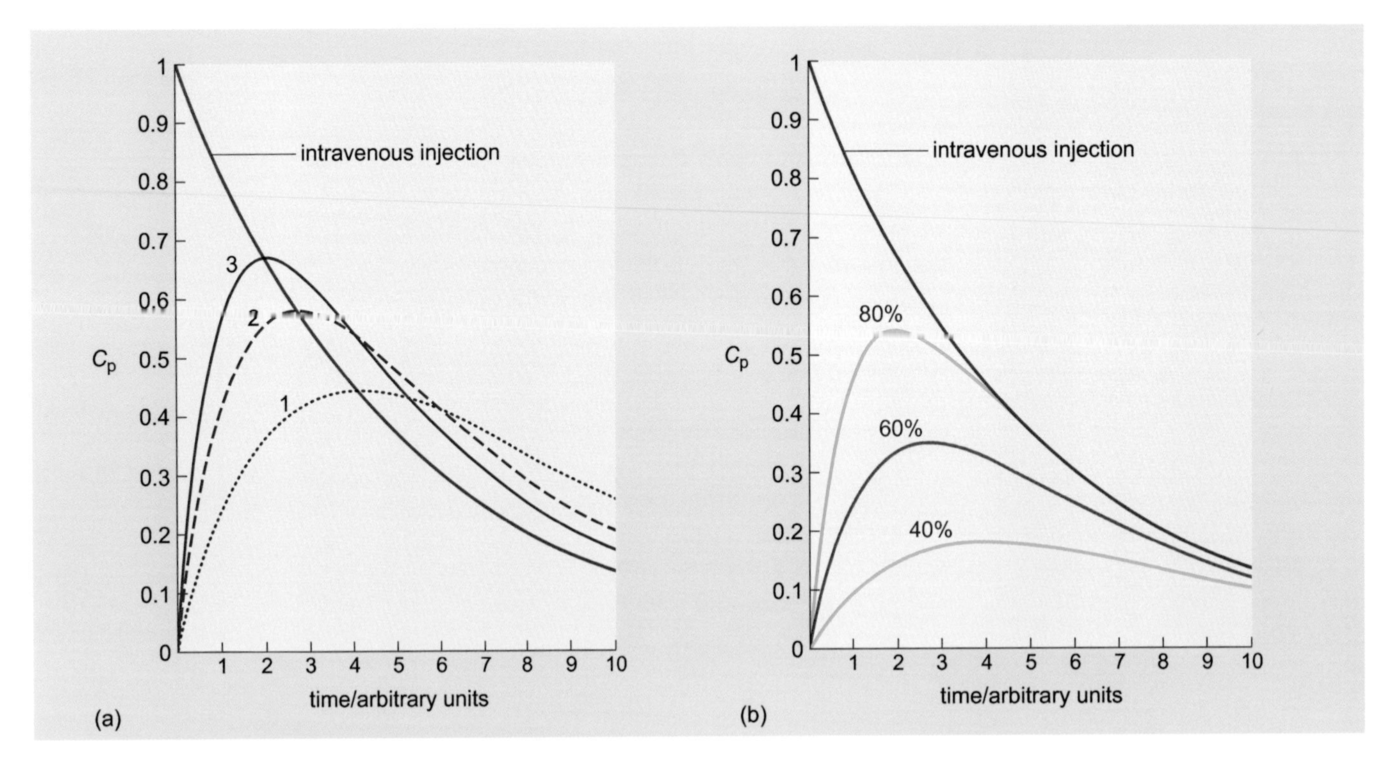

Figure 3.4 (a) Relative plasma concentration versus time plots for an intravenously injected drug (lilac), and three orally administered drugs (1, 2, 3) with different rates of absorption, but bioavailabilities (see text) of 100%. (b) Similar plots for drugs with bioavailabilities of 80%, 60% and 40%.

This means that although the drugs in Figure 3.4a pass through the body at different rates, the areas under the curves are in fact identical in these idealised examples, indicating that equal numbers of moles of drugs have passed through the patient.

Bioavailabilities of 100% for orally administered drugs are unusual, however, and it is much more common to see a situation like the one in Figure 3.4b, where the orally administered drugs clearly have smaller areas under the curves than the intravenous dose. The curves shown (with the intravenous curve for comparison) are based upon bioavailabilities of 80%, 60% and 40%. The causes of bioavailablity of less than 100% can be due, as we have seen, to a range of factors, such as very high polarity, poor solubility, chemical instability or excessive hydrophobicity, but low bioavailablity does not necessarily mean that the compound is a poor drug. If it is very potent, then low plasma concentrations may be sufficient for a therapeutic dose and the problem is more one of drug delivery than drug unsuitability.

3.2.8 Distribution

Once a drug has entered the bloodstream, it will rapidly distribute itself around the body. The concentration of the drug in any one locality in the body depends on the type of tissue in the immediate environment. We have seen already, when considering partition coefficients, that drugs partition themselves between aqueous and organic phases. Similar partitioning of a drug occurs in the body depending on the proportions of aqueous and lipid phases in the various tissues. Figure 3.4a shows an idealised C_p versus time plot for intravenous injection. In reality we would expect some deviation from this perfect curve, as equilibration with the tissues is not an instantaneous process and, thus, there is a lag before drug elimination processes can occur. The amount of deviation is dependent on the hydrophilic/hydrophobic balance of the drug. Generally speaking, the more hydrophobic the drug, the more deviation is observed. We would expect drugs that are polar, hydrophilic and/or heavily protein bound to be confined to mainly the blood volume in the body. On the other hand, drugs that are rather more hydrophobic and can penetrate cell walls will tend to distribute throughout most of the aqueous phases (non-plasma) of the body, thereby lowering the observed plasma concentration. Taking this further, highly hydrophobic drugs will tend to penetrate fatty tissue, and this seriously reduces the plasma concentration. In an ideal situation, the loss of drug from the bloodstream is a first-order process and, thus, a plot of log C_p against time is a straight line. Any deviation from linearity observed in such a plot reflects the type of non-ideal behaviour discussed above.

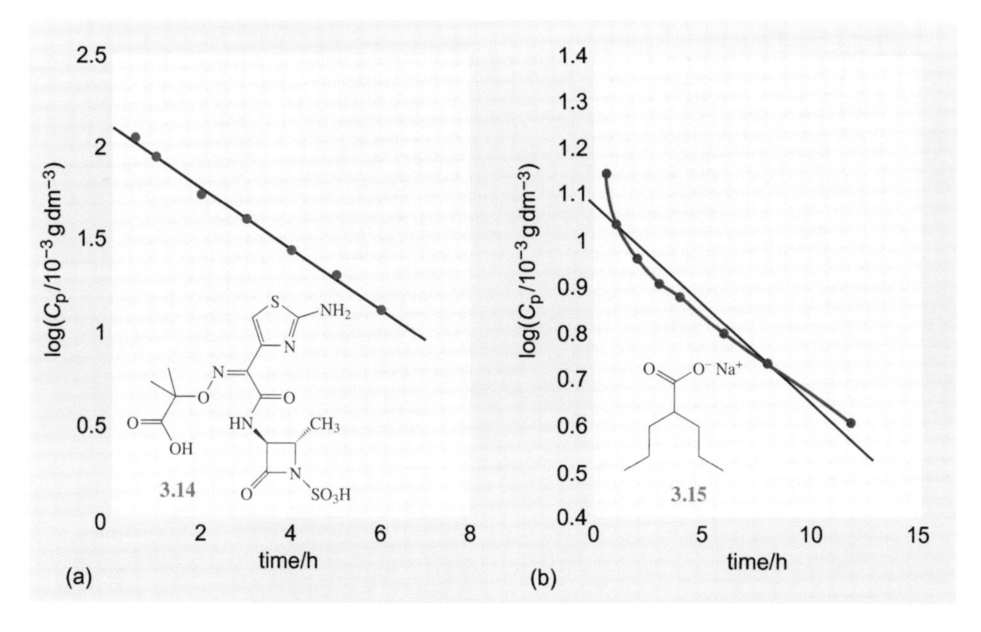

Figure 3.5 Log (C_p/10^{-3} g dm^{-3}) versus time plots for (a) aztreonam (**3.14**, 2.0 g dose) and (b) sodium valproate (**3.15**, 1.0 g dose).

Figure 3.5a shows a typical plot following a 2.0 g intravenous dose of the relatively hydrophilic antibiotic aztreonam (**3.14**). The plot shows very little deviation from a straight line, even in the early stages, suggesting that equilibration is rapid, with the drug concentration soon showing a first-order depletion in concentration, from which its plasma half-life can be deduced. Figure 3.5b, by contrast, shows that for a 1.0 g intravenous dose of the more hydrophobic valproate (**3.15**) there is a large deviation from linearity at the beginning. This suggests there is a significant equilibration period between aqueous and lipid regions lasting about 2 h before first-order depletion is observed.

Of great interest is the y-axis intercept of the linear part of each curve, as this gives us an apparent concentration of drug at zero time. From this we can calculate a parameter known as the **volume of distribution** V_d.

- ■ What are the y-axis intercepts in Figure 3.5a and b?

- □ For plot (a) the intercept is $\log (C_{p(zero\ time)}/10^{-3}\ g\ dm^{-3}) = 2.1$ and for plot (b) the intercept is $\log (C_{p(zero\ time)}/10^{-3}\ g\ dm^{-3}) = 1.07$

- ■ Is the apparent concentration of drug at zero time higher for **3.14** compared with **3.15** or lower?

- □ Since the y-axis intercept for Figure 3.5a is larger than that for Figure 3.5b, which is the log of the concentration, the apparent concentration of drug at zero time is higher for **3.14** than for **3.15.**

Since we can calculate the apparent concentration of drug at zero time from the y-axis intercept and we know how much drug was administered, we can calculate V_d the volume of the medium in which the drug is distributed. V_d is equal to 15.9 dm^3 for aztreonam (**3.14**) and 84 dm^3 for valproate (**3.15**).

What is the meaning of these values? Normally, the volumes calculated for V_d shown above are corrected for body mass of the individual patient, so using a typical mass of 79 kg we arrive at values of 0.2 $dm^3\ kg^{-1}$ for aztreonam and 1.06 $dm^3\ kg^{-1}$ for sodium valproate. These values can now be interpreted in terms of how much of the body's combined aqueous systems are being infiltrated by drug. If the blood volume for an average person is divided by their mass, then a figure of 0.07 $dm^3\ kg^{-1}$ is obtained. Repeating this calculation for the total body water gives a figure of 0.7 $dm^3\ kg^{-1}$. So any calculated V_d in excess of 0.7 $dm^3\ kg^{-1}$ is suggesting that the drug is being diluted to concentrations below that which is possible from considering the body water volume alone. This has to be explained in terms of the concentration of drug being lower than expected (making V_d appear larger) due to significant amounts being partitioned into the lipid-rich tissues. The larger the value of V_d the more the drug is being retained by lipids, and lipophilic (hydrophobic) drugs can have apparent V_d values from 1 to 200. Our calculations suggest, then, that aztreonam is penetrating cell membranes to some extent and its V_d is intermediate between blood volume and total body water. The much greater lipophilic character of valproate is reflected in a V_d that is significantly larger than 0.7 $dm^3\ kg^{-1}$. Table 3.4 gives V_d values for a number of familiar drugs.

Note that warfarin, an anticoagulant, is mainly confined to the blood volume, whereas imipramine (an antidepressant) is, as perhaps expected, much more concentrated in the lipids, which is consistent with its target: the lipid-rich nerve tissues.

Table 3.4 V_d values for a number of familiar drugs.

Drug	**Purpose**	$V_d/dm^3\ kg^{-1}$
warfarin	anticoagulant	0.11
salicylic acid	analgesic	0.14
atenolol	beta-blocker	0.7
imipramine	antidepressant	30
chloroquine	antimalarial	235

3.2.9 Metabolism

We have seen from Figure 3.4 that, once in the bloodstream, the plasma concentrations of drugs fall over time, usually with first-order kinetics. This concentration decay is associated with metabolic processes that eventually remove the drug from the body in a similar manner to toxic metabolites. These can either be passed out of the body through the urine or the faeces, but first they are usually chemically modified by the liver. This hepatic metabolism occurs in two phases. In **phase I**, functional groups are either oxidised or reduced, through enzymatic reactions, to molecules that are then passed on to **phase II.** Many of the phase I processes are catalysed by a large family of proteins found mainly in the liver called the cytochrome P450 enzymes. These enzymes work as oxidases, inserting oxygen atoms into selected C–H bonds of molecules, including drugs. The active site contains an iron (Fe^{2+}/Fe^{3+}) ion which can take part in redox reactions.

The overall equation can be written as

$$R{-}H + O_2 + 2H^+ + 2e^- \rightarrow R{-}OH + H_2O$$

Some examples of the kinds of oxidation reaction possible are shown below:

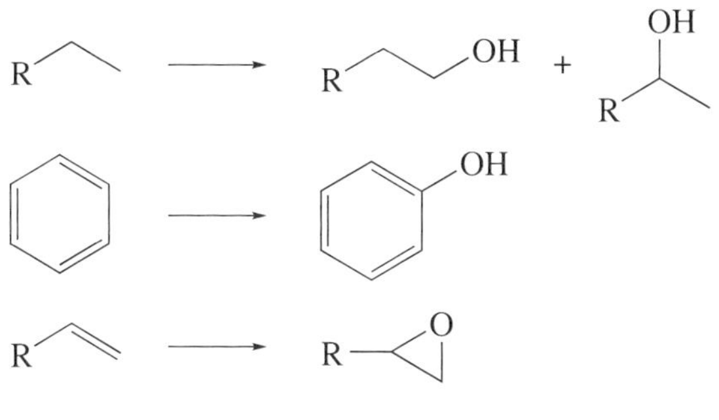

R OH + OH R

OH

R R O

The liver also contains reductase enzymes (such as P450 reductase, nitroreductase and azoreductase) which catalyse alternative **phase I reactions**, such as the examples shown below:

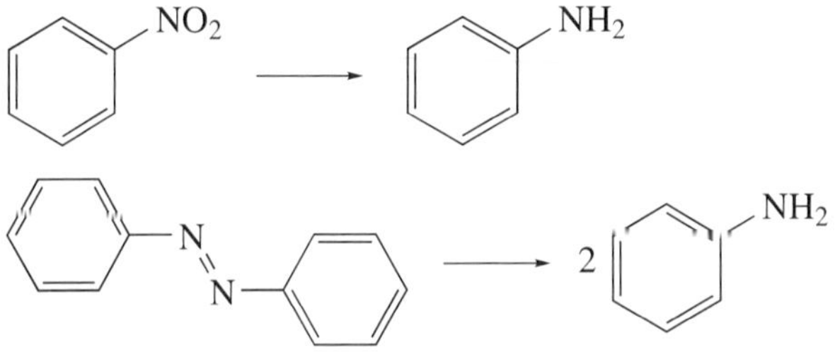

In phase II, the derivatives formed in phase I are joined to polar, hydrophilic groups such as sugar-like glucuronic acid, sulfate groups or ethanoyl (acetyl) groups which increases their hydrophilicity, allowing them to leave the body through the urine, or through bile into the intestine. The attachment of glucoronic acid requires an enzyme called UDP-glucuronosyl transferase (UGT) and a cofactor known as UDP-glucuronic acid (UDPGA, **3.16**). The glucuronic acid moiety is usually attached through any aromatic or aliphatic –OH groups formed in the phase I reactions (or already present):

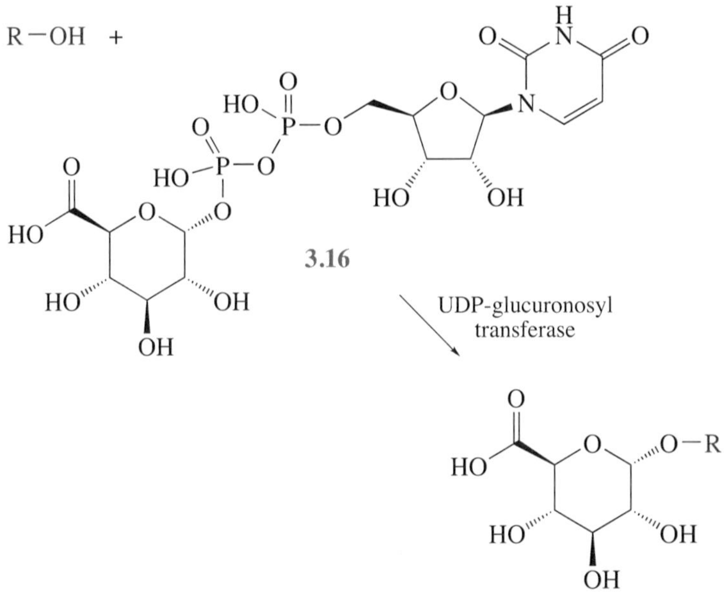

R–OH +

3.16

UDP-glucuronosyl transferase

(3.4)

glucuronic acid derivative

Alternatively, acetyl groups can be attached to amine functions through acetyl-CoA and *N*-acyltransferases. Other **phase II processes** are also possible, such as the attachment of glutathione instead of glucuronic acid, but the overall purpose is similar.

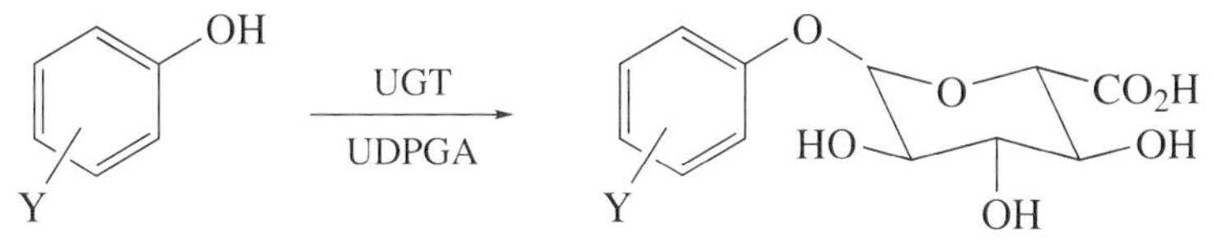

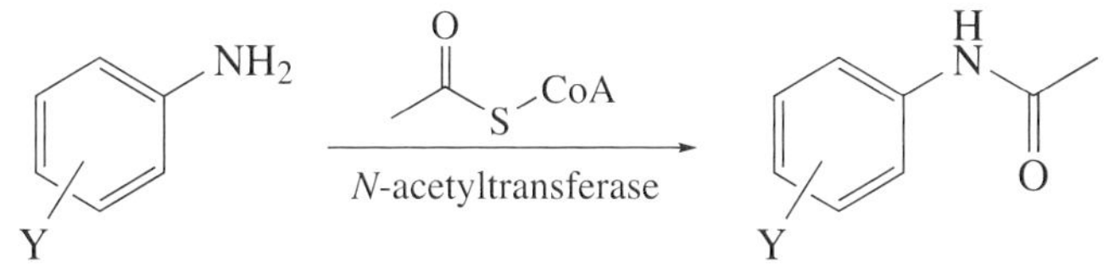

The possibility of adapting drugs to increase their metabolic stability has been used by drug developers, and one method is to attach strongly electron-withdrawing Y-groups (such as –CN) to the aromatic ring, or use a bulky substituent instead. Both of these approaches can slow down the rate of phase II metabolism, which, if the drug already possesses –OH or $-NH_2$ groups, can be beneficial for bioavailability. As always, though, the overall effect of the modifications must be investigated to ensure there are no undesirable changes to the drug's properties.

3.2.10 Elimination

Inevitably, drug molecules and their metabolites are eventually removed from the body by way of urine or bile. Small amounts may be lost by exhalation or through sweat, and since breast milk is produced by glands which are in essence modified sweat glands, it is important to understand any associated risks to breast feeding of infants. The role of the kidney in the elimination of drug metabolites is to allow some of the products of phase II metabolism to pass into the urine, mainly on the criterion of size, although the molecules concerned must be sufficiently water soluble for this to occur. Most of the remaining compounds, particularly the more hydrophobic fragments, are taken up by bile and moved into the gall bladder for storage and eventual release into the lower reaches of the alimentary canal. These processes are responsible for the **clearance** of the drug.

3.3 Summary of Section 3

Pharmacokinetics describes what the body does to a drug. It involves the study of:

- the chemical stability of the drug in body tissue/fluids
- the breakdown of the drug via metabolic processes
- the hydrophilic/hydrophobic balance of the drug
- molecular size
- the number of hydrogen-bonding interactions (which leads to Lipinski's 'rule of five').

The activity of a drug can be correlated using a range of physical parameters to create a QSAR. Properties correlated include:

- Partition coefficients that describe the partitioning of the drug between water and octanol. Partition coefficients can be easily predicted.
- Electronic substituent constants, such as σ, used in linear free energy relationships.

A Craig plot identifies the balance between hydrophobicity/hydrophilicity and electron-withdrawing/donating ability for particular substituents and thus aids in the identification of particular targets once a QSAR has been determined.

ADME processes describe the fate of the drug once in the body.

Absorption reflects the method by which the drug is administered. The blood plasma concentration of a drug usually decreases in a first-order fashion but may take time to reach a maximum depending upon the properties of the drug. Degradation and elimination may mean that the bioavailability is less than 100%.

Depending upon its hydrophobicity/hydrophilicity, a drug will be distributed in the body in different regions, such as the blood, all aqueous environments and lipid-rich tissue. Calculation of V_d, the volume of distribution, provides insight into the way the drug is distributed. A large V_d suggests the drug is not just distributed in the blood, but also in other aqueous environments. A very large V_d suggests the drug is partitioned into lipid-rich tissues.

Eventually, a drug is metabolised to make it more water soluble so that it can be excreted. Redox reactions are used in the phase I process, and phase II involves further functionalisation.

Drugs are eliminated from the body predominantly through the urine and faeces.

Study note

You should now return to the study planner on the module website before moving on to Unit 6.

Acknowledgements

Grateful acknowledgement is made to the following sources for permission to reproduce material in this book.

Cover

Adapted from pdb 1nnb, Bossart-Whitaker, P., Carson, M., Babu, Y.S., Smith, C.D., Laver, W.G., Air, G.M. (1993) 'Three-dimensional structure of influenza A N9 neuraminidase and its complex with the inhibitor 2-deoxy 2,3-dehydro-N-acetyl neuraminic acid', *Journal of Molecular Biology*, 232: 1069–83.

Unit 2 Section 1

Figure 1.4: Adapted from Dickerson, R.E. and Geis, I. (1969) *The Structure and Action of Proteins*, Harper and Row; Figure 1.6: Irving Geis/Geis Archives Trust; Figure 1.8: Alberts, B. et al. (2002) *Molecular Biology of the Cell*, 4th edn, Taylor and Francis; Figures 1.17 and 1.18: Courtesy of JEOL (UK) Ltd.; Figures 1.25 and 1.27: Voet, D. and Voet, J.G. (2004) *Biochemistry*, 3rd edn, John Wiley and Sons;

Unit 3 Section 1

Figure 1.10: Schlunzen, F. et al. (2001) 'Structural basis for the interaction of antibiotics with the peptidyl transferase centre in eubacteria', *Nature*, vol. 413, 25 October 2001, Macmillan Magazines Limited;

Unit 5 Section 3

Figure 3.3: Adapted from Patrick, G.L. (2005) *An Introduction to Medicinal Chemistry*, 3rd edn, Oxford University Press;

Every effort has been made to contact copyright holders. If any have been inadvertently overlooked the publishers will be pleased to make the necessary arrangements at the first opportunity.

Module team

Module Team Chair and Academic Editors

James Bruce (Chair)
Jim Iley
Peter Taylor

Module Team Authors

James Bruce
Peter Taylor
Yao-Zhong Xu

Curriculum Manager

Yvonne Ashmore

External Module Assessor

Dr Nick Greeves (University of Liverpool)

Consultants

Simon Ainge (King Henry VIII School, Coventry)
David Gamblin (St Paul's School, London)
Christopher Perry (University of Wolverhampton)
Clare Sansom (Birkbeck College, University of London)

Production Team

Rob Barnes
Greg Black
Martin Chiverton
Roger Courthold
Michael Francis
Sarah Gammon
Rebecca Graham
Rafael Hidalgo
Vivien Hoare
Chris Hough
Jason Jarratt
Martin Keeling
Corinne Owen
Will Rawes

Other Contributors

The S346 Module Team gratefully acknowledge the following S344, S377 and S304 Module Team members and Associate Lecturer for their contributions to S346 and for the use of their original materials:
Alan Bassindale, Jim Iley, Roger Hill, Jane Loughlin, Kevin McCullough (Heriot-Watt University), David Roberts, Peter Taylor